QP
301
B33

Barham, Jerry N.

Structural
kinesiology

18733 - 2

# Structural Kinesiology

# Structural Kinesiology

**Jerry N. Barham**
University of Northern Colorado

**Edna P. Wooten**
University of Oregon

The Macmillan Company, New York
Collier-Macmillan Publishers, London

The Macmillan Company
866 Third Avenue, New York, New York 10022

Collier-Macmillan Canada, Ltd., Toronto, Ontario

Library of Congress Catalog card number:  72–80072

Printing:  1 2 3 4 5 6 7 8      Year:  3 4 5 6 7 8 9

# Preface

This book is designed for use in the standard undergraduate course dealing with the structure and mechanical functions of the musculoskeletal system. It is suitable both for the student who has had a course in human anatomy and the student who has had no previous experience with the subject matter.

The rapid growth of the movement sciences in recent years has made it increasingly evident that the entire subject of kinesiology cannot be adequately covered in a single one-quarter or one-semester course. Indeed, many colleges and universities are offering separate courses in the various subdivisions such as those derived from mechanics, physiology, anatomy, psychology, and sociology. For this reason, the present text is limited to the structural components of human movement.

The text considers the basic and most essential facts of human structure and the movement problems most often found in general physical education programs. The specific movement problems studied, therefore, are not all-inclusive, but are given only as examples of the kinesiological applications of anatomical information.

The progression of concepts is from the basic to the applied, and from the general to the specific. The basic and more general materials are presented to enable the student to grasp the total concept before proceeding to the more specific movement applications involved.

The discussion concentrates, as mentioned before, on structural information primary to an understanding of the problems of human movement. To make such an emphasis possible, peripheral material that might be of value from a general education standpoint has been omitted.

Each chapter of this text is divided into three major parts: general student objectives, the text proper, and study guidelines, which include specific student objectives and hints as to how the subject matter might best be studied. The general and specific behavioral objectives to be achieved by the student in his study of each chapter are included to provide the student with (1) a check list of the behavior changes expected of him, and (2) a self-evaluation device through which he can check his progress.

In Chapter 1, we introduce the general concept of kinesiology, the academic and professional objectives, and a brief description of the subject of structural kinesiology. In the discussion of professional applications, emphasis is placed on the foundational role of structural kinesiology in areas such as activity instruction, adapted physical education, athletic training, and exercise programs.

The text as a whole is divided into nine parts. Part I deals with the basic concepts of musculoskeletal anatomy. The three chapters included in this part are devoted to the basic terminology and nomenclature of osteology (bones), arthrology (joints), and myology (muscles). These chapters are designed to give the student a background in the general features of the musculoskeletal system that will prepare him for detailed study of the unique features of the system. They also provide him with the basic vocabulary necessary for effectively dealing with the introductory chapters of the text.

Part II deals with anatomical mechanics and treats only those principles necessary for an understanding of the mechanical functions of the musculoskeletal system.

Part III is devoted to a general consideration of the motor ability factors of muscle strength, power, and endurance, with consideration also being given to the factors affecting the mobility and stability of joints. These are the primary motor ability factors usually associated with the musculature and leverage systems of the body.

Since the subject of structural kinesiology is not limited to basic and applied anatomy but is also concerned with the structural variables associated with general and regional anthropometry, Part IV briefly introduces the study of these variables.

Parts V through IX discuss the structural kinesiology of the (1) foot and leg, (2) thigh and hip, (3) trunk, (4) shoulder and arm, and (5) forearm and hand and each has two main considerations: the specific structure of the region studied and the movements and problems found in that region.

In order to eliminate completely the role of students as mere passive receivers of information, it is strongly recommended that this book be accompanied by appropriate laboratory work and by supplementary readings. A list of recommended readings is presented at the end of most chapters and in Appendix B. A programmed textbook has also been prepared to facilitate the learning of basic concepts.*

Special recognition and thanks are due Dr. J. V. Krause, Eastern Washington State College, for his assistance in developing the chapter format used in this text and for suggesting the inclusion of the study guidelines section.

J. N. B.
E. P. W.

---

*Jerry N. Barham and William L. Thomas: *Anatomical Kinesiology: A Programmed Text.* New York, The Macmillan Company, 1969.

# Contents

# Introduction

# 1

# Introduction

## 1.11 The Concept of Kinesiology

An intelligent approach to the subject of structural kinesiology demands that we settle at once upon an adequate and acceptable definition of the term. Kinesiology is a combination of two Greek verbs: *kinein* meaning to move, and *logos* meaning to study. Kinesiology is involved, therefore, with the study of movement.

Kinesiology has evolved through the years, as have other sciences, as being primarily concerned with the movement problems of human beings and is often defined as the study of *human movement*. Psychology is a parallel case in point. Psychology is defined by some psychologists as being the study of behavior, but in practice most psychologists are concerned primarily with the study of *human* behavior.

That the primary focus of kinesiology is human movement does not mean that kinesiologists are unconcerned with the movement of lower animals or even inorganic bodies. These types of movement are of concern, but usually only to the extent that they give further insight into the complexities of human movement. Much can be learned about human movement by observing the movements of lower animals or of nonliving objects. Sometimes this is the only way that systematic observations can be made and properly controlled experiments can be conducted. This study is called *comparative kinesiology* and is of the same value to the kinesiologists as is *comparative psychology* to the psychologist.

Since it primarily emphasizes the movements and movement problems of human beings, kinesiology is defined here as the body of knowledge devoted to the arts and sciences of human movement. This definition is the only one that is consistent with standard dictionary usage and is a consensus of the many definitions offered by scholars in the field. *Dorland's Medical Dictionary*,[1] for example, defines kinesiology as "the sum of what is known regarding human movement."

The sum of man's knowledge regarding human movement certainly includes the artistic expressions of a motor performer as much as it does the scientific principles that account for his specific movements. Kinesiology is, therefore, a broad and interdisciplinary body of knowledge that includes all factors affecting movement or that are in turn affected by movement, regardless of how remote the relationship may be.

Within this context, structural kinesiology can be defined as the specialized area of kinesiology that deals with the morphological components of human movement. The subject matter of this area is primarily derived from the supporting sciences of *human anatomy* which treats the structure of the organ systems of the body and *human anthropometry* which treats the variables associated with the gross structure measurements of the body and its parts.

## 1.12 The Academic and Professional Objectives of Structural Kinesiology

The structural kinesiologist is concerned not only with the solution of practical problems, but also with the advancement of man's knowledge of human movement as a natural phenomenon. He has, in other words, an academic as well as a practical interest in his subject.

It is easy to understand why scientists in general and college students in particular are interested in solving practical problems. These solutions often make an obvious and immediate difference. Not so generally recognized is that most great scientists, as well as many students of science, have been motivated by another incentive: the satisfaction of simply knowing and understanding nature. In many instances, we pursue questions not because we expect useful results, but because we are curious. We simply want to know the answer; we do not consider whether our knowledge will be useful.

It is pure curiosity that motivates the academic kinesiologist. Because of this, the field is only now gaining recognition as an academic discipline. An academic discipline as defined by Henry[2] is

an organized body of knowledge collectively embraced in a formal course of learning. The acquisition of such knowledge is assumed to be an adequate and worthy objective as such, without any demonstration or requirement of practical application. The content is theoretical and scholarly as distinguished from technical and professional.

[1]*Dorland's Illustrated Medical Dictionary*, 24th ed. (Philadelphia, W. B. Saunders Co., 1965), p. 781.
[2]Franklin M. Henry: "Physical Education as an Academic Discipline," *J. Health, Phys. Ed., Recreat.*, 35:32, 1964.

The theoretical and scholarly aspects of kinesiology are defined here as the academic objectives of the discipline, whereas the technical and practical aspects are defined as the professional objectives. The use of the term *objective* in this sense implies that the student of kinesiology should be guided in his study by two primary goals. First, he should aspire to become a scholar in the arts and sciences of human movement. His objective in this instance should be to acquire knowledge and understanding of motor performance as a natural phenomenon. Second, he should aspire to become a skillful practitioner in the professional applications of this body of knowledge. His objective should be to acquire an insight into how a knowledge of human movement can be used in the solving of professional problems.

The student is cautioned to avoid the fallacious notion that all knowledge or information of any value must have an immediate and practical application. Some need to be provided with the applications of each section of material as it is presented. Otherwise, they are not motivated to learn. A danger of this orientation lies in its limitation of scientific curiosity. Even more damaging, however, is its limitation of scientific insight. Sometimes the practical applications of knowledge come from the increased understandings acquired through the academic approach. It should be self-evident that the more a student knows and understands about the many facets of human movement, the better he can work with it as a professional practitioner. This view is supported by the observation that man's academic comprehension of a phenomenon usually precedes his practical control of it.

One of the ultimate aims of kinesiology, of course, is the solution of problems of practical importance, but a well-rounded view of the whole field is necessary to this end. The student should remember that the solutions of practical problems may be found only after a firm foundation of basic facts and principles has been acquired.

Since a vast majority of the students of this textbook will be primarily interested in becoming physical educators, the problems of this field of professional application will be emphasized.

The professional objectives of kinesiology in relation to physical education are (1) to develop an understanding of human movement and the variables operating in successful motor performance, (2) to present information that will enable a teacher or coach to analyze and evaluate a motor performance in terms of basic essentials, and (3) to develop the ability of the teacher and coach to discriminate between various operational systems or schools of thought in terms of scientific soundness.

Knowledge of structural kinesiology will allow the physical educator to perform many tasks which he would not be able to do otherwise. He will have, for instance, the anatomical foundations for the prescription of instrumental exercises, i.e., conditioning exercises for athletes, cosmetic exercises for body-building enthusiasts, therapeutic exercises for atypical persons, and hygienic exercises for the maintenance of health.

Knowledge of structural kinesiology is necessary for the proper management of kinetic or athletic injuries. Thus, an athletic trainer needs a detailed knowledge of this subject for effective work.

The teacher of motor activities needs a knowledge of structural kinesiology to provide him with a scientific basis for analyzing the structural components of a student's motor performance. Only through this means can a proper movement diagnosis be made and proper corrective measures be prescribed. These and other professional applications of structural kinesiology will be further discussed in section 1.14.

In summary, the academic objectives of structural kinesiology are related to subject matter comprehension and the professional objectives are related to practical applications. Only through mastery of both the academic and professional aspects of structural kinesiology can a student of physical education be truly educated in this part of his professional preparation.

## 1.13 The Subject of Structural Kinesiology

Academically, a structural kinesiologist is primarily interested in understanding the structure of the movement mechanisms of the human body and in understanding how variabilities in this structure affect the movement potentials of human beings. The unique contribution of the academic approach is in the selection and synthesis of facts and principles gained from the supporting sciences of human anatomy and human anthropometry. The organization of this material into a systematic and unique science of human movement and motor performance is the most valuable outcome. Specialists in the field are also, of course, actively engaged in the extension of knowledge through their own basic research.

One of the academic objectives of the structural kinesiologist is to understand the skeletal, muscular, and articular components of the musculoskeletal system and to understand how these components act as structural determinants of human movement. In a certain sense, structural kinesiology is a descriptive science which provides a picture of the structural components and the anatomical events that take place in movement. Emphasis is placed on the unique movement or series of movements, and the scientific aim is a clear account of these movements with a detailed description of the musculoskeletal mechanisms involved.

The student might conceive of this study as an anatomical geography lesson through which he becomes familiar with the important landmarks of the body. He must learn the location and the names of the various bones, muscles, and joints of the body. He must learn the important features of these structures and how they interrelate to form the framework and movement apparatus of the body.

In another sense, however, structural kinesiology is an analytical science that emphasizes the general or universal, as well as the specific, aspects of movement phenomena. Particular situations are sometimes regarded not from the point of view of their uniqueness but rather as manifestations of certain general principles. This approach requires an understanding of mechanical laws and an understanding of how these laws are involved in the effective operation of the musculoskeletal system.

In considering the analytical aspects of structural kinesiology, the student might conceive of the musculoskeletal system as a machine capable of performing mechanical work. This machine system is composed of weights (mass of body segments), levers (bones), centers of rotation (joints), and devices for producing force (muscles). The student should conceive of this machine as responding to the laws of mechanics just as any other system of weights and levers.

In order for the student to properly understand the workings of this mechanical system, it is important that he be able to identify and interpret the pertinent laws of mechanics, derived from physics, that pertain to the movements of the human body. He needs to understand how these mechanical factors interact with structural components in producing the observed variabilities in human movement patterns. The chapters under the group heading *Anatomical Mechanics* are designed to provide the foundations for these essential understandings.

In the study of the structure and mechanical functions of the musculoskeletal system, the student is advised to first master the information concerned with the general features of this system. He will then have the background for a more detailed study of the unique features involved. This plan provides the basis of organization in the text. The first ten chapters, for example, serve as a foundation for all that follow.

The basic and applied subject matters are presented in separate chapters. Part VI, for example, contains two chapters. The first chapter deals with the *structure* of the thigh and hip, and the second chapter deals with the *movements and problems* of the knee, thigh, and hip. Thus, the basic anatomy is presented in one chapter and is then immediately followed by a discussion of the professional applications of this information. These professional applications are so important that the next section of this chapter is devoted to a discussion of them.

The professional applications of structural kinesiology are particularly noticeable in (1) the teaching of motor skills, (2) the conduction of adapted physical education programs, (3) the conduction of exercise programs, and (4) the management of athletic injuries. The purpose of this section is to present a brief overview of the role that structural kinesiology can play in preparing the future physical educator in each of these four areas. This discussion will also give the rationale followed by the authors in organizing the *movements* and *problems* chapters of the text.

**1.14 The Professional Applications of Structural Kinesiology**

### Structural Kinesiology and the Teaching of Motor Skills

In the teaching of motor skills, a knowledge of structural kinesiology is especially important in describing and analyzing the movements to be taught. This added insight into the nature of a skill should be to the mutual benefit of both the teacher and the student. In making a movement description, the primary objective of the teacher is to present a clear picture of the timing and coordinations that he is trying to teach. This description is communicated to the student so that he, in turn, has a clear picture of what he is trying to learn. Thus, without the development and description of *movement models* both the teaching and the learning of motor skills would be minimal, if at all possible.

Movement descriptions involve not only the sequence of joint actions, but also their speed and accelerations. Therefore, the fundamental concepts of anatomical mechanics are foundational to these efforts. The description of joint actions in terms of their direction, range, leverage, sources of motive power, and integration into patterns, as well as the axes and planes in which they occur are also foundational to movement descriptions.

A knowledge of structural kinesiology should also be of value to the teacher in (1) analyzing the structural components involved in the external and internal mechanics of a performance, (2) analyzing the kinesiological requirements of activities, and (3) analyzing the kinesiological abilities and potentialities of students.

A performance analysis is made from both external and internal standpoints. An external analysis considers the gross body segments and their externally applied leverages, forces, and accelerations. An internal analysis considers the bone-muscle leverages and the internal factors that affect joint actions. Needless to say, the role of structural kinesiology in the development of these *movement models* is indispensable.

In the teaching of motor skills, and in the administration of physical education programs, it is very important that students participate in activities in which they will probably succeed. To accomplish this requires not only an analysis of the kinesiological abilities required in the various activities offered in the program, but also an analysis of the kinesiological aptitudes of the student. Therefore, structural kinesiology helps the teacher to match student to activity and activity to student.

## Structural Kinesiology and the Adapted Physical Education Program

If structural kinesiology is foundational to the teaching of motor skills to the normal student, it is certainly of importance—indeed, essential—to the teacher of adapted physical education. The adapted physical education program is the epitome of the individualized program in that it is usually designed specifically for an individual child. Thus, the ability to analyze the movement difficulties usually associated with certain handicapping conditions and the ability to prescribe an individualized program are the major prerequisites to becoming a competent adapted physical education teacher.

The analysis of movement difficulties requires an understanding of not only the nature of various handicapping conditions, but also the effects of these conditions upon the movement patterns of children. Since the movement apparatus, consisting of the bones, joints, muscles, and nerves, of the body, is most often affected in handicapping conditions, the value of structural kinesiology in the preparation of the adapted physical educator should now be self-evident.

**Structural Kinesiology and the Conduction of Exercise Programs**

All competent teachers of exercise are practicing structural kinesiologists. How else can movement deficiencies be properly diagnosed and corrective exercises be properly prescribed, except through the analytical techniques of structural kinesiology?

The aims of exercises in the total program of physical education seem to be (1) to develop the strength, power, and endurance of specific muscles, (2) to improve the possible range of motion (flexibility) of specific joints, (3) to improve posture in general and to correct specific faults, and (4) to build habits of good body mechanics. Knowledge of the specific muscles, bones, and joints involved is mandatory for competent administration of an exercise. For example, group exercises accomplish all the above purposes, but individually prescribed ones are far more effective. It is in the area of individualized programming that structural kinesiology makes its greatest contribution.

A thorough background in structural kinesiology enables the instructor to know what conditions can be helped by exercises and to select the exercises best fitted to the individual's needs. It also enables him to recognize the kinesiological requirements of certain sport skills and dance techniques and to select the exercises best suited to preparing students to meet these requirements.

**Structural Kinesiology and the Management of Athletic Injuries**

Like the teacher of exercise, the professionally trained first aider and the athletic trainer are practicing structural kinesiologists. This is evidenced by the fact that a detailed knowledge of the bones, joints, and muscles of the body is essential for the prevention of or proper administration to fractures, sprains, and strains. It should be self-evident, therefore, that no competent first aider or athletic trainer would attempt to treat an injury that he did not understand, and that the foundations for this understanding are found in structural kinesiology.

In studying the basic concepts of this chapter, the student is advised to master not only the general student objectives given at the beginning of the chapter, but also the following specific student objectives for each section.

**1.20 Study Guidelines**

**1.21 The Concept of Kinesiology**

    A. Specific Student Objectives

        1. Describe the derivation of the term kinesiology.
        2. State the primary concern of kinesiology.
        3. Define comparative kinesiology.
        4. Define kinesiology.
        5. Define structural kinesiology.

### 1.22 The Academic and Professional Objectives of Structural Kinesiology

A. Specific Student Objectives

1. State the primary motivation of the academic kinesiologist.
2. Give Henry's definition of an academic discipline.
3. Differentiate between the academic and professional objectives of kinesiology.
4. Give the academic objective of kinesiology.
5. Give the professional objective of kinesiology.
6. Give the three professional objectives of kinesiology in relation to physical education.

### 1.23 The Subject of Structural Kinesiology

A. Specific Student Objectives

1. Justify structural kinesiology as a descriptive science.
2. Justify structural kinesiology as an analytical science.
3. State the plan of organization of this textbook.

### 1.24 The Professional Applications of Structural Kinesiology

A. Specific Student Objectives

1. *Introduction*

   a. Identify four areas in which the professional applications of structural kinesiology are particularly noticeable.

2. *Structural Kinesiology and the Teaching of Motor Skills*

   a. Identify the primary objective of the teacher in making a movement description.
   b. Identify three areas in which the analytical approach of structural kinesiology can be applied.
   c. Differentiate between external and internal mechanics.
   d. State how structural kinesiology can assist the teacher in matching the aptitude of the student with activity requirements.

3. *Structural Kinesiology and the Adapted Physical Education Program*

   a. Identify the abilities which summarize the major prerequisites to becoming a competent adapted physical education teacher.
   b. Justify the inclusion of structural kinesiology in the professional preparation of a teacher of adapted physical education.

4. *Structural Kinesiology and the Conducting of Exercise Programs*

    a. Identify the four purposes of exercise in the total program of physical education.

    b. Justify the statement that all competent teachers of exercise are practicing structural kinesiologists.

5. *Structural Kinesiology and the Management of Athletic Injuries*

    a. Justify the statement that all professionally trained first aiders and athletic trainers are practicing structural kinesiologists.

**1.30 Recommended Supplementary Readings**

Abernathy, Ruth, and Maryann Waltz: "Toward a Discipline: First Steps First," *Quest*, Monograph II:1–7, April, 1964.

Barham, Jerry N.: "Organizational Structure of Kinesiology," *The Physical Educator*, 20:120–21, October, 1963.

_____: "Toward a Science and Discipline of Human Movement," *J. Health, Phys. Ed. Recreat.*, 37:65–68, October, 1966.

Brown, Camille: "The Structure of Knowledge of Physical Education," *Quest*, Monograph IX:53–67, December, 1967.

Henry, Franklin M.: "Physical Education an Academic Discipline," *J. Health, Phys. Ed. Recreat.*, 35:32, September, 1964.

Locke, Lawrence F.: "Kinesiology: A Word or a Discipline," unpublished paper presented at the annual convention of the American Association for Health, Physical Education and Recreation, Las Vegas, March 10, 1967.

_____: "The Movement Movement," *J. Health, Phys. Ed. Recreat.*, 37:26–27, January, 1966.

Mackenzie, Marlin M.: *Toward a New Curriculum in Physical Education.* New York, McGraw-Hill Book Company, 1969.

Miller, Ben W.: "Kinesiology: The Academic Core of Physical Education," unpublished paper presented at the annual convention of the American Association for Health, Physical Education and Recreation, Minneapolis, May 3, 1963.

Morehouse, Laurence F.: "A Concept of Kinesiology and Physical Education as Academic Disciplines," unpublished paper commissioned by the School of Education, Northwestern University, Evanston, Ill., April, 1965.

Rarick, G. Lawrence: "The Domain of Physical Education as a Discipline," *Quest*, Monograph IX:49–52, December, 1967.

Redfern, Betty: "Physical Education as an Academic Discipline," *The New Era*, 46:37–40, February, 1965.

Sage, George H.: "The Emerging Directions in Kinesiology," unpublished paper presented at the annual convention of the American Association for Health, Physical Education and Recreation, St. Louis, March 29, 1968.

Smith, Nancy W.: "Movement as an Academic Discipline," *J. Health, Phys. Ed. Recreat.*, 35:63–65, November-December, 1964.

Stish, Eugene E.: "Anthropokinetics," *J. Health, Phys. Ed. Recreat.*, 35:33, November-December, 1964.

Wooten, Edna P.: "The Structural Base of Human Movement," *J. Health, Phys. Ed. Recreat.*, 36:59, October, 1965.

# Part I

# Basic Concepts
# of
# Musculoskeletal
# Anatomy

# 2

# Basic Concepts
of Osteology

## 2.11 The Kinesiological Importance of Bones

Osteology (os″te-ol′o-je)[1] is the study of the skeletal system. The bones of the body that comprise the skeleton, along with cartilage, are of interest to students of human movement for several reasons. Probably the most important is that they work with muscles as the principal organs in maintaining the upright position of the body and in providing the lever systems necessary for locomotion. Bones work with muscles to support the body against the pull of gravity much as steel girders support our modern buildings, and they provide the levers necessary for the production of our bodily movements.

The protection of the vital organs of the body from external forces is another important function of bones. They form hard, bony "boxes," which enclose and protect the delicate structures of the body. The skull, for example, protects the brain, and the rib cage protects the lungs and heart. Along with providing the structural framework of the body, bones give shape to the body and contribute to the unique appearance of each individual. Body builds and facial features, for example, are determined mainly by bony struc-

---

[1] In the phonetic spellings used in this book the primary (′) and secondary (″) accents are indicated in polysyllabic words (as in zi″go-mat′ik); an unstressed syllable is followed by a hyphen.

tures. The formation of blood cells, the storage of calcium, iron, and certain other metals that would be extremely toxic if free in the body, and possibly the formation of antibodies are some additional functions of bones.

More specifically, bones are of interest to kinesiologists because they (1) serve as points of attachment for muscles and ligaments, (2) enter into the formation of joints, (3) serve as landmarks for body measurements, (4) are frequent sites of movement injuries, and (5) are important variables in movement performances.

## 2.12 Divisions of the Skeleton

The human skeleton is divisible into two main parts: the axial skeleton and the appendicular (app"en-dik'u-lar) skeleton. The axial skeleton is composed of the bones of the head and trunk which form the upright part or axis of the body. The appendicular skeleton consists of the bones of the upper and lower extremities which are attached to the axial skeleton as appendages. The bones found in each of these divisions are listed in Table 2–1 and are illustrated in Figures 2–1, 2–2, 2–3, and 2–4. As can be seen in Table 2–1, the adult human skeleton has approximately 199 bones: 73 in the axial skeleton, 64 in the upper extremity, and 62 in the lower extremity.

Fig. 2–1. The human skeleton.

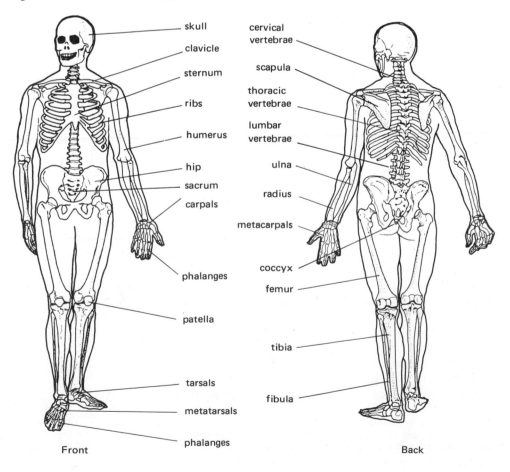

skull
clavicle
sternum
ribs
humerus
hip
sacrum
carpals
phalanges
patella
tarsals
metatarsals
phalanges

Front

cervical vertebrae
scapula
thoracic vertebrae
lumbar vertebrae
ulna
radius
metacarpals
coccyx
femur
tibia
fibula

Back

**Table 2–1. The Bones That Comprise the Axial and Appendicular Skeletons of the Human Body**

### Axial Skeleton

| | No. |
|---|---|
| A. *Skull or head* | |
| 1. *Cranium* (kra′ne-um), brain case | |
|    a. Occipital (ok-sip′i-tal), base of skull | 1 |
|    b. Parietal (pah-ri′e-tal), crown | 2 |
|    c. Frontal (fron′tl), forehead | 1 |
|    d. Temporal (tem′por-al), ear region | 2 |
|    e. Ethmoid (eth′moid), between cranial and nasal cavities | 1 |
|    f. Sphenoid (sfe′noid), base of brain and back of orbit | 1 |
| | 8 |
| 2. *Face,* anterior skull | |
|    a. Nasal (na′zal) | 2 |
|    b. Vomer (vo′mer) | 1 |
|    c. Inferior nasal concha (kong′kah), inferior turbinated | 2 |
|    d. Lacrimal (lak′ri-mal) | 2 |
|    e. Zygomatic (zi″go-mat′ik), or malar (ma′lar) | 2 |
|    f. Palatine (pal′a-tin), or palate (pal′at) | 2 |
|    g. Maxilla (mak-sil′ah), upper jaw | 2 |
|    h. Mandible (man′di-bl), lower jaw | 1 |
| | 14 |

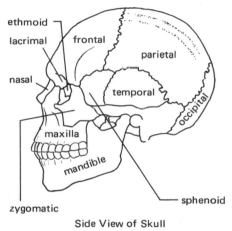

Fig. 2–2. The human skull.

| | Child | Adult |
|---|---|---|
| B. *Trunk* | | |
| 1. *Vertebral* (vur′te-bral), or *spinal column* | | |
|    a. Movable, or true vertebrae (vur′te-bre) | | |
|      (1) *Cervical* (ser′vi-kal), in the neck | 7 | 7 |
|      (2) *Thoracic* (tho-ras′ik), or dorsal, in the thorax | 12 | 12 |
|      (3) *Lumbar* (lum′ber), in the lower back | 5 | 5 |
|    b. Fixed, or false vertebrae | | |
|      (1) *Sacral* (sa′kral), fused into *sacrum* (sa′krum) in adult | 5 | 1 |
|      (2) *Coccygeal* (kok-sij′e-al), fused into *coccyx* (kok′siks) in adult | 4 | 1 |
| | 33 | 26 |
| 2. *Thorax* (tho′raks), chest | | |
|    a. *Costae* (kos′te), ribs, 12 each side | | 24 |
|    b. *Sternum* (stur′num), breastbone | | 1 |
| | | 25 |

ethmoid
lacrimal
frontal
parietal
nasal
temporal
occipital
maxilla
mandible
sphenoid
zygomatic

**Side View of Skull**

### Appendicular Skeleton

| | No. |
|---|---|
| A. *Superior or upper extremity* | |
| 1. *Shoulder girdle* | |
|    a. Clavicle (klav′i-kl), collarbone | 1 |
|    b. Scapula (skap′u-lah), shoulder blade | 1 |
| 2. *Upper limb* | |
|    a. Humerus (hu′mer-us), arm bone | 1 |
|    b. Ulna (ul′nah), large bone of forearm | 1 |
|    c. Radius (ra′de-us), small bone of forearm | 1 |
|    d. Carpus (kar′pus), or ossa carpi (os″ah kar′pi), wrist | 8 |

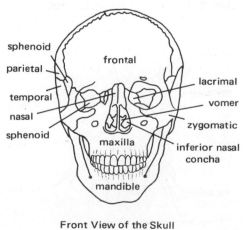

sphenoid
parietal
temporal
nasal
sphenoid
frontal
lacrimal
vomer
zygomatic
inferior nasal concha
maxilla
mandible

**Front View of the Skull**

**Table 2–1. The Bones That Comprise the Axial and Appendicular Skeletons of the Human Body (continued)**

---

*Appendicular Skeleton* (continued)

---

    (1)  Proximal or upper row

        (a)  Navicular (nah-vik′u-lah) or scaphoid (skaf′oid)
        (b)  Lunate (loo′nat), or semilunar (sem″e-loo′nar)
        (c)  Triquetral (tri-kwe′tral), or cuneiform (kyoo′ne-i-form) or triangular
        (d)  Pisiform (pi′si-form)

    (2)  Distal or lower row

        (a)  Trapezium (trah-pe′ze-um), or greater multangular
        (b)  Trapezoid (trap′e-zoid), or lesser multangular
        (c)  Capitate (kap′i-tat), or os magnum (os-mag′num)
        (d)  Hamate, or unciform (un′si-form)

  e.  Metacarpus (met″ah-kar′pus), body of hand

    (1)  Metacarpals (met″ah-kar′pals)             5

  f.  Phalanges (fa-lan′jez), 2 in thumb, 3 in each finger     14
                                              32

                               32 × 2 = 64

B.  *Inferior or lower extremity*

  1.  Os coxa (os-kok′sah), or ossa innominate (os″ah-i-nom′i-nat), hipbone       1

    a.  Ilium (il′e-um)
    b.  Ischium (is′ke-um)
    c.  Pubis (pyoo′bis)

  2.  Femur (fe′mur), thighbone       1
  3.  Patella (pah-tel′ah), kneecap       1
  4.  Tibia (tib′e-ah), large bone of leg       1
  5.  Fibula (fib′u-lah), small bone of leg       1
  6.  Tarsus (tar′sus), ossa tarsi (os′ah tar′si), ankle       7

    a.  Talus (ta′lus), or os calcis (os kal-sis)
    b.  Calcaneus (kal-ka′ne-us), astragalus (as-trag′ah-lus)
    c.  Cuboid (kyoo′boid)
    d.  Navicular (nah-vik′u-lar), or scaphoid (skaf′oid)
    e.  Cuneiform (kyoo′ne-i-form), three bones, called 1st, 2nd, and 3rd

  7.  Metatarsus (met″ah-tar′sus), sole and lower instep

    a.  Metatarsals (met″ah-tar′sals)       5

  8.  Phalanges (fa-lan′jez), 2 in big toe and 3 in each of the other toes     14
                                                31

                             31 × 2 = 62

---

**Fig. 2–3. Bones of the right wrist.**

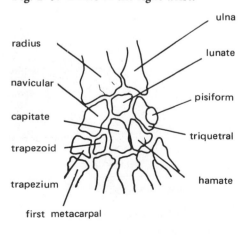

ulna
radius
lunate
navicular
pisiform
capitate
triquetral
trapezoid
trapezium
hamate
first metacarpal

## Classification of Bones

As can be seen in Figure 2–1, the bones of the body vary markedly in their sizes and shapes. Therefore, it has been found convenient to classify bones as follows:

  A.  *Long bones:* humerus, radius, ulna, metacarpals, phalanges, clavicle, femur, tibia, fibula, and metatarsals.

Fig. 2-4. Bones of the left foot.

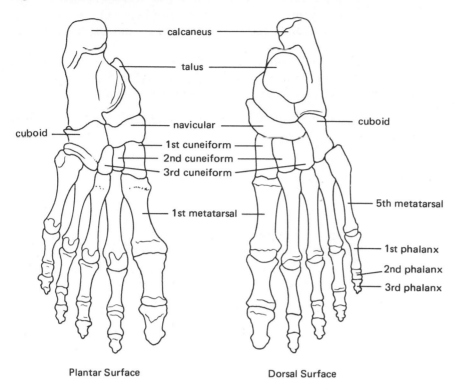

calcaneus

talus

cuboid

navicular

cuboid

1st cuneiform

2nd cuneiform

3rd cuneiform

5th metatarsal

1st metatarsal

1st phalanx

2nd phalanx

3rd phalanx

Plantar Surface                    Dorsal Surface

B. *Short bones*: carpals and tarsals.
C. *Flat bones*: ribs, sternum, scapula, and several of the cranial bones.
D. *Irregular bones*: vertebrae, sacrum, coccyx, and several of the facial bones.

Over a period of years anatomists have developed special names for certain bone structures and for ways of referring to the bones or body segments. In order to define the parts of a bone, as well as to relate the bone to other structures such as muscles, it is essential that the student be familiar with some of the more common terms. Some of the reference terms used in describing the upright body and its parts are

**2.13 Markings and Terminology**

1. *Superior*: toward the head end of the body; upper; example: the hip is superior to the knee.
2. *Inferior*: away from the head; lower; example: the knee is inferior to the hip.
3. *Anterior or ventral*: front; example: the kneecap is located anterior to the knee joint.
4. *Posterior* (pos-te're-or), or *dorsal*: back; example: the shoulder blade is on the posterior surface of the trunk.
5. *Medial or mesial*: toward the midline of the body; example: the big toe is on the medial side of the foot.
6. *Lateral*: away from the midline of the body; example: the little toe is on the lateral side of the foot.

7. *Proximal*: near or toward a point of reference, usually the trunk or midline of the body or the beginning or source of a part; example: the proximal end of the thigh bone is at the hip.
8. *Distal*: away from a point of reference usually the trunk or the midline of the body or the source of a part; example: the distal end of the thigh bone is at the knee.

Some important descriptive terms used in identifying the markings on bones are

### Projections or Processes

A. Those projections or processes which fit into joints

1. *Condyle*: a rounded projection that enters into the formation of a joint; example: condyles of femur.
2. *Head*: a rounded projection beyond a narrow necklike portion; example: head of humerus.

B. Those projections or processes to which muscles attach

1. *Trochanter*: a very large process; example: greater trochanter of femur.
2. *Tuberosity*: a large rounded projection, example: greater tuberosity of humerus.
3. *Tubercle*: a small rounded projection; example: adductor tubercle of femur.
4. *Crest*: a ridge; example: iliac crest.
5. *Line*: a less prominent ridge; example: intertrochanteric line of femur.
6. *Spinous process or spine*: a sharp projection; example: anterosuperior iliac spine.

### Depressions or Openings

A. *Fossa*: a pitlike depression or hollow; example: olecranon fossa on the humerus.
B. *Fovea*: a deep pit; example: the fovea on the head of the radius.
C. *Groove*: a long ditchlike hollow; example: bicipital groove on humerus.
D. *Foramen*: hole; example: obturator foramen on hipbone.

## 2.14 Microscopic Structure of Bone

On cutting open a bone one can see that it is composed of a dense, outer *compact* layer or cortex enclosing a spongy network of delicate, interlacing plates or trabeculae. Compact bone varies in hardness and thickness but is distinguished by the fact that it is laid down in layers around blood vessels and appears solid. The *spongy* or *cancellous* (kan'se-lus) bone appears spongy in texture, because it consists of very thin trabeculae that meet other trabeculae at various

**Fig. 2–5. Diagram of a cross section of osseous tissue.**

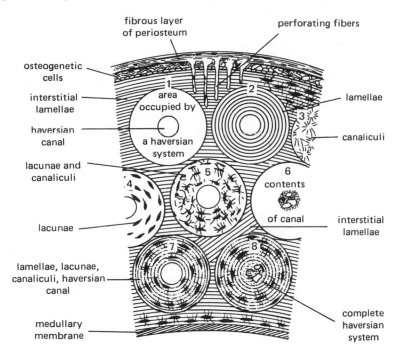

angles with relatively large spaces between the plates. The only difference, however, between compact and cancellous bone is in the degree of porosity; their compositions are identical.

The microscopic *haversian* (ha-ver'shan) system (Fig. 2–5) is the structural basis of compact bone. This system consists of a central canal called a *haversian* canal which is usually aligned with the long axis of the bone. The canal contains small blood vessels, lymph vessels, and nerve fibers. Bone tissue is formed around each haversian canal by bone-forming cells called osteoblasts, and the bone is laid down in very thin cylindrical concentric layers known as *lamella* (lah-mel'ah). Between the lamellae are many small cavities called *lacuna* (lah-ku'nah), each of which contains an osteocyte (bone cell). Delicate channels, called canaliculi (kan"ah-lik'u-li) radiate in all directions from the lacunae to form communications with other lacunae, with haversian canals, and with *Volkmann's canals*. Volkmann's canals connect haversian canals with the periosteum or outer membrane of the bone. All these passageways are filled with blood vessels and/or tissue fluid.

In spongy bone the trabeculae consist of parallel lamellae separated here and there by tiny lacunae containing bone cells. Typical haversian systems are seen only in the thicker trabeculae.

The relative amounts of compact and spongy (cancellous) substances vary in different bones and in different parts of the same bone, according to the strength required and the functions to be performed. These and other differences found in typical long, short, flat, and irregular bones are as follows:

**2.15  Gross Structure of Bones**

**Fig. 2–6. Diagram of longitudinal section of a long bone.**

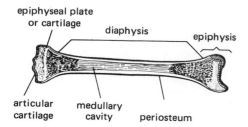

*Structure of Long Bones.* Each long bone (Fig. 2–6) of the body consists of a shaft and two extremities. Some of the unique characteristics of long bones are

A. Shaft or Diaphysis (di-af′i-sis)

The shaft is a hollow tube with walls composed of compact bone. The hollowness of the shaft decreases the weight of the bone and increases its strength. Since a given quantity of matter is stronger when arranged as a hollow cylinder than as a solid structure of equal length, the shaft provides strong support to the bone without cumbersome weight.

B. Extremity or Epiphyses (i-pif′i-sis)

The extremities are somewhat bulbous in shape and are composed almost exclusively of light, cancellous bone with only a thin outer layer of compact bone. Thus, the extremities are light despite their size. To give added strength, the arrangement of the layers of bone corresponds to the lines of stress. The extremities also provide generous space for muscle attachments and their size ensures steadier play to the joints.

C. Articular Cartilage

The articular cartilage is a thin layer of very hard cartilage that covers the articular surfaces of a bone and serves to prevent excessive wear and tear of the bone.

D. Medullary (med′u-lar″e) or Marrow Cavity

The medullary cavity runs the length of the diaphysis and contains marrow.

E. Marrow

Marrow is of two distinct kinds: red and yellow. Red blood cells are formed in the red marrow and are responsible for its color. Red marrow is found in the articular ends of the long bones, mainly the femur and humerus, and in the cancellous tissue. Yellow marrow is found in the medullary canals of the long bones and extends into the spaces of the cancellous tissue. The high fat content of yellow marrow determines its color.

F. Membranes

1. *Periosteum* (per″i-os′te-um). The periosteum is a fibrous membrane that covers the external surface of bones with the exception of the joint surfaces. Many of the periosteum's fibers penetrate the underlying bone to weld these two structures to each other. It is composed of two layers; an outer, dense fibrous connective tissue layer and an inner, loosely arranged osteogenic or bone-producing layer. The fibers of muscle tendons interlace with periosteal fibers to anchor muscles firmly to the bone.

   In young bones the osteogenic inner layer contains bone-producing cells (osteoblasts) and is richly supplied with blood vessels, which enter the bone through Volkmann's canals. The osteogenic layer is of great importance during the development and growth of bones and throughout life in the regeneration of bone following fractures.

2. *Endosteum* (en-dos'te-um). The endosteum is a membrane that lines the medullary cavity and haversian canals. It is composed of cells that become active osteoblasts as needed.

***Structure of Short Bones.*** Short bones are polyhedral in shape and consist of a core of cancellous bone encased in a thin layer of compact bone.

***Structure of Flat Bones.*** Flat bones consist of a layer of cancellous tissue lying between two plates of compact tissue. The cancellous bones of the skull, ribs, and sternum contain red marrow. Despite their name these bones are seldom truly flat, but show varying curvatures. Because of their design, they are used to protect, as in the skull and thorax, or to provide broad surfaces for muscular attachments, as in the scapula.

***Structure of Irregular Bones.*** Irregular bones are similar in structure to short bones; that is, a thin layer of compact bone forms a casing for cancellous bone.

**2.16  Growth of Bones**

The process of bone formation, called *ossification*, involves the formation of osseous tissue and definite bones. In the embryo, models of the different bones appear in the form of either a connective tissue membrane or a hyaline cartilage. Therefore, ossification, which means the depositing of bone salts in an organic matrix, occurs either *intramembranously* or *intracartilaginously*. Intracartilaginous (in"trah-kar"ti-laj'i-nus) ossification is also called endochrondral (en"do-kon'dral) ossification. Flat bones ossify intramembranously, short bones intracartilaginously, and long bones by both methods, but mainly intracartilaginously.

In the growth of long bones there are always at least three centers of ossification, namely, a primary center located in the center of the future shaft and called the *diaphysis*, and secondary centers, at least one of which is at each end of the future bone, called the *epiphyses*. The diaphysis, with the exception of the carpal and tarsal bones, appears soon after the second fetal month, whereas the epiphyses, with one or two exceptions, do not appear until postnatal life. The diaphysis "radiates" and the epiphysis enlarges until they fuse, in some rare cases as late as 25 years of age. This intracartilaginous ossification also progresses circumferentially (oppositional growth) as well as longitudinally, and finally all of the original cartilage has been replaced by bone. During the growth of the bone the original cartilage that separates the diaphysis from the end of the epiphysis is called the epiphyseal (ep"i-fiz'e-al) cartilage or the epiphyseal plate. When the epiphyseal cartilage ceases to proliferate, bony union called *closure* takes place between the diaphysis and epiphysis and usually leaves an elevated ridge called the *epiphyseal line* on the surface of the matured bone. The most recently formed bone at the end of the diaphysis is called the *metaphysis* (me-taf′i-sis)—a zone of spongy bone between the epiphyseal plate and the diaphysis. As the bone is growing in length, a *bone collar* ossifies intramembranously in the periosteum around the shaft defining its outside diameter.

The subperiosteal deposition of bone by the deeper layer of the periosteum increases the *width* of a bone and tends to increase the thickness of its outer compact layer. This thickening, however, is limited in the long bones by a coincident absorption from within as a result of the activity of osteoclasts (bone-absorbing cells) that are slowly enlarging the medullary cavity. Growth in *length* of long bones is the result of the ossification of the epiphyseal cartilage.

## 2.20 Study Guidelines

In studying the basic concepts of this chapter, the student is advised to master not only the general objectives given at the beginning of the chapter, but also the following specific objectives for each section. Study suggestions (hints) are also given for some of the sections.

### 2.21 The General Function of Bones

A. Specific Student Objectives

1. Define osteology.
2. Give four mechanical functions of bone.
3. Give three physiological functions of bone.
4. Give five reasons why kinesiologists are interested in bones.

### 2.22 Divisions of the Skeleton

A. Specific Student Objectives

1. Differentiate between the axial skeleton and the appendicular skeleton.
2. Approximately how many bones are found in

   a. the adult human skeleton?
   b. the lower extremity?
   c. the trunk?
   d. the upper extremity?

3. Give the common and the technical names of each bone in the lower extremity, in the trunk, and in the upper extremity.
4. Give the correct pronunciation of each bone in the body.
5. Give the location of each bone in the body.
6. Describe the shape or general appearance of each bone in the body.
7. Give the number of bones found in each region of the body, e.g., the foot.
8. Classify each bone of the body as a long, short, flat, or irregular bone.

B. Study Hints

In studying Table 2–1, the student should locate each bone in the illustrations and then on a mounted skeleton. Following this procedure should give the student a broad overview of the skeletal system and a background for the more detailed discussions which follow. Upon completion of this introductory study, the student should be familiar with the following information:

1. The common and technical names of each bone; e.g., the collarbone is called the clavicle.
2. The pronunciation of the technical names; e.g., the name of the upper jaw bone is maxilla, which is pronounced mak-sil'ah. As mentioned before, in the phonetic spellings used in this book the primary (') and secondary (") accents are indicated in polysyllable words (as in zi"go-mat'ik); an unstressed syllable is followed by a hyphen.
3. The location of each bone in the body; e.g., the humerus is located in the arm.
4. The shape or general appearance of each bone; e.g., the femur or thigh bone is a long bone with marked enlargements at each end. The student should be able to locate the femur, for example, in a box of dismounted bones.
5. The number of bones found in each region of the body; e.g., the forearm contains two bones, the wrist contains eight bones.

## 2.23 Markings and Terminology

A. Specific Student Objectives

1. Differentiate between the following terms:

    a. superior and inferior
    b. anterior and posterior
    c. medial and lateral
    d. proximal and distal
    e. condyle and head
    f. trochanter, tuberosity, and tubercle
    g. crest and line
    h. fossa and fovea
    i. groove and spine

2. Define a foramen.
3. Identify the two classifications of projections or processes as used in this book.

## 2.24 Microscopic Structure of Bone

A. Specific Student Objectives

1. Identify and contrast the two types of bone tissue.

2. Define the following terms:

    a. haversian system
    b. haversian canal
    c. lamella
    d. lacuna
    e. canaliculi
    f. Volkmann's canals

### 2.25 Gross Structure of Bones

A. Specific Student Objectives

1. Define the following terms:

    a. diaphysis
    b. epiphyses
    c. articular cartilage
    d. medullary cavity
    e. red marrow
    f. yellow marrow
    g. periosteum
    h. endosteum

2. State at least one mechanical or physiological function for each of the following structures.

    a. the epiphyses
    b. the articular cartilage
    c. the red marrow
    d. the periosteum

3. Of what benefit is the hollowness of the shaft of long bones?
4. Identify the two layers of the periosteum by both name and function.

### 2.26 Growth of Bones

A. Specific Student Objectives

1. Define the following terms:

    a. ossification
    b. intramembranous ossification
    c. intracartilaginous ossification
    d. primary and secondary centers of ossification
    e. epiphyseal plate
    f. closure
    g. epiphyseal line
    h. metaphysis

### 2.30 Recommended Supplementary Readings

The student should consult any recent basic anatomy text for supplementary readings in general osteology. A list of selected anatomy texts is given in Appendix B.

# 3

# Basic Concepts
# of Arthrology

Arthrology (ar-throl'o-je) is the study of joints. A joint or articulation is the junction or connection between two bones or between bones and cartilage. Since joints are the sites at which human movement takes place, they are of special interest to kinesiologists. The identification of joint actions is usually the starting point in the anatomical analysis of a movement performance and in the prescription of exercises. Joints are also of interest because they are frequent sites of movement injuries, and a knowledge of arthrology is usually deemed a prerequisite in the proper management of these injuries.

**3.11  The Kinesiological Importance of Joints**

Although humans seem capable of performing a variety of different movements, only two basic types exist. The body or a part can be moved as a whole from one place to another in a straight line, called *linear movement,* or it can be moved around the arc of a circle, called *circular, angular,* or *rotatory movement.* The terms circular, angular, and rotatory are synonymous from the standpoint of mechanics and can be used interchangeably in the description of movements.

**3.12  The Planes and Axes of Joint Movements**

Both linear and angular movements are found in the human anatomy. For example, the linear movement of the body as a whole in running a hundred-yard dash is produced by the angular movements of the limbs.

Even though the movements of the body at one time or another involve both types, angular movement is most often found in the musculoskeletal system; e.g., a bony lever rotates at a joint because of the force imparted to it by a muscle contraction. These angular movements all occur in a definite plane and around a definite axis.

The three planes of motion (Fig. 3–1) that correspond to the three dimensions of space are

A. *Sagittal* (saj'i-tal) or *anteroposterior plane*: This is a vertical plane that passes through the center of gravity of a body from front to back and, divides it into right and left sections.

B. *Frontal or lateral plane*: This is a vertical plane that passes through the center of gravity of a body from side to side and divides it into front and back sections.

C. *Transverse or horizontal plane*: This is a horizontal plane that passes through the center of gravity of a body and divides it into upper and lower sections.

**Fig. 3–1. The three cardinal planes of space.**

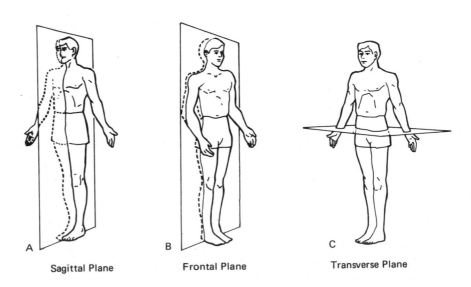

A — Sagittal Plane  B — Frontal Plane  C — Transverse Plane

When a plane is laid through the center of gravity of a body, as above, it is called a *cardinal plane*. Planes drawn through the center of gravity of a body segment or through the center of a joint, as is often the case, are called *secondary planes*.

The angular motion of a body part occurs around a center of rotation or *axis*. The three axes of motion, called the X, Y, and Z axes, are located at the intersection of the three planes of space as shown in Figure 3–2. Each of these axes is perpendicular to the plane in which the motion occurs and is defined as follows:

A. *Frontal or X-axis*: This axis passes horizontally from side to side perpendicular to the sagittal plane.

B. *Vertical or Y-axis:* This axis passes perpendicular to the ground and to the transverse plane.

C. *Sagittal or Z-axis:* This axis passes horizontally from front to back and is perpendicular to the frontal plane.

**Fig. 3-2. The three axes of motion located at the intersection of the three planes.**

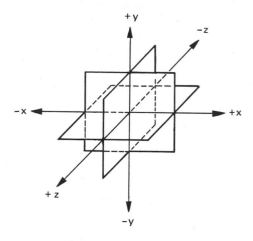

The three types of joints in the human body are (1) diarthroses (di"ar-thro'sis) or freely movable, (2) amphiarthroses (am"fe-ar-thro'sis) or slightly movable, and (3) synarthroses (sin"ar-thro'sis) or immovable. Some of the subdivisions and important features that characterize each of these types are given in the following sections.

**3.13 The Classification of Joints**

## The Diarthrodial Joints

Diarthrodial joints are distinguished by the presence of an articular cavity and by having freedom of movement. Six types of movable joints can be determined anatomically by the shape of their articular surfaces. These six diarthrodial joints can be further classified into four groups on the basis of the number of axes around which the joint surfaces can rotate:

A. Nonaxial joints

1. Sliding, or arthrodial joints

B. Uniaxial joints

1. Hinge, or ginglymus (jin'gli-mus) joints
2. Pivot, or trochoid (tro'koid) joints

C. Biaxial joints

1. Condyloid, or ellipsoid (e-lip'soid) joints
2. Saddle, or reciprocal reception joints

D. Triaxial joints

1. Ball-and-socket, or enarthrodial joints

*Sliding Joints.* Sliding joints permit gliding, or linear movements only, as in the joints between the carpal bones of the wrist, between the tarsal bones of the ankle, and between the articular processes of the vertebrae. Gliding movements, however, are to some extent common to all diarthrodial joints. The articular surfaces of these joints are nearly flat, or one surface may be slightly concave and the other slightly convex.

*Hinge Joints.* Hinge joints allow angular movements in one plane, like a door on its hinges. The articular surfaces of these joints are shaped to permit motion only in the forward and backward (sagittal) plane. Such movements are called flexion and extension and may be seen in the joint between the humerus and ulna, in the knee and ankle joints, and in the articulations of the phalanges.

*Pivot Joints.* Pivot joints allow rotatory movements only around one axis. In this type of joint a ring rotates around a pivot, or a pivotlike process rotates within a ring of bone and cartilage. A good example of a pivot joint is the articulation between the atlas (first cervical vertebra) and axis (second cervical vertebra). The atlas contains a ring formed in front by the anterior arch and in back by the transverse ligament. The odontoid process of the axis forms a pivot and around this pivot the ring of the atlas rotates carrying the head with it. Another example is found in the superior articulation of the radius and ulna, where the head of the radius rotates within the ring formed by the radial notch of the annular ligament.

*Condyloid Joints.* Condyloid joints permit movements in two planes: sagittal and frontal. When an oval-shaped head, or condyle, of a bone is received into a circular or elliptical cavity, it is said to form a condyloid joint; an example is the wrist joint. Movements permitted in this type of joint include flexion and extension in the sagittal plane, and abduction and adduction in the frontal plane. No axial rotation, however, is allowed.

*Saddle Joints.* Saddle joints are like the condyloid joints in that they provide for angular movements in two planes, but their structures are different. The articular surface of each of the articular bones is concave in one direction and convex in another, at right angles to the former. The metacarpal bone of the thumb articulates with the trapezium of the wrist by a saddle joint. The movements of these joints are the same as those of condyloid joints.

*Ball-and-Socket Joints.* Ball-and-socket joints permit angular movements in all directions and also a pivot movement. In this type of joint a more or less rounded head fits into a cuplike cavity, as does, for example, the head of the femur into the acetabulum of the hip, and the head of the humerus into the glenoid cavity of the scapula. The shoulder joint is the most freely movable joint in the body.

## Amphiarthrodial Joints

Amphiarthrodial joints are characterized as having a continuous union, lacking an articular cavity, and being only slightly movable. The two types of slightly movable joints are

A. *Symphysis* (sim"fi-sis): In these joints the bones are united by a plate or disk of fibrocartilage of considerable thickness. These fibrocartilages not only bind the bones firmly in place, but also function as buffers or shock absorbers; example: the articulation between the two pubic bones, called the symphysis pubis.

B. *Syndesmosis* (sin"des-mo'sis): In this type of joint the bony surfaces are united by an interosseous ligament; example: the radioulnar union formed by the thin interosseous membrane occupying the interval between the shafts of the radius and ulna.

## Synarthrodial Joints

Synarthrodial joints are characterized as having a continuous union, lacking an articular cavity, and being immovable. The four types of immovable joints, classified on the basis of the type of intervening process, are

A. *Sutures* (su'turs): These joints are formed by processes and indentations interlocking; example: the sutures between the parietal bones of the skull.

B. *Schindylesis* (skin"di-le'sis): These joints are formed when a thin plate of bone is received in a cleft or fissure of another bone; example: the reception of the vomer in the fissure between the maxillae and between the palatine bones.

C. *Gomphosis* (gom-fo'sis): These joints are formed when a conical process fits into a socket; example: roots of teeth into the alveoli of the maxillae and mandible.

D. *Synchondrosis* (sin"kon-dro'sis): This is a temporary joint in which cartilage, either fibrous or hyaline, forms a union; example: epiphyseal unions, which are transitory and disappear when ossification is completed.

A typical diarthrodial joint is illustrated in Figure 3–3. Regardless of the shape of the articulating surfaces, all diarthrodial joints have the following structures in common.

**3.14 The Architecture of Diarthrodial Joints**

A. *The articular surfaces*: These are the bone portions that are in contact with and move upon each other. These surfaces are constructed of a specially hard, compact, osseous substance, the *articular lamella*, which provides an unyielding support for the articular cartilage and differs from ordinary compact bone in that it is denser, contains no haversian canals, and is not covered with periosteum.

**Fig. 3-3. A typical diarthrodial joint.**

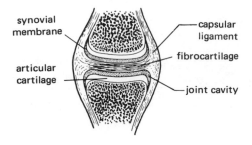

B. *The articular cartilage*: This is a layer of the original cartilage that persists over the articular surfaces after ossification is completed. This cartilage offers a much smoother surface than can be obtained from the bone itself; thus it serves to increase freedom of movement by reducing friction. It is thickest over the areas of greatest pressure in the joints.

C. *The articular disk*: This is additional cartilage located in some joints. In some joints the articular surfaces are incongruent, so that they are never in contact over their whole extent. This incongruence is compensated for, in some cases, by the interposition of an articular cartilaginous disk or meniscus, which serves to adapt the surfaces to each other, as in the knee joint. In some cases the disk may entirely separate the articular surfaces, as between the bodies of the vertebrae. The disk may also divide the articular cavity into two portions, as in the sternoclavicular articulation. In some joints, the articular margins of the bony sockets are provided with a fibrocartilaginous structure which tends to deepen the socket, as in the glenoid lip of the hip joint.

D. *The articular capsule*: This is a sleevelike, fibrous sheath attached to the circumference of the articular extremity of each bone so as to form an envelope surrounding the articulation. The outer layer of the capsule is composed of fibrous connective tissue and is continuous with the periosteum near the borders of the articular surfaces of the bones. The capsule tends to bind the bones together, but is sufficiently loose and flexible in most joints to permit freedom of movement. It also serves as a protective covering for the joint and as a support for the synovial membrane.

E. *Ligaments*: These are accessory strengthening fibrous bands that assist in holding the bones in apposition. They may be incorporated in the articular capsule or appear as independent structures. Most ligaments blend with the fibrous capsule on their deep surfaces and are, therefore, really local thickenings of the capsule. Where a capsule is particularly thin, the joint is usually protected by the adjacent tendon of a muscle. In the case of hinge joints, the anterior and posterior parts of the capsules are regularly thin and protected by the muscles passing in front and behind the joint, while the medial and lateral surfaces are reinforced by well-developed ligaments.

Ligaments play an important part as limiters of movement. Although the type of movement allowed at a joint usually depends primarily on the shape of the articular surfaces, ligaments sometimes guide the movement, and they regularly assist muscles in limiting the amount of movement allowed at a joint. They are also an important source of stability to the joint.

F. *The synovial membrane*: This is the inner layer of the articular capsule which serves as the source of synovia. *Synovia* is a thick, viscid fluid, which resembles in appearance the white of an egg. The synovial fluid forms a film over the articular cartilages and serves to lubricate them. It also is the main source of nutrition for joint cartilage. In some joints, the synovial membrane is prolonged into folds that increase the area of contact between apposed surfaces, as in the knee joint. These folds, which may contain fat, serve as joint cushions to fill in the spaces and to break the force of movements. Sometimes these folds become detached, resulting in impaired and painful movement of the joint. The membrane lines all parts of the joint cavity except over the articular cartilages.

The joints found in all parts of the body, excluding the skull, are listed in Table 3-1 and are illustrated in Figures 3-4, 3-5, and 3-6.

**3.15 The Joints of the Body**

**Table 3-1. The Joints of the Human Body (excluding the skull)**

---

### *The Lower Extremity*

---

A. *The foot*

1. The interphalangeal articulations (hinge joints): articulations between the phalanges.
2. The metatarsophalangeal articulations (condyloid): articulations between the metatarsals and the proximal phalanges.
3. The intermetatarsal articulations (sliding joints): two sets of articulations are included:

   a. The distal intermetatarsal articulations: articulations formed by the adjacent sides of the distal extremities of the metatarsal bones.
   b. The proximal intermetatarsal articulations: articulations formed by the adjacent sides of the proximal extremities of the metatarsal bones.

4. The tarsometatarsal articulations (sliding joints): articulations formed by the proximal ends of the metatarsal bones and the adjacent tarsal bones.
5. The intertarsal articulations (sliding joints): articulations between the individual tarsal bones.

   a. The subtalar joint: articulation between the talus and calcaneus.
   b. The transverse tarsal or midtarsal joint: two joints are included:

      (1) Calcaneocuboid joint: articulation between the calcaneus and the cuboid located on the lateral side of the transverse tarsal joint.
      (2) Talonavicular joint: articulation between the talus and navicular located on the medial side of the transverse tarsal joint.

      These two joints stretch across the foot almost transversely and combined they form a horizontal S.

   c. The anterior intertarsal or cuneonavicular joint: articulation between the navicular and the cuneiforms. This joint also extends slightly between the cuneiforms and between the cuboid and the lateral cuneiform.

B. *The ankle joint or talocrural articulation* (hinge joint)

   Articulation formed by the tibia and fibula articulating with the superior surface of the talus.

C. *The tibiofibular articulations*

   Three joints are included:

1. The inferior tibiofibular articulation (sliding joint): inferior articulation between the tibia and fibula.

**Fig. 3–4.  The joints of the lower extremity.**

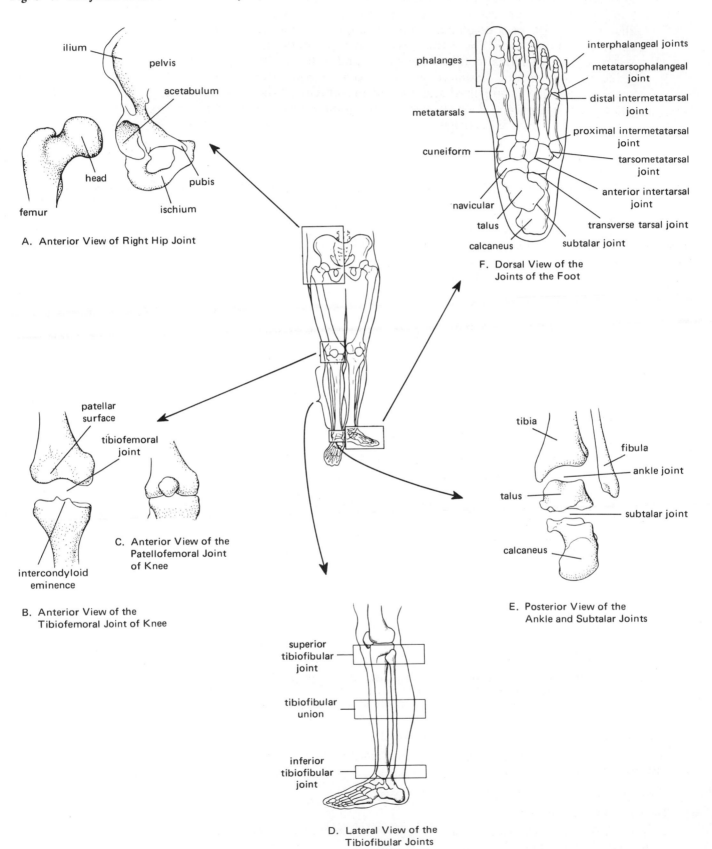

A.  Anterior View of Right Hip Joint

B.  Anterior View of the
    Tibiofemoral Joint of Knee

C.  Anterior View of the
    Patellofemoral Joint
    of Knee

D.  Lateral View of the
    Tibiofibular Joints

E.  Posterior View of the
    Ankle and Subtalar Joints

F.  Dorsal View of the
    Joints of the Foot

**Table 3-1. The Joints of the Human Body (excluding the skull) (continued)**

### *The Lower Extremity (continued)*

   2. The tibiofibular union (syndesmoses): the union of the shafts of the tibia and fibula by means of an interosseous membrane.
   3. The superior tibiofibular articulation (sliding joint): superior articulation between the tibia and fibula.

D. *The knee joint* (hinge joint)

   This joint may be regarded as a double one; a patellofemoral articulation, and a tibiofemoral articulation.

E. *The hip joint* (ball-and-socket joint)

   Articulation between the femur and the coxal bone.

F. *The pelvis*

   1. The symphysis pubis (symphysis): articulation of the two pubic bones where these come together and complete the pelvis anteriorly.
   2. The sacroiliac articulation (sliding joint): articulation between the sacrum and ilium.

### *The Trunk*

A. *The spinal column*

   1. The intervertebral articulations:

      a. The articulations of the bodies of the vertebrae (symphysis): intervertebral fibrocartilaginous disks are interposed between the bodies of adjacent vertebrae.
      b. The articulations of the neural arches (sliding joints): articulations between the articular processes of adjacent vertebrae.
      c. The atlantoaxial articulations: two types of joints are included:

         (1) The lateral atlantoaxial joints (sliding joints): articulation between the superior articular processes of the second cervical vertebra called the axis and the inferior articular process of the first cervical vertebra called the atlas.
         (2) The atlantodental joint (pivot joint): articulation formed by the toothlike process (dens) of the axis which fits into a ring on the posterior surface of the atlas.

   2. The atlantooccipital articulation (condyloid joint): articulation between the atlas and the occipital bone of the skull.

B. *The thorax*

   1. The costovertebral articulation:

      a. The capitular articulation (sliding joint): articulation between the ribs and the bodies of the thoracic vertebrae.
      b. The costotransverse articulation (sliding joint): articulation between the ribs and the transverse processes of the corresponding thoracic vertebrae.

   2. The intersternal articulations:

      a. The superior intersternal joint (synchondrosis): articulation between the inferior border of the manubrium and the superior border of the body.
      b. The inferior intersternal joint (synchondrosis): articulation between the inferior border of the body and the superior border of the xiphoid process.

   3. The costochondral joints (synchondrosis): articulations between the sternal ends of the ribs and the costal cartilages.

**Table 3-1. The Joints of the Human Body (excluding the skull) (continued)**

---

### *The Trunk (continued)*

---

4. The sternocostal joints (synchondrosis): articulations between the lateral borders of the sternum and the sternal ends of the costal cartilages.
5. The interchondral joints (sliding joints): articulations between the contiguous borders of the sixth to the tenth costal cartilages.

---

### *The Upper Extremity*

---

A. *The shoulder girdle*

1. The sternoclavicular joint (sliding joint): articulation between the medial or sternal end of the clavicle and the manubrium of the sternum and the cartilage of the first rib.
2. The acromioclavicular joint (sliding joint): articulation between the lateral or acromial end of the clavicle and the medial edge of the acromion process of the scapula.
3. The coracoclavicular union (syndesmoses): The coracoclavicular ligament connects the clavicle with the coracoid process of the scapula.

B. *The shoulder joint* (ball-and-socket joint)

Articulation between the humerus and the scapula.

---

**Fig. 3-5. The joints of the trunk.**

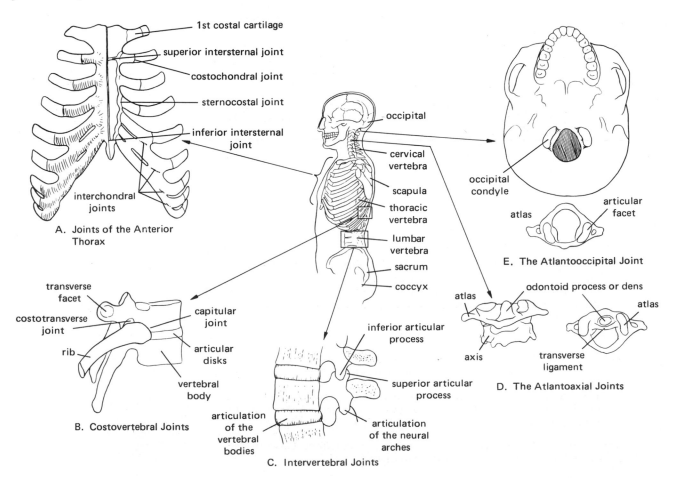

1st costal cartilage
superior intersternal joint
costochondral joint
sternocostal joint
inferior intersternal joint
interchondral joints

A. Joints of the Anterior Thorax

occipital
cervical vertebra
scapula
thoracic vertebra
lumbar vertebra
sacrum
coccyx

occipital condyle
atlas
articular facet

E. The Atlantooccipital Joint

transverse facet
costotransverse joint
rib
capitular joint
articular disks
vertebral body

B. Costovertebral Joints

inferior articular process
superior articular process
articulation of the vertebral bodies
articulation of the neural arches

C. Intervertebral Joints

atlas
odontoid process or dens
atlas
axis
transverse ligament

D. The Atlantoaxial Joints

**Fig. 3-6. The joints of the upper extremity.**

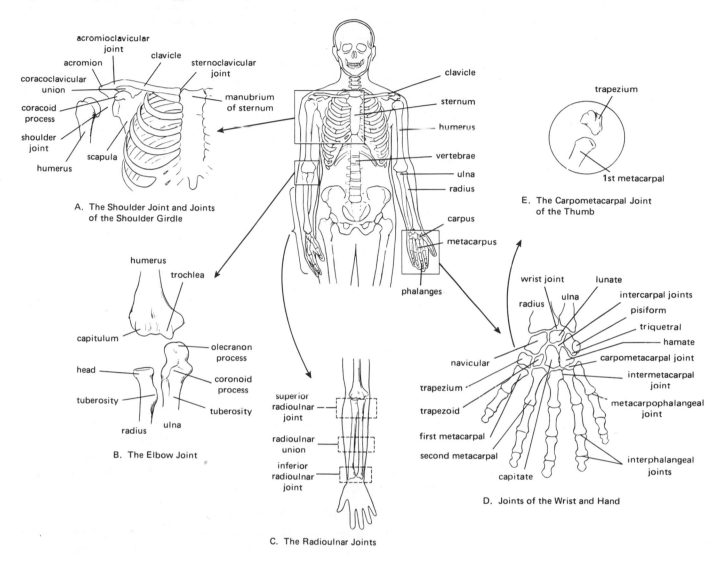

A. The Shoulder Joint and Joints of the Shoulder Girdle

B. The Elbow Joint

C. The Radioulnar Joints

D. Joints of the Wrist and Hand

E. The Carpometacarpal Joint of the Thumb

**Table 3-1. The Joints of the Human Body (excluding the skull) (continued)**

*The Upper Extremity (continued)*

C. *The elbow joint* (hinge joint)

Articulation of the humerus with the ulna and the radius.

D. *The radioulnar joints*

Three joints are included:

1. The superior radioulnar joint (pivot joint): articulation between the superior extremities of the radius and ulna.
2. The inferior radioulnar joint (pivot joint): articulation between the inferior extremities of the radius and ulna.
3. The radioulnar union (syndesmoses): the space between the shafts of the radius and ulna is occupied by a thin interosseous membrane.

Table 3–1. **The Joints of the Human Body (excluding the skull) (continued)**

*The Upper Extremity (continued)*

E. *The wrist or radiocarpal joint* (condyloid joint)

Articulation between the radius and the navicular, lunate, and triquetral bones.

F. *The intercarpal joints* (sliding joints)

Articulations between the individual carpal bones.

G. *The carpometacarpal joints* (saddle joint at thumb, sliding joints at the medial four articulations)

Articulations between the metacarpals and the distal row of carpal bones.

H. *The intermetacarpal joints* (sliding joints)

Articulations between the adjacent sides of the proximal extremities of the medial four metacarpal bones.

I. *The metacarpophalangeal joints* (hinge joint at thumb, condyloid joints at the medial four articulations)

Articulations between the metacarpal bones and the proximal phalanges.

J. *The interphalangeal joints* (hinge joints)

Articulations between the phalanges.

---

## 3.16 The Fundamental Joint Movements

When defining specific joint movements, it is always assumed that the body is in the anatomical position: that is, the individual is standing upright, arms at his sides with the palms of his hands facing forward. The linear and angular movements that occur at the diarthrodial joints of the body are

A. Linear or Gliding Movement

This is the simplest kind of motion that can take place in a joint and is the characteristic movement of the sliding joints. In this type of movement one surface moves over another without any angular or rotatory movement; example: the costovertebral articulations permit a slight gliding of the heads and tubercles of the ribs on the bodies and transverse processes of the vertebrae.

B. Angular Movement

This type of movement occurs in the spinal column and between long bones, and by it the angle between two bones is either increased or decreased. When the anatomical position is used as a frame of reference, we can see that these movements occur in a definite plane and around a definite axis as follows:

1. *Movements in the Sagittal Plane About a Frontal Axis*

    a. *Flexion*: a movement in which the anterior or posterior surface of one bone approaches the anterior or posterior surface of another bone; example: bringing the front surface of the thigh toward the abdomen is hip flexion.

b. *Extension*:  a movement in which a bone is returned to the anatomical position from the flexed position; hence, the reverse of flexion.

c. *Hyperextension*:  the movement of a limb or body part beyond the extended position.

2. *Movements in the Frontal Plane About a Sagittal Axis*

a. *Abduction*:  the movement of a body part away from the center line of the body; example:  lifting the arm out to the side of the body.  Once started, the movement is called abduction throughout its entire range, even though, as in the case of the abducting arm at the shoulder joint, the arm actually comes back toward the body after passing above the horizontal or during the second 90 degrees of the movement. In the spinal column, abduction is also called *lateral flexion.*

b. *Adduction*:  the reverse of abduction.  It means brought to or nearer the middle line of the body; example:  bringing the arm to the side of the body from the abducted position.

   *Note*:  at the wrist, abduction is also called *radial flexion*, and adduction is also called *ulnar flexion.* Both abduction and adduction have a different meaning when used with reference to the fingers and toes. Abduction and adduction of the fingers refer to an imaginary line drawn through the middle finger; of the toes, to an imaginary line drawn through the middle toe.  In the foot, flexion is sometimes referred to as *dorsal flexion,* and extension is referred to as *plantar flexion.*  The movements of the thumb as defined in Table 3–2 do not follow the rules identified here.

3. *Movements in the Transverse Plane About a Vertical Axis*

a. *Rotation*:  movement in which a bone moves around a central or long axis, often an imaginary one, without undergoing any displacement from this axis. *Inward or medial rotation* occurs when the anterior surface of a bone turns inward.  *Outward or lateral rotation* occurs when the anterior surface of a bone turns outward.   Inward rotation of the forearm is called *pronation*, and outward rotation of the forearm is called *supination*.  Lifting the medial border of the foot, outward rotation, is called *inversion*; lifting the lateral border of the foot, inward rotation, is called *eversion.*

4. *Movement in both the Sagittal and Frontal Planes*

a. *Circumduction*:  a movement in which a body part describes a cone, with the apex at the joint and the base at the distal end of the part.  It does not involve rotation; therefore, it may occur in biaxial joints by a combination of flexion, abduction, extension, and adduction; example: swinging the limbs (arms and legs) in a circle.

**3.17 Movements Allowed at the Different Diarthrodial Joints of the Body**

The movements allowed at the different diarthrodial joints of the body are listed in Table 3-2 and illustrated in Figures 3-7 through 3-18.

**Table 3-2. The Diarthrodial Joint Movements of the Human Body (excluding the skull)**

---

*Lower Extremity*

---

**Fig. 3-7. Inversion and eversion of the foot.**

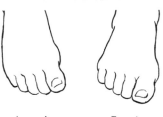

Inversion       Eversion

A. *The foot*

1. *The interphalangeal articulations* (hinge joints): These joints being of the hinge type permit only *flexion* and *extension*. Extension at these joints is drawing the toes dorsally or upward and flexion is drawing them downward.

2. *The metatarsophalangeal articulations* (condyloid joints): In addition to *flexion* and *extension*, these joints permit limited *abduction* and *adduction*. Abduction is drawing the first and second toes, and the fourth and fifth toes away from the middle or third toe. Adduction is the movement of these toes toward the middle one. Lateral movement of the middle toe is abduction, and a medial movement of this toe is adduction.

3. *The intermetatarsal, tarsometatarsal,* and *intertarsal articulations* (sliding joints). The movements at these joints are of a gliding nature, resembling a restricted form of flexion, extension, abduction, and adduction. Slight *abduction* and *adduction* of the front part of the foot on the rear occurs mostly at the talonavicular articulation. *Inversion* and *eversion* occur at both the subtalar and transverse tarsal articulations. Inversion is turning the sole of the foot medially, while eversion is turning the sole of the foot laterally. The combined movement of adduction and inversion is called *supination,* and the combined movement of abduction and eversion is called *pronation.*

B. *The ankle joint* (hinge joint)

Being a hinge joint, the movements of the ankle are only flexion and extension. *Flexion* (dorsi flexion) is a movement of the dorsal surface of the foot toward the anterior surface of the leg, while *extension* (plantar flexion) is the reverse action.

C. *The tibiofibular articulations*

The inferior and superior tibiofibular articulations being sliding joints merely allow gliding movements which are passive in character in that they complement the movements of the ankle joint. Thus during flexion of the ankle the fibula tends to be displaced upward and during extension it is displaced downward. These movements are resisted by the interosseous membrane.

D. *The knee joint* (hinge joint)

Being a hinge joint, the knee permits *flexion* and *extension.* In addition, a certain amount of free rotation is possible during flexion, the range of rotation being greatest at 90° of flexion at which position it amounts to about 50°. No free rotation is possible in the fully extended knee. Rotation of the flexed knee is identified as being either *inward* or *outward.*

**Fig. 3-8. Dorsiflexion and plantar flexion of the ankle joint.**

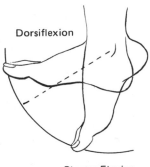

Dorsiflexion

Plantar Flexion

**Table 3-2. The Diarthrodial Joint Movements of the Human Body (excluding the skull) (continued)**

### Lower Extremity (continued)

E. *The hip joint* (ball-and-socket joint)

Since a ball-and-socket joint is a triaxial joint, it is capable of movements in all directions. Thus the hip joint permits *flexion* (swinging the leg forward), *extension* (return to anatomical position), and hyperextension (swinging the leg backward from the anatomical position). Hyperextension is extremely limited by the iliofemoral ligament at the front of the joint.

This joint also permits *abduction* (swinging the leg sideward away from the midline of the body), *adduction* (return to anatomical position), and *hyperadduction* (swinging the leg across the body) which is possible only when the other leg is moved out of the way.

*Outward rotation, inward rotation,* and *circumduction* are also permitted. Outward rotation is a movement of the femur around its vertical axis so that the knee is turned outward. Inward rotation is a movement of the femur around its vertical axis so that the knee is turned inward. Circumduction is a combination of flexion, abduction, extension, and adduction, performed sequentially in either direction.

F. *The pelvis*

The main movements of the pelvis take place at the sacroiliac articulation which is the only diarthrodial joint (sliding joint) in the pelvis. The sacroiliac joint is essentially a sturdy one and the slight movement which is permitted is gliding both upward and downward, as well as forward and backward and a rotation around a transverse axis in such a manner that the pelvis can be tilted slightly.

### The Trunk

A. *The spinal column*

The movements of the vertebrae and head are flexion (bending forward), *extension* (return to anatomical position from flexion), *hyperextension* (bending backward from the anatomical position), *abduction* or *lateral flexion* (bending sideward), *adduction* (return to anatomical position from abduction), and *rotation* (twisting) in the cervical and thoracic regions. Rotation of the head takes place at the atlantodental joint (pivot joint). *Circumduction* of the spinal column is a circular movement of the upper trunk on the lower, being a combination of flexion, lateral flexion, and hyperextension, but not including rotation. Circumduction of the head takes place at the atlantooccipital articulation (condyloid joint) as well as does flexion, extension, and lateral flexion.

B. *The thorax*

The movements of the thorax are those concerned with the process of breathing, i.e., inhalation and exhalation. Inhalation is brought about by the elevation of the ribs and the consequent forward thrust of the sternum and the lateral displacement of the shafts of the ribs. The center of rotation for the elevation of the ribs is at the capitular and costotransverse articulations. In exhalation the movements of these joints are the reverse of those that take place in inhalation.

C. *Integrated movements of the pelvis*

The joints at which the integrated movements of the pelvis occur are the two hip joints, the sacroiliac joint, and the joints of the lumbar spine, particularly the lumbosacral articulations.

The integrated movements of the pelvis are *flexion, increased inclination,* or *forward tilt,* which is a rotation of the pelvis forward so that the symphy-

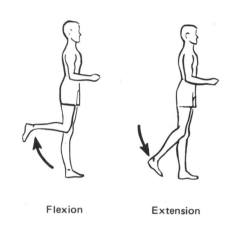

**Fig. 3-9. Flexion and extension of the knee joint.**

Flexion          Extension

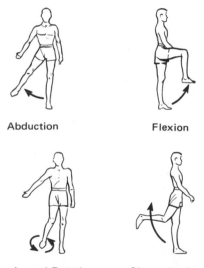

**Fig. 3-10. Selected movements of the hip joint.**

Abduction          Flexion

Inward Rotation          Circumduction

**Fig. 3-11. Selected movements of the vertebral column.**

Flexion of the
Trunk on the Thighs

Hyperextension
of the Spine

Lateral Flexion
of the Spine

Flexion of the
Thighs on the Trunk
Flexion of the Knees

**Fig. 3-12. (*A*) Movement of the thorax in inspiration. (*B*) Changes in position
of diaphragm and abdominal wall and in size of thoracic cavity during
repiration.**

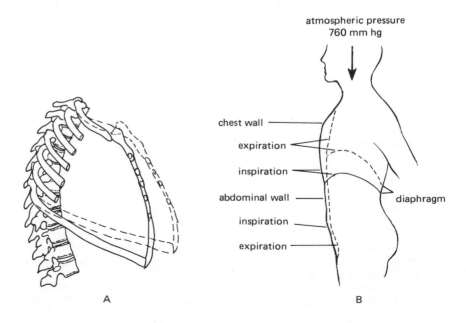

atmospheric pressure
760 mm hg

chest wall

expiration

inspiration

abdominal wall

inspiration

expiration

diaphragm

A

B

Table 3-2. The Diarthrodial Joint Movements of the Human Body
(excluding the skull) (continued)

### The Trunk (continued)

sis pubis turns downward and the posterior surface of the sacrum turns upward, and *extension, decreased inclination,* or *backward tilt,* which is the
reverse of flexion. *Lateral tilt* is a rotation of the pelvis such that one iliac
crest is lowered and the other raised. The tilt is named in terms of the side
moved downward being either right or left. *Circumduction* is a rolling of
the hips and is a combination of flexion, extension, and lateral tilt. *Rotation* or *lateral twist* is a rotation of the pelvis in the horizontal plane about a
vertical axis. The movement is named in terms of the direction toward
which the front of the pelvis turns.

### The Upper Extremity

A. *The shoulder girdle*

The movements of the shoulder girdle, expressed in terms of the movements
of the scapula, are *elevation* (hunching the shoulders), *depression* (return
from the position of elevation), *abduction* or *protraction* (a lateral movement of the scapula away from the spinal column), *adduction* or *retraction*
(a medial movement of the scapula toward the spinal column), *upward rotation* (a rotation of the scapula so that the glenoid fossa faces somewhat upward, *downward rotation* (return from the position of upward rotation),

Fig. 3-13. Selected movements of the shoulder girdle.

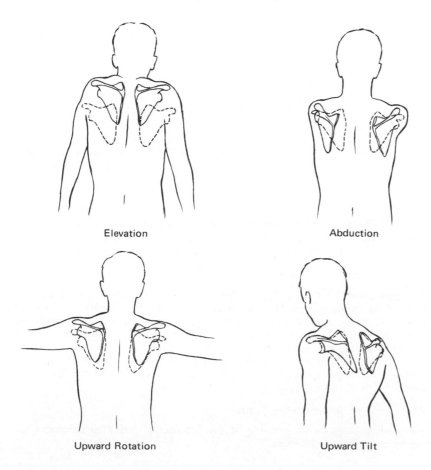

Elevation

Abduction

Upward Rotation

Upward Tilt

**Fig. 3–14. Selected movements of the shoulder joint.**

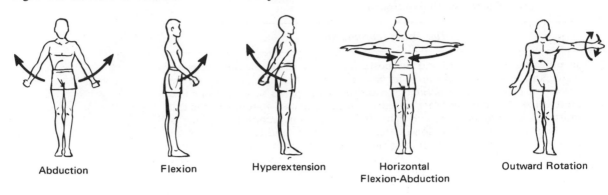

Abduction    Flexion    Hyperextension    Horizontal Flexion-Abduction    Outward Rotation

### Table 3-2. The Diarthrodial Joint Movements of the Human Body (excluding the skull) (continued)

#### *The Upper Extremity (continued)*

*upward tilt* (a forward rotation of the scapula so that its posterior surface faces slightly upward and the inferior angle protrudes from the back), and *reduction of upward tilt* (the return movement from upward tilt). The rolling of the shoulders is called *circumduction*.

B. *The shoulder joint* (ball-and-socket joint)

The movements of the shoulder joint, and therefore of the humerus, are *flexion* (swinging forward), *hyperflexion* (flexion continued beyond 180°) *extension* (return from flexion), *hyperextension* (swinging backward beyond the anatomical position), *abduction* (swinging sideward), *adduction* (return from abduction), *outward* and *inward rotation* (rotation around the vertical axis of the humerus), *horizontal flexion-adduction* (a forward, sidearm movement of the abducted humerus in a horizontal plane), *horizontal extension-abduction* (a backward, sidearm movement of the flexed humerus in a horizontal plane). Swinging the limbs in a circle is called *circumduction*.

C. *The elbow joint* (hinge joint)

The movements of the elbow joint are *flexion* (bringing the anterior forearm toward the anterior surface of the arm) and *extension* (the reverse of flexion).

D. *The radioulnar joints*

The superior and inferior radioulnar joints (pivot joints) permit *pronation* (a rotation of the forearm so that the palm of the hand faces downward when the forearm is horizontal) and *supination* (a rotation of the forearm so that the palm of the hand faces upward when the forearm is horizontal).

E. *The wrist joint* (condyloid joint)

The movements of the wrist joint are flexion (movement of the palmar surface of the hand toward the anterior surface of the forearm), *extension* (return from flexion), *hyperextension* (movement of the dorsal surface of the hand toward the posterior surface of the forearm), *abduction or radial flexion* (bending the hand laterally), *adduction* or *ulnar flexion* (bending the hand medially), and *circumduction* (a movement of the hand at the wrist whereby the fingertips describe a circle, and the hand as a whole describes a cone).

F. *The intercarpal joints* (sliding joints)

The gliding movements possible at the intercarpal joints complement the movements of the wrist joint.

**Fig. 3–15. Pronation and supination of the forearm.**

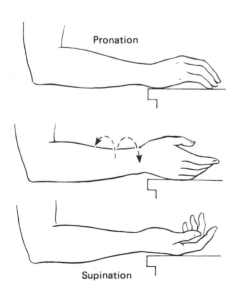

Pronation

Supination

Table 3–2. **The Diarthrodial Joint Movements of the Human Body (excluding the skull) (continued)**

*The Upper Extremities (continued)*

G. *The carpometacarpal and intermetacarpal joints of the fingers* (sliding joints)

These joints permit only a slight amount of flexion and extension, which supplement the movements of the wrist.

H. *The carpometacarpal joint of the thumb* (saddle joint).

This joint allows *abduction* (a forward movement of the thumb at right angles to the palm), *adduction* (return movement from abduction), *hyperadduction* (a backward movement of the thumb at right angles to the hand), *extension* (a lateral movement of the thumb away from the index finger), *flexion* (return movement from extension), *hyperflexion* (a medial movement of the thumb from a position of slight abduction—the thumb slides across the front of the palm), *circumduction* (a combination of all the movements described above, performed in sequence in either direction), and *opposition* (touching the tip of the thumb to the tip of any of the four fingers).

I. *The metacarpophalangeal joints of the fingers* (condyloid joints)

The movements allowed at these joints are *flexion* (movement of the anterior surface of the finger toward the palmar surface of the hand), *extension* (return movement from flexion), *hyperextension* (a slight movement of the posterior surface of the fingers toward the dorsal surface of the hand), and *circumduction* (a circular movement of the fingers).
   *Abduction* of the fourth and fifth and index fingers is a movement of these fingers away from the middle finger; *adduction* is the reverse movement. *Abduction* of the middle finger, also called *radial flexion*, is a movement of this finger laterally; *adduction*, or *ulnar flexion*, is the movement of the middle finger medially.

J. *The metacarpophalangeal joint of the thumb* (hinge joint)

This joint allows only *flexion* and *extension*.

K. *The interphalangeal joints* (hinge joints)

Being hinge joints, these articulations allow only *flexion* (curling the fingers) and *extension* (straightening the fingers). *Hyperextension* is slight, if present at all.

---

**Fig. 3–16. Selected movements of the wrist.**

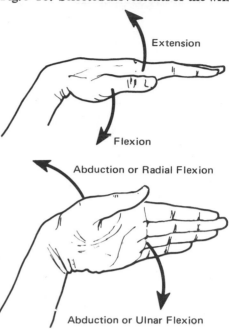

Extension

Flexion

Abduction or Radial Flexion

Abduction or Ulnar Flexion

**Fig. 3–17. Abduction and adduction of the fingers.**

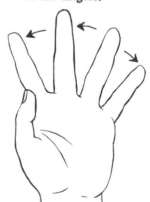

Adduction

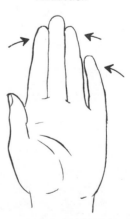

Abduction

**Fig. 3–18. Selected movements of the thumb at the carpometacarpal joint.**

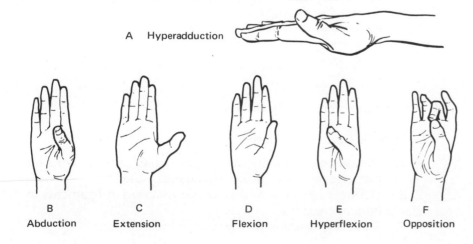

A  Hyperadduction

B
Abduction

C
Extension

D
Flexion

E
Hyperflexion

F
Opposition

**3.20  Study Guidelines**

In studying the basic concepts of this chapter, the student is advised to master not only the general objectives given at the beginning of the chapter, but also the following specific objectives for each section. Study suggestions (hints) are also given for some of the sections.

### 3.21  The Kinesiological Importance of Joints

A.  Specific Student Objectives

1.  Define arthrology.
2.  Define a joint or articulation.
3.  Give four reasons why the study of joints is important in kinesiology.

### 3.22  The Planes and Axes of Joint Movements

A.  Specific Student Objectives

1.  Identify and define the two basic types of movement found in the human anatomy.
2.  Identify and define the three planes of motion.
3.  Identify and define the three axes of motion.
4.  Differentiate between cardinal and secondary planes.

### 3.23  The Classification of Joints

A.  Specific Student Objectives

1.  Identify and define the three major types of joints found in the human body.
2.  Identify and define the six types of diarthrodial joints.
3.  Give an example of each type of diarthrodial joint found in the human anatomy.
4.  Define the following terms:

    a.  synarthroses
    b.  suture
    c.  schindylesis
    d.  synchondrosis
    e.  amphiarthroses
    f.  symphysis
    g.  syndesmosis

### 3.24  The Architecture of Diarthrodial Joints

A.  Specific Student Objectives

1.  Define the following terms:  articular lamella, articular cartilage, articular disks, articular capsule.
2.  Define a ligament and state the function of ligaments in human anatomy.
3.  State the function of the synovial membrane.

## 3.25 The Joints of the Body

A. Specific Student Objectives

1. Give the name of each diarthrodial joint in the lower extremity, in the trunk, and in the upper extremity.
2. Give the names of the bones that enter into the formation of each diarthrodial joint in the body.
3. Identify each diarthrodial joint in the body by type.
4. Give the number of axes of motion allowed at each diarthrodial joint in the body.
5. Identify the unique architecture of each diarthrodial joint of the body.

B. Study Hints

In studying Table 3–1, the student should locate each joint in the illustrations and then on a mounted skeleton. The student should also ask himself the following questions:

1. What is the name of the joint, and what bones are involved in its formation? It should be noted that the name of the joint is derived from the names of the bones involved. For example, the metatarsophalangeal joints are the articulations between the metatarsals and the proximal phalanges.
2. What type of joint is it? Study should be given to the shape of the articular surfaces of the bones involved in the joint. Reviewing the definitions given for the different joint classifications should prove beneficial in determining the type of joint involved.
3. How many axes of motion will the joint allow?
4. What is the unique architecture of the particular joint? Attention should be given to the shape of the articular surfaces, the location of the articular cartilage, the presence of articular disks, and the approximate location of the articular capsule and ligaments. Glancing ahead to the chapters dealing with the joints of the lower extremity, trunk, and upper extremity might prove profitable at this time.

## 3.26 The Fundamental Joint Movements

A. Specific Student Objectives

1. Define the anatomical position.
2. Differentiate between linear and angular movements.
3. Define the following terms:

    a. flexion
    b. extension
    c. abduction
    d. adduction
    e. rotation
    f. circumduction

4. Identify the fundamental joint movements that occur in the sagittal plane about a frontal axis.
5. Identify the fundamental joint movements that occur in the frontal plane about a sagittal axis.
6. Identify the fundamental joint movement that occurs in the transverse plane about a vertical axis.
7. Identify the fundamental joint movement that occurs in the sagittal and frontal planes.

### 3.27 Movements Allowed at the Different Diarthrodial Joints of the Body

A. Specific Student Objectives

1. Identify the movements allowed at each diarthrodial joint of the body excluding those of the skull.
2. Identify the specific joints and the specific joint actions involved in the performance of a given total body movement.

B. Study Hints

In studying Table 3–2, the student should locate each joint on a mounted skeleton and follow these exercises:

1. The student should study each joint by asking himself the following questions:

   a. What type of joint is involved? In other words, is the joint a sliding, hinge, pivot, condyloid, saddle, or ball-and-socket joint?
   b. How many axes of motion does the joint have? In other words, is the joint a nonaxial, uniaxial, biaxial or triaxial joint?
   c. What type of movement will the joint allow? In other words, will the joint allow only linear or angular movement, or will it allow both types of movement?
   d. What specific actions will the joint allow? The following classification of joints according to type, axes, and actions should be helpful in the analysis of specific joint actions:

| *Type of Joint* | *Actions Allowed* |
|---|---|
| (1) *Nonaxial* | |
|    (a) Sliding | Gliding |
| (2) *Uniaxial* | |
|    (a) Hinge | Flexion and extension |
|    (b) Pivot | Rotation |
| (3) *Biaxial* | |
|    (a) Condyloid | Flexion and extension |
| | Abduction and adduction |
|    (b) Saddle | Same as condyloid |

(4) *Triaxial*
    (a) Ball-and-socket        Flexion and extension
                                   Abduction and adduction
                                   Rotation

e. What specific plane and what specific axis is used in the performance of each joint action?

It should be remembered that when the *anatomical position* is used as a frame of reference, each fundamental joint movement occurs in a definite plane and around a definite axis. Flexion and extension, for instance, occur in the sagittal plane about a frontal axis. Likewise, abduction and adduction occur in the frontal plane and about a sagittal axis, and rotation occurs in the transverse plane about a vertical axis. Since circumduction involves flexion, abduction, extension, and adduction performed in sequence, it occurs in both the sagittal and frontal planes.

2. The student should practice the performance of each joint action on himself by following these steps:

a. Locate the joint in his own body.
b. Perform the joint actions by following the description of each action given in Table 3–2.

3. The student should practice analyzing the joint actions involved in several total body movements. For example, what specific joints, and what specific joint actions are involved in the performance of the following activities?

a. Walking
b. Throwing
c. Jumping
d. Chin ups
e. Push ups

The student should consult any recent anatomy text for supplementary readings in general arthrology. A list of selected anatomy texts is given in Appendix B.

**4.11 Recommended Supplementary Readings**

# 4

# Basic Concepts
# of Myology

Myology is that branch of anatomy which deals with the muscular system. This system is of obvious importance to students of human movement in that muscles generate the forces which move the human body and its parts.

All movements of the body and its segments are the result of muscle force and/or the application of some external force. The most common form of external force that acts upon the body is gravity. Without doubt, however, the majority of bodily movements can be attributed to the contraction of muscles. The fingers close over a tennis racket or a ball because the flexors of the fingers are acting. One opens a window by flexion of the elbow and pushes it closed by extensors. Likewise, it is the muscles of the neck that turn the head to look at something over the shoulder, muscles of the back that contract to lift the trunk after bending forward to tie one's shoes, and flexors of the thigh that lift the thigh to make it easier to reach the shoes to be tied. In short, muscle contraction is the source of energy for all movements in which the body and its extremities are raised or held in position against the pull of gravity.

**4.11   The Kinesiological Importance of Muscles**

## 4.12 Characteristics of Muscle Tissue

Muscles are able to perform their special functions because of the following four properties of muscle tissue:

A. *Irritability*, or *excitability*: This is the property of receiving stimuli and responding to them. All cells possess this property. The response of any tissue to stimulation is to perform its special function, which in the case of muscle tissue is contraction.

B. *Contractility*: This is the property that enables muscles to change their shape and become shorter and thicker. This property is characteristic of all protoplasm, but is more highly developed in muscle tissue than in any other.

C. *Extensibility*: This is the property that enables muscles to be stretched or extended.

D. *Elasticity*: This is the property that enables muscles to readily return to their original form when a stretching force is removed.

## 4.13 Types of Muscle Tissue

Muscle tissue is composed, as is every other tissue, of cells and intercellular substance. The cells are elongated and are called *fibers*. The intercellular substance consists of a small amount of cement, which holds the cells to the framework of connective tissue in which they are embedded.

Muscular tissue may be classified according to its structure or location:

| *Structure* | *Location* |
|---|---|
| Striated, or cross-striped | Skeletal |
| Nonstriated, or smooth | Visceral |
| Indistinctly striated | Cardiac |

The *striated* muscle tissue receives its name because of the parallel cross stripes, or striae, that characterize its microscopic appearance. This tissue is called *skeletal* because it forms the muscles attached to the skeleton. In addition, it is sometimes called *somatic* because it helps to form the body wall, and *voluntary* because the movements accomplished are in most instances under conscious control.

The *nonstriated* or *smooth* muscle tissue is so called because it does not exhibit cross stripes or striae. It is called *visceral* because it forms the muscular portion of the visceral organs.

*Cardiac* muscle tissue forms the heart. It is also indistinctly striated in that the transverse striations are less distinct than those in skeletal muscles. The cells are also smaller than those found in the skeletal muscle system.

Since smooth and cardiac muscle tissues are usually studied in detail in human physiology courses, only the skeletal muscles will be considered in this book.

The skeletal muscles found in the lower extremity, trunk, and upper extremity are listed in Table 4–1 and are illustrated in Figures 4–1 through 4–8, as well as in the figures of Chapters 11, 12, 14, 16, 18, and 20.

**4.14  The Skeletal Muscles
of the Body**

**Table 4–1. The Skeletal Muscles of the Body (excluding the skull)**

*The Lower Extremity*

A. *The intrinsic muscles of the foot* (Fig. 4–1)

These muscles are located entirely in the foot and do not cross the ankle joint.

1. *The dorsal muscle of the foot:* This muscle is located on the top (dorsum) of the foot.

a. The extensor digitorum brevis (Figs. 4–1 and 11–7)

**Fig. 4–1. The intrinsic muscles of the foot.**

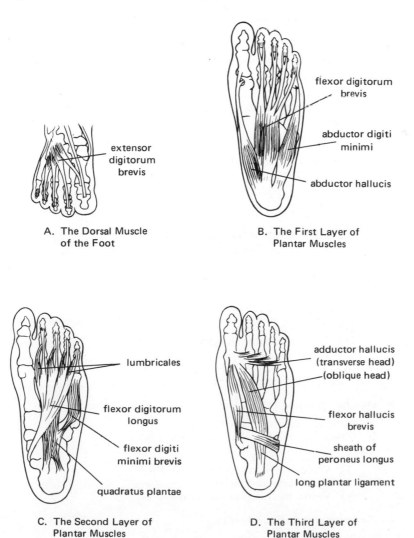

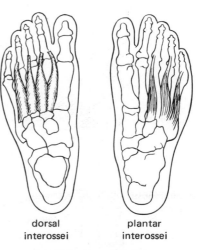

**Fig. 4–2. The muscles of the leg.**

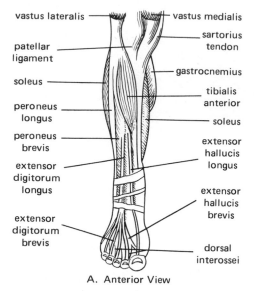

vastus lateralis
vastus medialis
patellar ligament
sartorius tendon
soleus
gastrocnemius
peroneus longus
tibialis anterior
peroneus brevis
soleus
extensor digitorum longus
extensor hallucis longus
extensor hallucis brevis
extensor digitorum brevis
dorsal interossei

A. Anterior View

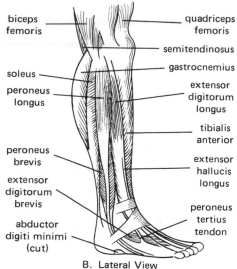

biceps femoris
quadriceps femoris
semitendinosus
soleus
gastrocnemius
peroneus longus
extensor digitorum longus
tibialis anterior
peroneus brevis
extensor hallucis longus
extensor digitorum brevis
abductor digiti minimi (cut)
peroneus tertius tendon

B. Lateral View

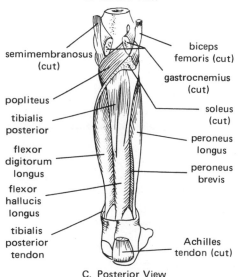

semimembranosus (cut)
biceps femoris (cut)
popliteus
gastrocnemius (cut)
tibialis posterior
soleus (cut)
flexor digitorum longus
peroneus longus
flexor hallucis longus
peroneus brevis
tibialis posterior tendon
Achilles tendon (cut)

C. Posterior View

**Table 4–1. The Skeletal Muscles of the Body (excluding the skull) (continued)**

*The Lower Extremity (continued)*

2. *The plantar muscles of the foot:* These muscles are located on the bottom of the foot.

   a. The first or superficial layer (Figs. 4–1 and 11–8)

      (1) Abductor hallucis (hal'lucis)
      (2) Abductor digiti minimi
      (3) Flexor digitorum brevis

   b. The second layer (Figs. 4–1 and 11–9)

      (1) Quadratus plantae
      (2) Flexor digiti minimi brevis
      (3) Lumbricales (lum"bre-ka'les)

   c. The third layer (Figs. 4–1 and 11–10)

      (1) Adductor hallucis
      (2) Flexor hallucis brevis

   d. The fourth or deep layer (Figs. 4–1 and 11–11)

      (1) Plantar interossei (in"ter-os'e-i)
      (2) Dorsal interossei

B. *The muscles of the leg*

   1. *Anterior group* (Figs. 4–2 and 12–6)

      a. Tibialis (tib"e-a'lis) anterior
      b. Extensor digitorum longus
      c. Peroneus tertius (tur'she-us)
      d. Extensor hallucis longus

   2. *Lateral group* (Figs. 4–2 and 12–7)

      a. Peroneus (per"o-ne'us) longus
      b. Peroneus brevis

   3. *Posterior group* (Fig. 4–2)

      a. Superficial layer (Fig. 12–8)

         (1) Gastrocnemius (gas"trok-ne'me-us)

      b. Middle layer (Fig. 12–9)

         (1) Soleus
         (2) Plantaris

      c. Deep layer (Fig. 12–10)

         (1) Tibialis posterior
         (2) Flexor digitorum longus
         (3) Flexor hallucis longus

C. *The muscles of the thigh* (Fig. 4–3)

   1. *Anterior group*

      a. Sartorius (sar-tor'e-us) (Fig. 14–14)
      b. Quadriceps femoris (fem'oris) (Fig. 14–15)

         (1) Rectus femoris
         (2) Vastus medialis (vas'tus me"di-alis)
         (3) Vastus lateralis (lat'er-alis)
         (4) Vastus intermedius (in"ter-me'di-us)

   2. *Posterior group* (Fig. 14–16)

      a. Popliteus (pop"lit'e-us)

**Table 4-1.  The Skeletal Muscles of the Body (excluding the skull) (continued)**

---

*The Lower Extremity (continued)*

---

    b.  Hamstrings (Fig. 14–17)

        (1)  Semitendinosus (sem″e-ten′di-no-sus)
        (2)  Semimembranosus (sem″e-mem′brano″sus)
        (3)  Biceps femoris

  3.  *Medial group* (Fig. 14–18)

    a.  Gracilis (gras′i-lis)
    b.  Pectineus (pek-tin′e-us)
    c.  Adductor longus
    d.  Adductor brevis
    e.  Adductor magnus

D.  *The muscles of the hip* (Fig. 4–3)

  1.  *Anterior group*  (Fig. 14–19)

    a.  Iliacus (il-i′ah-kus)
    b.  Psoas (so′as)

  2.  *Posterior group*  (Figs. 14–20, through 14–23)

    a.  Tensor fasciae latac
    b.  Gluteus maximus
    c.  Gluteus medius

**Fig. 4-3.  The muscles of the thigh and hip.**

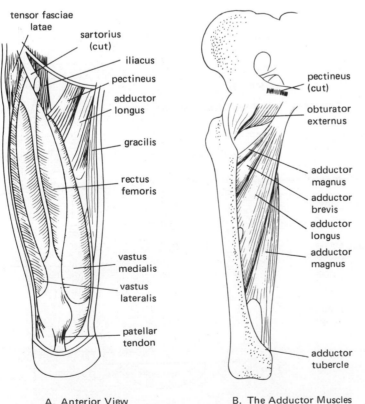

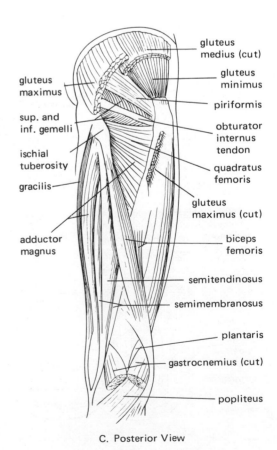

A. Anterior View        B. The Adductor Muscles        C. Posterior View

**Table 4–1. The Skeletal Muscles of the Body (excluding the skull) (continued)**

---

*The Lower Extremity (continued)*

---

  d. Gluteus minimus
  e. The six deep outward rotators (Fig. 14–23)

    (1) Piriformis (pir″i-for′mis)
    (2) Superior gemellus (je-mel′us)
    (3) Inferior gemellus
    (4) Obturator internus
    (5) Obturator externus
    (6) Quadratus femoris

---

*The Trunk*

---

A. *The muscles of the abdomen* (Figs. 4–4 and 4–5)

  1. *Anterior group* (Figs. 16–12 through 16–14)

    a. Rectus abdominis
    b. External oblique
    c. Internal oblique
    d. Transversus abdominis, also called transversalis

  2. *Posterior group* (Fig. 16–15)

    a. Quadratus lumborum

**Fig. 4–4.** (*A*) The superficial muscles of the anterior aspect of the trunk.
    (*B*) The superficial muscles on the posterior aspect of the trunk.
    (*C*) The deeper muscles on the posterior aspect of the trunk.

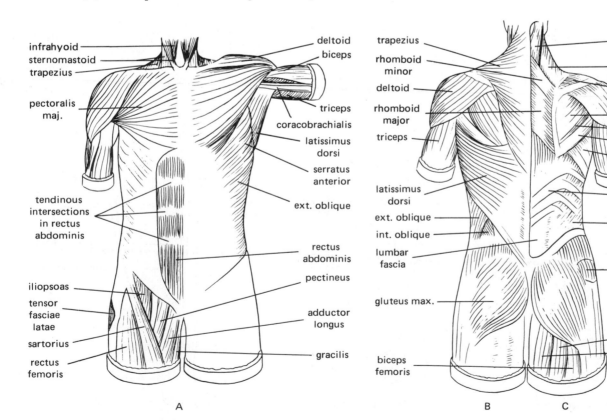

**Fig. 4-5. The deeper muscles on the anterior (*A*) and posterior (*B*) abdominal wall.**

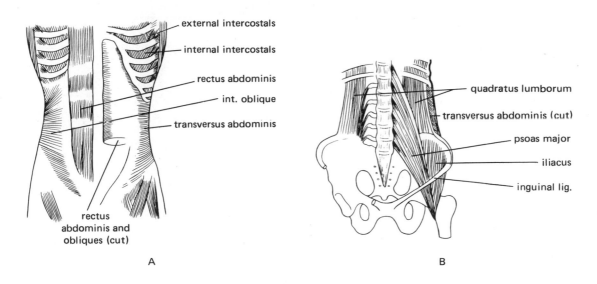

A                                                                    B

Table 4-1. The Skeletal Muscles of the Body (excluding the skull) (continued)

*The Trunk (continued)*

B. *The muscles of the thorax*

1. *Internal*

   a. Diaphragm (Fig. 16–16)
   b. Transversus thoracis (Fig. 16–17)

2. *External*

   a. Anterior and lateral (Fig. 16–18)

      (1) External intercostals
      (2) Internal intercostals

   b. Posterior (Fig. 16–19)

      (1) Serratus posterior superior
      (2) Serratus posterior inferior

C. *The muscles of the back* (Fig. 4–4 and 4–5)

1. *The superficial layer* (Fig. 16–20): These muscles are collectively called the *erector spinae* muscles and were once called the *sacrospinalis* (sa″kro-spi-na′lis) muscles.

   a. Iliocostalis (il″e-o-kos-ta′lis): lateral group

      (1) Iliocostalis thoracis
      (2) Iliocostalis cervicis

   b. Longissimus (lon-jis′i-mus): middle group

      (1) Longissimus thoracis
      (2) Longissimus cervicis
      (3) Longissimus capitis

   c. Spinalis (spi-na′lis): medial group

      (1) Spinalis thoracis
      (2) Spinalis cervicis

**Table 4–1.  The Skeletal Muscles of the Body (excluding the skull) (continued)**

*The Trunk (continued)*

    2.  *The middle layer* (Fig. 16–21):  These muscles—collectively *semispinalis.*

        a.  Semispinalis thoracis
        b.  Semispinalis cervicis
        c.  Semispinalis capitis

    3.  *The deep layer* (Fig. 16–22):  These muscles are collectively called the *deep posterior muscles of the spine.*

        a.  Multifidus
        b.  Rotatores, longus and brevis
        c.  Interspinalis
        d.  Intertransversus, lateralis and medius
        e.  Levator costae, longus and brevis

D.  *The muscles of the neck* (Fig. 4–4)

    1.  *Anterior*

        a.  Sternocleidomastoid (ster″no-kli″do-mas′toid) (Fig. 16–25)
        b.  Prevertebral (pre-ver′te-bral) muscles (Fig. 16–23)

            (1)  Longus capitis
            (2)  Longus colli
            (3)  Rectus capitis anterior
            (4)  Rectus capitis lateralis

**Fig. 4-6.  Superficial muscles of the anterior (*A*) and posterior (*B*) shoulder, arm, and forearm.**

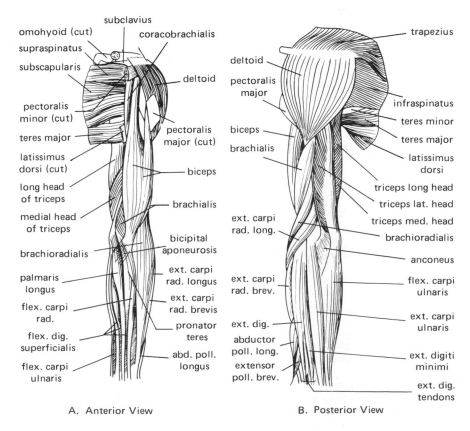

A. Anterior View           B. Posterior View

**Table 4-1. The Skeletal Muscles of the Body (excluding the skull) (continued)**

### *The Trunk (continued)*

    c. Hyoid (hi′oid) muscles (Fig. 16–24)

        (1) Suprahyoids

            (a) Mylohyoid
            (b) Geniohyoid
            (c) Digastric
            (d) Stylohyoid

        (2) Infrahyoids

            (a) Thyrohyoid
            (b) Sternothyroid
            (c) Sternohyoid
            (d) Omohyoid

  2. *Lateral group*

    a. The three scaleni muscles (Fig. 16–26)

        (1) Scalenus (ska-le′nus) anterior
        (2) Scalenus posterior
        (3) Scalenus medius

  3. *Posterior group*

    a. The two spleni muscles (Fig. 16–27)

        (1) Splenius (sple′ne-us) capitis
        (2) Splenius cervicis

    b. The suboccipitals (sub″ok-sip′i-tals) (Fig. 16–28)

        (1) Obliquus capitis superior
        (2) Obliquus capitis inferior
        (3) Rectus capitis posterior minor
        (4) Rectus capitis posterior major

### *The Upper Extremity*

A. *The muscles of the shoulder region* (Fig. 4–6)

  1. Muscles of the shoulder region with proximal attachments on the trunk

    a. Anterior group (Fig. 18–11)

        (1) Pectoralis (pek″to-ra′lis) major
        (2) Pectoralis minor
        (3) Subclavius (sub-kla′ve-us)
        (4) Serratus (scr-ra′tus) anterior

    b. Posterior group (Fig. 18–12)

        (1) Trapezius (trah-pe′ze-us) (Fig. 18–14)
        (2) Rhomboids (rhom′boids) major and minor
        (3) Levator scapulae
        (4) Latissimus dorsi (lah-tis′i-mus dor′si) (Fig. 18–15)

  2. *Muscles of the shoulder region with proximal attachments on the scapula*

    a. Anterior (Fig. 18–13)

        (1) Subscapularis (sub″skap-u-la′ris)

    b. Posterior group (Fig. 18–12)

        (1) Deltoids
        (2) Supraspinatus (su″prah-spi-na′tus)
        (3) Infraspinatus (in″frah-spi-na′tus)
        (4) Teres (te′rez) major
        (5) Teres minor

**Table 4-1. The Skeletal Muscles of the Body (excluding the skull) (continued)**

### *The Upper Extremity (continued)*

B. *The muscles of the arm* (Fig. 4–6)

   1. *Anterior or flexor group* (Fig. 18–16)

      a. Biceps brachii
      b. Coracobrachialis (kor″ah-ko-bra″ke-a′lis)
      c. Brachialis (bra″ke-a′lis) (Fig. 18–17)

   2. *Posterior or extensor group* (Fig. 18–18)

      a. Triceps brachii
      b. Anconeus (an-ko′ne-us)

C. *The muscles of the forearm* (Figs. 4–6 and 4–7)

   1. *Anterior group*: This group comprises the flexors of the wrist and fingers, and the pronators of the forearm.

      a. *Superficial subdivision* (Figs. 20–10 and 20–11): All five of these muscles arise by a common tendon from the medial epicondyle of the humerus and are (named from the lateral to the medial side):

         (1) Pronator teres
         (2) Flexor carpi radialis
         (3) Palmaris longus
         (4) Flexor digitorum superficialis
         (5) Flexor carpi ulnaris

      b. *Deep subdivision* (Figs. 20–11 and 20–12)

         (1) Flexor digitorum profundus
         (2) Flexor pollicis longus
         (3) Pronator quadratus

   2. *Posterior group*: This group comprises the extensors of the hand and fingers and the supinators of the forearm.

      a. *Superficial subdivision* (Figs. 20–13 and 20–14): The majority of these muscles take their proximal attachments from a common tendon on the lateral epicondyle of the humerus. These muscles are (named from the lateral to the medial side).

         (1) Brachioradialis
         (2) Extensor carpi radialis longus
         (3) Extensor carpi radialis brevis
         (4) Extensor digitorum
         (5) Extensor digiti minimi
         (6) Extensor carpi ulnaris

      b. *Deep subdivision* (Fig. 20–15)

         (1) Supinator
         (2) Abductor pollicis longus
         (3) Extensor pollicis longus
         (4) Extensor pollicis brevis
         (5) Extensor indicis

D. *The intrinsic muscles of the hand* (Fig. 4–8)

   1. *Muscles of the thumb* (Fig. 20–16): these muscles form a prominence called the thenar eminence which forms the proximal and lateral boundary of the palm.

      a. Abductor pollicis brevis
      b. Opponens pollicis
      c. Flexor pollicis brevis
      d. Adductor pollicis

**Fig. 4–7. The deeper muscles of the anterior (*A-B*) and posterior (*C*) forearm.**

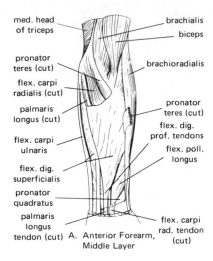

A. Anterior Forearm, Middle Layer

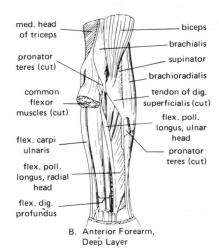

B. Anterior Forearm, Deep Layer

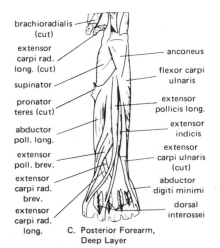

C. Posterior Forearm, Deep Layer

**Fig. 4-8. The muscles of the hand.** (*A*) Fascia of palmar surface of the hand. (*B*) Palmar surface of the hand and wrist with the thenar and hypothenar muscles. (*C*) Adductor pollicis and opponens digiti minimi.

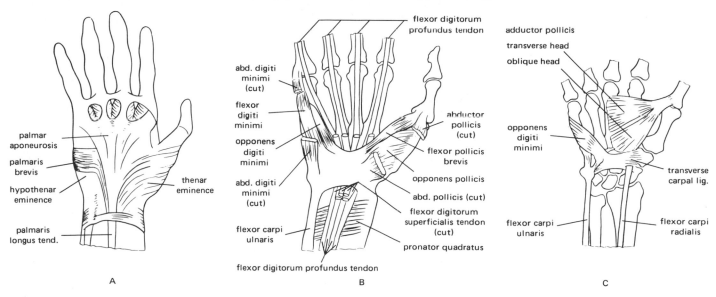

A       B       C

---

**Table 4-1. The Skeletal Muscles of the Body (excluding the skull) (continued)**

---

### *The Upper Extremity (continued)*

---

2. *Muscles of the little finger* (Fig. 20–17): these muscles form a prominence called the hypothenar eminence which forms the medial border of the palm.

   a. Abductor digiti minimi
   b. Flexor digiti minimi
   c. Opponens digiti minimi

3. *The lumbricales* (Fig. 20–18)

4. *The interosseous muscles* (Fig. 20–19)

   a. The palmar interossei
   b. The dorsal interossei

---

Each skeletal muscle listed in Table 4–1 is considered an independent motor organ with a connective tissue framework (stroma) and an arterial, venous, lymphatic, and nerve supply. The skeletal muscles vary considerably in size, shape, and arrangement of fibers. Some are broad and sheetlike, others are triangular or quadrate, still others are cylindrical or fusiform (spindle-shaped).

In general, a muscle that is long and slender is weak but can shorten through a relatively large distance, whereas a muscle that is short and broad has much strength of contraction but can exert it through a proportionately shorter distance. The arrangement of fibers varies in different muscles. In some muscles the fibers are parallel to the long axis of the muscle, in some they converge to a narrow attachment, and in some they are oblique and may even be curved, as in the sphincters of the face. Muscles have been classified, therefore,

## 4.15 Structure of Skeletal Muscles

according to the arrangement of their fibers. The two main classifications are (1) *fusiform* and (2) *penniform*. In the fusiform arrangement the fibers are parallel to the long axis of the muscle; in the penniform (feather-shaped) arrangement the fibers are attached obliquely to a tendon. The three main classifications of penniform muscles (Fig. 4–9) are

**Fig. 4–9. Examples of different fiber arrangements in skeletal muscles.**

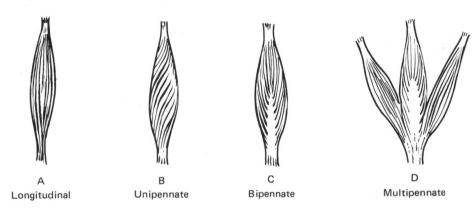

| A | B | C | D |
| --- | --- | --- | --- |
| Longitudinal | Unipennate | Bipennate | Multipennate |

A. *Unipennate*: muscle fibers are arranged to one side of the tendon; example: extensor digitorum longus located in the leg.
B. *Bipennate*: muscle fibers are arranged on both sides of a tendon; example: flexor hallucis longus and gastrocnemius in the leg.
C. *Multipennate*: muscle fibers converge to several tendons, giving a herringbone effect; example: middle deltoid.

**The Muscle Fiber**

Regardless of their arrangement in the different muscles, all muscle fibers (cells) are basically the same in both structure and function. Figure 4–10*A* shows a fusiform muscle consisting of a bulky central part called the *belly* that tapers off to form two extremities. The muscle fibers are located in the belly, whereas the extremities are composed mostly of fibrous connective tissue which forms the tendons that attach the muscle to its bony levers. The muscle fibers contract on stimulation, and the force of contraction is transmitted to the bones through the tendons.

Figures 4–10*B* and *C* illustrate the muscle fibers, which appear striated in the light microscope. Also illustrated here are the endplates of motor nerves, which are the small branching structures at the surface of the fibers, and the many mitochondria and nuclei located on the inside of the fiber.

Figures 4–10*D*, *E*, and *F* illustrate the myofibrils—the unique structures of muscles. Each muscle fiber contains a thousand or more longitudinal myofibrils arranged in bundles within the fiber. The

**Fig. 4-10. The structure of a muscle fiber. (Redrawn from H. E. Huxley: "The Contraction of Muscle," *Scientific American*, November, 1968.)**

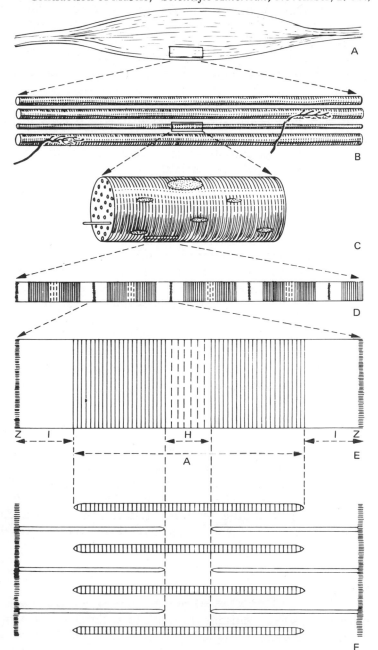

myofibrils, in turn, are composed of many small fibrils composed of actin and myosin molecules, which are the actual contractile elements of the muscle.

Figure 4-10*D* illustrates several sarcomeres showing the dark and light bands that give the characteristic striated appearance to skeletal muscles. A single sarcomere is illustrated in Figure 4-10*E*. The dark band is called the A-band or anisotropic band, and the light band is called the I-band or isotropic band. The actin and myosin filaments are illustrated in Figure 4-10*F*. The actin filament is the thin filament, and the myosin filament is the thick filament. It should be noted that it is the arrangement of the actin and myosin filaments in the fiber that makes the light and dark bands, the A-band corresponding to the myosin filaments and the I-band corresponding to the segment of the fiber between successive myosin filaments. It should also be noted that the myosin and actin filaments interdigitate. During muscle contraction, the actin filaments slide inward among the myosin filaments, which results in the shortening of the muscle.

The muscle fiber is enclosed by a membrane called the sarcolemma, and immediately beneath the sarcolemma, is a plasma membrane which is the true cell membrane of the muscle fiber and capable of transmitting action potentials in the same manner that the nerve membrane transmits action potentials.

## Connective Tissue Framework

Each individual muscle fiber is surrounded by a fibrous, connective tissue sheath called the *endomysium* (en″do-mis′e-um), which serves to bind the adjacent fibers together. The fibers are also aggregated into parallel bundles or *fasciculi* (fah-sik′u-li) of varying girth and length, bound together by another fibrous, connective tissue sheath called the *perimysium*. The small bundles formed by the perimysium are called primary fasciculi. A third fibrous, connective tissue sheath called the *epimysium* envelops the entire muscle and extends into it as partitions dividing the primary bundles into larger bundles called secondary fasciculi.

The endomysium, perimysium, and epimysium, which form the connective tissue framework of the muscle (Fig. 4–11), serve two important functions. First, they bind the muscle parts together; second, they harness the force of muscle contraction and transmit this force to the bony attachments. The second function is possible because all three types of connective tissue extend beyond the ends of the muscle fibers to form the *tendon*. Indeed, the tendon consists mostly of extensions of the connective tissue framework of the muscle belly.

## Nerve Supply

The nerve cells that transmit impulses to skeletal muscle fibers are called motor *neurons*. Actually, from several hundred to several thousand motor neurons enter each muscle with each neuron dividing and spreading throughout the muscle. A single motor neuron innervates an average of 150 muscle fibers, which means that stimulation of one neuron will cause contraction of 150 muscle fibers at the same time. All the fibers innervated by the same neuron are called a *motor unit* because they always contract in unison.

The motor units operate under the all-or-none law. That is, when stimulated by a neuron, all the muscle fibers of the unit will contract to the full extent of their ability at that time or they will not contract at all.

It is especially important that all the muscle fibers in a motor unit do not lie side by side, but are spread throughout the muscle belly.

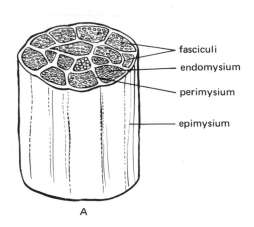

**Fig. 4–11. The connective tissue framework of a skeletal muscle.**

fasciculi
endomysium
perimysium
epimysium

A

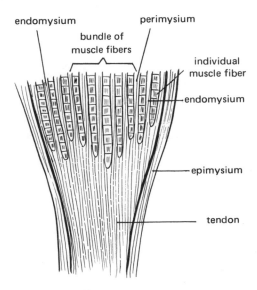

endomysium    perimysium
bundle of muscle fibers
individual muscle fiber
endomysium
epimysium
tendon

B

Because of this, stimulation of the motor unit causes a weak contraction in a broad area of the muscle, rather than a strong contraction at one specific point.

Those muscles that control very fine movements usually have only a few muscle fibers in each motor unit, which means that the ratio of motor neurons to muscle fibers is very high. For instance, the finger muscles, which must control the extremely discrete movements of the fingers, have very few fibers in each motor unit. On the other hand, postural muscles, which usually exhibit only very gross movements, may have as many as 200 or more fibers to the motor unit.

In the study of skeletal muscles and their actions it is important to keep certain key concepts in mind. A few of these concepts are as follows:

**4.16 Skeletal Muscle Functions**

1. *The unique function of skeletal muscles is to contract.* Skeletal muscles can do only two things: contract and relax. Contraction, however, is the unique function of muscles, and contraction produces the force that moves or prevents the movement of the body and its parts. Muscle contractions have been classified as follows:

   A. Isotonic contractions

   Contractions during which the length of the muscle changes. The two types of isotonic contractions are

   1. *Concentric, or shortening contraction:* a contraction in which the muscle shortens and produces movement of the bony levers to which it is attached.
   2. *Eccentric, or lengthening contraction:* a contraction in which the force of contraction is gradually released and the length of the muscle is allowed to increase, or to return to its normal resting length. The length of the muscle can also be increased when an external force greater than the force of the contraction is applied.

   B. Isometric, or static contraction

   A contraction in which the length of the muscle does not change appreciably.

2. *Skeletal muscles contract only when stimulated.* Muscles can be stimulated to contract by many types of stimuli, such as externally applied electricity. The natural stimulation of a muscle, however, is by its innervation. Therefore, in normal functioning the skeletal muscles are under the direct control of the nervous system, and its own functions depend upon nerve stimulations.

3. *Skeletal muscles produce movements by pulling on bones.* The bones of the body serve as levers, as will be discussed in Chapter 5, and the joints of the body serve as fulcrums of these levers. When a muscle contracts, it applies a pulling force on a bony lever and causes the lever to rotate about its joint fulcrum. Therefore, a

skeletal muscle, its motor nerve, the bony levers to which it is attached, and the joint(s) that its tendon crosses work together as a physiological unit, always functioning together, each being practically useless without the normal functioning of the others.

4. *The joint actions produced by a muscle depend upon the location of the muscle and its line of pull in relation to the joint.* Muscles located on the anterior side of the arm with lines of pull anterior to the elbow joint, for instance, produce elbow flexion, whereas muscles located on the posterior side of the arm with lines of pull posterior to the elbow joint produce elbow extension. Perhaps it should be noted that muscles that move a part usually do not lie over that part. In most cases the body of a muscle lies *proximal* to the part moved with only its tendon crossing over the joint.

5. *Muscle and gravitational forces work together to produce many bodily movements.* The lifting of a weight against the force of gravity, for instance, is produced by muscle forces, whereas the gradual lowering of the weight to its resting place is produced by the force of gravity. The muscles control the lowering of the weight through the gradual relaxation of their contractions. Therefore, the same muscles are involved in both the lifting and the lowering of the weight. In lifting the weight, concentric contractions are involved; in lowering the weight, eccentric contractions are involved.

6. *Skeletal muscles almost always act in groups rather than alone.* In other words, joint actions are usually produced by muscles working as members of a team. The various roles a muscle may play on the team are as follows:

A. *Prime movers*: the muscles whose contractions are primarily responsible for producing a joint movement.

B. *Emergency mover*: a muscle called into action to assist the prime movers only when an exceptional amount of force is needed.

C. *Antagonist*: a muscle whose contraction tends to produce a joint action exactly opposite to the joint action of the prime movers.

D. *Fixator or stabilizer*: a muscle that contracts isometrically to anchor or to steady a bone or body part against the pull of the other contracting muscles, or against the application of some external force.

E. *Neutralizer*: a muscle that acts to prevent an undesired action of another contracting muscle. For instance, if a muscle both extends and adducts, but only extension is desired in the movement, an abductor contracts to neutralize the adduction action of the mover.

**4.17 Classification of Muscle-Produced Movements**

The different types of bodily movements produced through muscle forces are classified as (1) postural movements, (2) ballistic movements, and (3) tension movements.

The movement of holding still, as in the maintenance of a football stance, is called a *postural* or a *fixation* movement. Although the body appears to be still, it is actually moving from side to side and to and fro over the base of support. This constant movement, called tremor, is due to the asynchronous summations occurring in the muscles. This type of movement is involved in all balance activities where the to-and-fro movements must be controlled by counter-movements to maintain the center of gravity of the body above the base of support.

A *ballistic* movement is one in which a forceful muscle contraction initiates the movement of a body part, but once initiated the movement continues on its own momentum. This type of movement is characteristic of such activities as throwing, striking, and kicking. The skillful execution of these movements requires that the movements be performed ballistically and not with a constant muscular contraction throughout the joint range of movement.

Movements that require constant muscular contraction throughout the range of movement are called *tension* movements. This type of movement is characteristic of the sprinting start in track, called a fast tension movement, and handwriting, called a slow tension movement.

Some movements found in sports and in everyday living require the utilization of all three types of movement. Running, for instance, requires the fixation of the trunk in the upright position, tension movement in the driving leg, and ballistic movement of the recovery leg. Some mixing of the three types of movement, in fact, is common in most complex motor skills.

## 4.18 Muscle Analysis of Joint Actions

In studying the muscles involved in the production of particular joint actions, it is important to remember that the joint actions are, in general, the *outcomes* of a series of events. The actions are initiated in the brain and/or spinal cord. The patterns of nerve impulses originating in the brain and/or spinal cord stimulate the muscle contractions that *produce* the joint actions.

In making a muscle analysis of a movement performance it is recommended that a list be prepared of all the joint actions that occur in the movement. Second, a list should be prepared of all the muscles that might be involved in producing each joint action. Third, a list should be prepared of all the additional joint actions each muscle listed in step two might have. It is possible that some or all of the undesired actions may be neutralized within the list. If not all of the undesired actions are neutralized, additional muscles must contract as neutralizers and these muscles should be listed as involved in the movement. Fourth, with the fact that a muscle as it contracts pulls on all bones to which it is attached in mind, the bones that must be stabilized should be identified and a list of the muscles that must be employed as stabilizers should be prepared. Consideration should also be given to the antagonistic muscles, which must be relaxed in order for the joint action to proceed smoothly.

In addition to the above procedures, muscles and their actions should be studied in the anatomical kinesiology laboratory. Some laboratory procedures found to be especially useful are

A. Study of a mounted skeleton. Here the student notices the location of a muscle, its points of attachment, its direction of pull, the relation of the line of pull to the joint, and its leverage.

B. Pulling upon the partly dissected muscles of a cadaver, either human or lower animal, and noticing the resulting joint actions.

C. Stimulation of individual muscles by electric current and noticing the resulting joint actions.

D. Study of subjects who have lost the use of certain muscles, to determine what loss of force and movement have resulted.

E. Palpation of the active muscles during the performance of a joint action.

F. Measuring the electrical activity in a muscle during the performance of a joint action through the use of electromyography.

Methods A, B, and C have their values from the standpoint of the educational laboratory, but caution should be taken to avoid the mistaken notion that because a muscle is situated in such a way that it *can* produce a movement that it necessarily *will* be involved in the production of that movement. Muscles act in groups and their actions depend not only upon their anatomical location, but also upon the neuronal organization of the circuits that control them. Methods E and F have been recommended by some kinesiologists as being the most valuable because they involve study of the normal living body and they tell us more conclusively what muscles contract in certain exercises and what movements call certain muscles into action. Probably the most satisfactory method of all is that employing electromyography.

### Electromyography

Electromyography is based on the fact that a completely relaxed or inactive muscle has no electrical activity associated with it. When, on the other hand, a muscle is engaged in contraction, action potentials appear. These action potentials can be measured by needle electrodes placed in the muscle or by skin electrodes placed over a muscle. In both cases, the electrodes are connected with an oscilloscope so that the action potentials may be viewed and recorded. With the aid of electromyography, it is now possible to tell what muscles, or even what parts of a muscle, participate in a movement. This method has taken much of the guesswork out of the study of muscles and the roles that particular muscles play in the production of various bodily movements.

In studying the basic concepts of this chapter, the student is advised to master not only the general objectives given at the beginning of the chapter, but also the following specific objectives for each section. Study suggestions (hints) are also given for some of the sections.

### 4.21   The Kinesiological Importance of Muscles

A. Specific Student Objectives

1. Define myology.
2. Give a reason why the study of muscles is important in kinesiology.

### 4.22   Characteristics of Muscle Tissue

A. Specific Student Objectives

1. Define the following four properties of muscle tissue:
   a. irritability
   b. contractility
   c. extensibility
   d. elasticity

### 4.23   Types of Muscle Tissue

A. Specific Student Objectives

1. Identify the three types of muscle tissue as classified by their structure and location.
2. Define the following terms:  somatic, visceral muscles, smooth muscles, skeletal muscles.

### 4.24   The Skeletal Muscles of the Body

A. Specific Student Objectives

1. Identify the muscles located in each region of the lower extremity, the trunk, and the upper extremity.

B. Study Hints

In studying muscle anatomy in general and Table 4–1 in particular, students are advised to do a minimum amount of pure memorizing.  It is much better to "think through" the information to be learned, than it is to resort to rote memory.  The following steps, therefore, are recommended:

*Step 1.*  The student should familiarize himself with the general locations, names, and appearances of the muscles found in the various regions of the body.  He should not proceed to the next step until he can identify each muscle to be studied by its name on a wall chart, or in the illustrations of the chapter.

In trying to remember the names of muscles it is helpful to remember that the name of a muscle often describes one or more of the following features about the muscle:

A. Its points of attachment; example: the sternocleido-mastoid muscle is named for its attachments on the sternum, clavicle, and mastoid process of the temporal bone.

The following definitions should prove helpful in associating the names of muscles with their attachments:

1. Muscles in the extremities

   a. *Digitorum*: a muscle attaching to the digits, that is, attaching to either the toes or fingers.
   b. *Digiti minimi*: a muscle attaching to the little toe or to the little finger.
   c. *Hallucis*: a muscle attaching to the big toe.
   d. *Pollicis*: a muscle attaching to the thumb.
   e. *Plantar*: of or pertaining to the sole of the foot; example: the quadratus plantae attaches in the sole of the foot.
   f. *Palmar*: pertains to or situated in the palm of the hand; example: the palmaris longus attaches in the palm of the hand.
   g. *Carpi*: a muscle attaching in the carpus or wrist.

2. Muscles in the trunk

   a. *Capitis*: a muscle attaching to the head.
   b. *Cervicis*: a muscle attaching to the cervical region or neck.
   c. *Thoracis*: a muscle attaching to the thorax.
   d. *Lumborum*: a muscle attaching to the lumbar region.

B. Number of divisions composing the muscle; example: biceps, triceps, or quadriceps.
C. Its location; example: tibialis or femoris.
D. Direction of its fibers; example: rectus (straight) or transversus.
E. Its shape; example: deltoid (triangular), trapezius (kite shaped), or quadratus.
F. Its action; example: flexor, extensor, or abductor. The following terms are used to name muscles according to their main actions:

   1. *Flexors*: decrease the angle of a joint. This occurs between the anterior surfaces of the bones except in the knee and toe joints.
   2. *Extensors*: return of the part from flexion to the normal anatomical position; increase in the angle of a joint.
   3. *Abductors*: move the bone away from the midline.
   4. *Adductors*: move the bone toward the midline.
   5. *Rotators*: cause a part to pivot upon its axis.

6. *Levators*: raise a part.
7. *Depressors*: lower a part.
8. *Sphincters*: reduce the size of an opening.
9. *Tensors*: tense a part, make it more rigid.
10. *Supinators*: turn the palm of the hand upward.
11. *Pronators*: turn the palm of the hand downward.

G. Its length:

1. *Longus*: the longer of two muscles; example: extensor digitorum longus.
2. *Brevis*: the shorter of two muscles; example: extensor digitorum brevis.

*Step 2.* The student should try to determine what bones each individual muscle attaches to from the knowledge gained in step one. In this book, the attachments of the muscles located in the extremities are identified as proximal and distal. The attachments of the muscles located on the axial skeleton are identified as upper or lower for those muscles whose line of pull is more or less vertical, and medial and lateral for those muscles whose line of pull is more nearly horizontal.

It is important that the student not try to learn too many details about muscle attachments at first.

*Step 3.* The student should try to determine the actions of each muscle from his knowledge of the following:

A. The general location of the muscle, i.e., whether the muscle is located on the anterior, posterior, medial, or lateral regions of the body part. As a general rule, posterior muscles produce posterior movements, anterior muscles produce anterior movements, and so forth.
B. The joints crossed by the muscle. A muscle cannot produce an action at a joint unless its tendon crosses over that particular joint. Some muscles, like the brachialis, cross over only one joint; others, like the hamstrings, cross over two joints; still others, like the extensor digitorum longus, cross over several joints. As a general rule, muscles produce actions at all joints that they cross.
C. The relation of the muscle's line of pull to the center of the joint. A muscle whose line of pull is directly anterior to the center of a joint, for instance, will *definitely* cause an anterior movement of the joint, if it produces a movement at all and this action is not neutralized by the pull of another muscle. The same relationship is true of muscles whose line of pull is located on the posterior, medial, or lateral sides of the joint center.
D. The possible axes of motion of the joint as determined by the structure of the joint itself. Hinge joints, as mentioned in the last chapter, are uniaxial joints and allow *only* flexion and extension. Pivot joints are also uniaxial joints, but allow only inward or outward rotation in the extremities or rotation right or left in the trunk.
   Condyloid and saddle joints are biaxial joints that

allow (1) flexion and extension and (2) abduction and adduction.

The ball-and-socket joints are, of course, triaxial joints that allow movement in all three planes of space, i.e., (1) flexion and extension, (2) abduction and adduction, and (3) rotation.

*Step 4.* The student should try to determine the muscles that produce each possible movement at each joint. That is, he should try to figure out the muscles that produce, for example, flexion of the elbow. The procedures recommended in step three should also prove helpful in this effort.

*Summary:* In the study of muscles it is extremely important that the student learn to associate the names of the muscles with the appearances and general locations of the muscles. This association is just as important in learning the names of muscles as it is in learning the names of people.

Second, it is important that the student become more knowledgeable about the precise location of the muscle in the body by learning its bony attachments.

Third, the actions of the muscle should be studied from two points of view: (1) individual action and (2) group actions. The individual action is closely associated with the anatomy of the muscle because, mechanically, the action is directly affected by the attachment of its two ends. In the study of group actions, it should be remembered that a muscle may be associated with one group of muscles in one action and a different group for another, possibly even antagonistic action.

## 4.25 Structure of Skeletal Muscles

A. Specific Student Objectives

1. Differentiate between a fusiform and a penniform muscle.
2. Identify and define the three main types of penniform muscles.
3. Define the following parts of a muscle fiber:

   a. myofibril
   b. sarcomere
   c. actin filaments
   d. myosin filaments
   e. sarcolemma

4. Define the following terms that apply to the connective tissue framework of a muscle:

   a. endomysium
   b. fasciculi
   c. perimysium
   d. epimysium

5. Define the following terms that apply to the nerve supply to a muscle:

   a. motor neuron
   b. motor unit
   c. all-or-none law

## 4.26  Skeletal Muscle Functions

A. Specific Student Objectives

1. Differentiate between isotonic and isometric contractions.
2. Differentiate between concentric and eccentric contractions.
3. Identify the unique function of a skeletal muscle.
4. Identify the six key concepts associated with skeletal muscle functions.
5. Define the following terms:

   a. prime mover
   b. emergency mover
   c. antagonist
   d. fixator or stabilizer
   e. neutralizer

## 4.27  Classification of Muscle-Produced Movements

A. Specific Student Objectives

1. Differentiate between postural, ballistic, and tension movements.
2. Give an example of a postural movement.
'3. Give an example of a ballistic movement.
4. Give an example of a tension movement.

## 4.28  Muscle Analysis of Joint Actions

A. Specific Student Objectives

1. Identify the six ways in which muscles may be studied in the anatomical kinesiology laboratory.
2. Which methods have been recommended by kinesiologists as being the most valuable because they involve study of the normal living body?
3. Define electromyography.
4. Identify the four steps recommended for use in making a muscle analysis of a movement performance.

**4.30 Recommended Supplementary Readings**

The student should consult any recent anatomy text for supplementary readings in general myology. A list of selected anatomy texts is given in Appendix B.

# Part II

# Anatomical Mechanics

# 5

# The Mechanical Function
# of Bones

**5.11    The Machine Function of Bones**

A machine may be defined as any device wherein mechanical energy is applied at one point and mechanical energy in a more useful form is delivered at another. Mechanical energy, like force, is defined simply as any energy tending to either cause or to change the movements of a body.

The three major components of a machine *system* are (1) a source of input energy called the *mover*, (2) a *machine* that changes the energy into a more useful form, and (3) a *utilization device* that takes the energy delivered to it and produces the movements of a body.

Human movements such as running, jumping, lifting, pulling, and throwing may be taken as examples of the mechanical capabilities of the musculoskeletal system. These movements are produced by skeletal muscles that apply force to bony machines operating at the joints of the body. The various segments of the body involved in a throwing movement, for example, may be considered the *utilization devices* that use the mechanical energy delivered to them through the bony machines in the production of mechanical work. The skeletal muscles are, of course, the *movers* of this mechanical system, and their function in this respect can be likened to that of the electric motor, water turbine, or the gasoline engine in other systems. The bones of the body in their function as *machines* may be compared to the combination of levers, pulley wheels, and gears of an automobile, and the body segments in producing mechanical work may be compared to the airplane propeller, the wheels of a car, or the hands of a clock.

It is evident from the above discussion that the movement apparatus of the human body, consisting of the bones, muscles, and joints of the musculoskeletal system, is indeed a mechanical machine system, and experience indicates that its operations conform to the laws of mechanics just as do all such systems. One of the purposes of this book, therefore, is to show how the principles of mechanics governing the operations of mechanical machine systems may be found in and applied to the human anatomy. In this chapter we will be concerned with the primary function of bones in the musculoskeletal system: to supply the simple machines necessary for the production of human movements.

The three simple machines found in the musculoskeletal system are (1) the lever, (2) the wheel and axle, and (3) the pulley.

## 5.12  The Lever

The lever is one of the simplest of all mechanical devices that may rightfully be called a machine. In fact, any rigid object free to turn about a center of rotation when a force is applied to it can be classified a lever. The object may rightfully be called a machine because on turning it overcomes a resistance and thereby produces mechanical work. The resistance consists of the weight of the object plus any external load added to it.

The important points on a lever are (1) the point about which it turns, (2) the point at which force is applied to it, and (3) the point at which the resistance to its movement is concentrated. These three points along with the classes of levers are shown in their simplest form in Figure 5–1. In each illustration the axis $A$ is the pivot point or fulcrum about which the lever is made to turn, $R$ is the point at which the resistance or load to be lifted is concentrated, and $F$ is the point at which force is applied. The arrangement of these three points provides the basis for the classification of levers. Since there are three points, there are three possible arrangements of these points. Any one of the three may be situated between the other two. In a first-class lever (diagram $A$) the axis is located between the force and the resistance. In a second-class lever (diagram $B$) the resistance is located between the axis and the force; in a third-class lever (diagram $C$) the force is located between the axis and resistance.

In Figure 5–1 the distance $r$ is called the lever arm of the resistance or load, and the distance $f$ is the lever arm of the applied force. The *lever arm* of any force, which includes the resistance force, is defined as the perpendicular distance from the line of action of the force to the fulcrum.

As discussed before, a bony lever is a machine capable of changing the mechanical energy of muscle contraction into a more useful form. The three functions levers are capable of performing along these lines are (1) the magnification of a force, which is possible when the force arm is longer than the resistance arm; (2) an increase in the speed and range of motion through which a force may act, which is possible when the resistance arm is longer than the force arm; and (3) the balancing of forces, which is possible when the lengths of the force and resistance arms are equal.

Numerous examples of these three lever functions and of the three types of levers are used in everyday life. Diagrams of three such devices are shown in Figure 5-2. In the seesaw of A the horizontal line FAR represents a lever of the first class with A as the axis, R the weight of one boy, and F the weight of the other boy. Since the relative lengths of the force and resistance arms can vary in a first-class lever depending upon the location of the axis, this type of lever can be used to perform all three functions of a lever. The wheel barrow in B employs a second-class lever with the axis A at the wheel. The heavily loaded barrow is lifted to a rolling position by applying a smaller force F at the handles, which illustrates that a second-class lever is designed for the magnification of force. The loaded shovel in C illustrates a third-class lever, the fulcrum being located in the man's left hand. This class of lever is designed to increase the speed and range of motion through which the force acts.

**Fig. 5-1. Lever classification.**

A. First Class—Type I

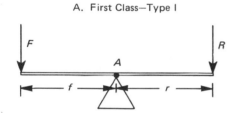

**Fig. 5-2. Illustrations of the three classes of levers as commonly found in everyday life.**

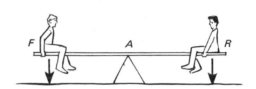

B. Second Class—Type II

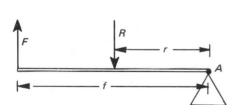

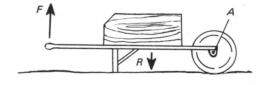

C. Third Class—Type III

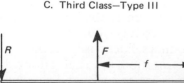

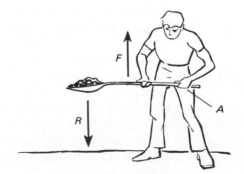

Every bone in the body acts as a lever at one time or another in the production of bodily movements. The bones may act either alone or in combination to form the lever systems of the musculoskeletal system. In fact, the body as a whole acts as a complex third-class lever in performing, for example, a correctly executed tennis serve. In this case, a right-handed server pivots over his left foot $A$ and transfers his body weight $F$ into the serve, which overcomes the resistance of the racket $R$. This lever system greatly increases the speed with which the racket strikes the ball.

The type of lever employed in a lever system often depends upon the type of movement intended. As illustrated in Figure 5-3, all three types of levers may be found in the movements of the foot. Tapping the toes, for example, involves the use of a first-class lever, standing on the toes involves a second-class lever when we focus on the actions of the plantar flexors, and lifting a weight with the foot involves a third-class lever. In $A$ and $C$ the axis $A$ is at the ankle joint, whereas in $B$ the axis is at the ball of the foot (metatarsal arch). The force $F$ involved in tapping the toes (downward movement only) and standing on the toes ($A$ and $B$) comes from the plantar flexors of the ankle joint (calf muscles), whereas lifting a weight with the foot ($C$) involves the dorsi flexors (muscles located on the front of the leg). The resistance $R$ involved in tapping the toes is the weight of the foot; in standing on the toes, the weight of the body; in lifting a weight with the foot, the weight of the object lifted plus the weight of the foot.

A vast majority of the levers of the human body are of the third class, which means that humans are built for speed more than they are for strength. The first-class levers are few in number, but are still more numerous than the second-class levers.

*Lever Arms.* The lever arm of any force, as defined before, is the perpendicular distance from the fulcrum to the line of action of that force. This is illustrated in Figure 5-4, which shows the top view of a flat object, pivoted about an axis perpendicular to the plane of the diagram and passing through point $A$. The body is acted on by two forces, $F_1$ and $F_2$, lying in the plane of the diagram. The lever arm of $F_1$ is the perpendicular distance $AB$ with a length $f_1$, and the lever arm of $F_2$ is the perpendicular distance $AC$ with a length $f_2$.

*Torque.* A single force acting on a body and tending to produce rotation is said to exert a *torque*. Torque is synonymous with force moment and is defined as force multiplied by the length of the lever arm (torque = force × lever arm, or $T = F \times f$). Hence, if we assume that the magnitude of $F_1$ in Figure 5-4 is 10 lb and the length of its lever arm $f_1$ is 5 ft, the torque produced will equal 50 ft-lb, i.e., $T_1 = F_1 \times f_1 = 10$ lb × 5 ft = 50 ft-lb.

The effect on a body of a torque of any given magnitude depends on the direction of its *line of action* in relation to the body's axis of rotation. Thus, in Figure 5-4, force $F_1$ produces counterclockwise rotation about the axis, whereas $F_2$ produces clockwise rotation. To distinguish between these directions of rotation, we shall adopt the convention that counterclockwise torques are negative and clockwise torques are positive. Hence, the torque of $F_1$ is negative; that of $F_2$ is positive.

**Fig. 5-3.** Illustration of the three classes of levers as found in the movements of the foot.

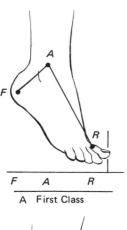

A First Class

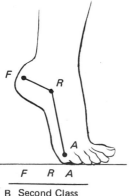

B Second Class

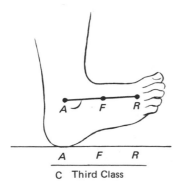

C Third Class

*The Law of the Lever.* A lever is said to be in a state of equilibrium when the algebraic sum of all the torques acting upon it equals zero. That is, a lever is in equilibrium when the sum of all the torques tending to produce clockwise rotation equals the sum of all the torques tending to produce counterclockwise rotation. This is known as the law of the lever.

The law of the lever is of value in that it enables us to calculate the amount of force needed to balance a known resistance by means of a known lever, or to calculate the point at which to place the fulcrum in order to balance a known resistance with a given force. If we remember that the resistance torque equals the resistance $R$ times the length of the resistance arm $r$ and that the force torque equals the force $F$ times the length of the force arm $f$, we can use the following formula to express the law of the lever:

$$F \times f = R \times r$$

If any three of the four values are known, the remaining one can be calculated by the formula.

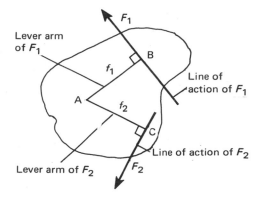

Fig. 5-4. **The torque of a force about an axis is the product of the force and its lever arm.**

*Mechanical Advantage.* The mechanical advantage of a machine may be defined as the ratio of the output force delivered by the machine to the amount of input force applied by the mover. With a simple machine such as the lever, the output force is represented by the resistance $R$, the input force is represented by $F$. The mechanical advantage of a lever, therefore, is given by dividing the force into the resistance, i.e., $MA = R/F$. By transposing the law of the lever ($F \times f = R \times r$), the mechanical advantage can also be expressed as the ratio of the lever arms, i.e., $MA = R/F = f/r$.

As an example of the use of mechanical advantage, let us suppose that a man weighing 150 lb wishes to lift a stone weighing 1500 lb by means of a lever. The mechanical advantage required of the lever must therefore be $MA = R/F = 1500/150 = 10$. Thus, the force arm of the lever must be 10 times as long as the resistance arm.

*Levers and the Conservation of Energy.* As was discussed before, levers are used for three different purposes: (1) to gain force at the expense of range of motion, which will be referred to as the *magnification of force*; (2) to gain speed and range of motion at the expense of force, which will be referred to as the *magnification of displacement*; or (3) to balance forces.

In the second-class lever the force arm coincides with the total lever; hence, the force arm is longer than the resistance arm, and the lever has the effect of *magnifying force*. In the third-class lever the resistance arm coincides with the total lever; hence, the resistance arm is longer than the force arm, and the lever has the effect of *magnifying displacement*. In the first-class lever, however, the arms may be of equal length or either arm may be longer depending upon the relative position of the fulcrum.

The law of the conservation of energy states that energy is always conserved in its transformation from one form to another. Even though a lever is capable of magnifying either force or displacement, energy relations show that the user of the lever is not getting "something for nothing." The law of conservation of energy requires that the *work* done *by* the machine be no greater than the work done *on* the machine.

Mechanical work is defined as the force multiplied by the distance through which the force is applied ($W = F \times D$). Using force and resistance once again, we can define the work done *on* a machine as equal to the input force $F$ times the distance $d$ through which the force acts ($F \times d$), and the work done *by* the machine as equal to the resistance $R$ times the distance or height $h$ that the resistance is moved ($R \times h$). By the law of conservation of energy, we know that the output work ($R \times h$) equals the input work ($F \times d$).

By transposing the law of conservation of energy ($R \times h = F \times d$), we obtain $R/F = d/h$, which shows that the mechanical advantage, defined as the ratio of the forces $R/F$, is also given by the inverse ratio of the distance through which the force operates $d/h$. The latter is called the reduction or the magnification of the displacements. If $d$ is greater than $h$, there is a reduction in the displacements, the force arm $f$ is greater than the resistance arm $r$, and the mechanical advantage $R/F$ is greater than unity with the effect that force is magnified. If $d$ is smaller than $h$, there is a magnification in the displacement, the force arm $f$ is less than the resistance arm $r$, and the mechanical advantage is less than unity.

By combining the equation $MA = R/F = f/r$ with the equation $R/F = d/h$, a relation between lever arms and displacement is obtained; $f/r = d/h$. This effect is illustrated in Figure 5–5, which shows that the two triangles $ARB$ and $AFC$ are similar and that their corresponding sides are proportional.

**Fig. 5–5.** An illustration of the relationship between lever arms and displacement.

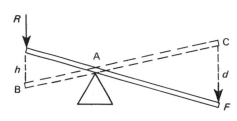

## 5.13 The Wheel and Axle

The wheel and axle is a simple machine involving the principle of the lever. It consists of a wheel attached to a central axle about which it revolves. The force causing the rotation can either be applied to the rim of the wheel, as on the steering wheel of an automobile, or to the axle, as on the rear wheel of a bicycle.

In a wheel and axle with the force applied at the rim of the wheel, as on a steering wheel, the force is magnified at the expense of speed and distance. The turning effect of the wheel exerts a torque equal to the force times the radius of the wheel. The radius in this case corresponds to the force arm of a lever. The larger the diameter of the wheel, the greater is the magnification of the force.

In a wheel and axle with the force applied at the axle, as on the rear wheel of a bicycle, speed and range of motion (displacement) are magnified at the expense of force.

The mechanical advantage of a wheel and axle with the force applied to the wheel is given by the ratio of the radius of the wheel $r_w$ to the radius of the axle $r_a$, or $MA = r_w/r_a$. A wheel and axle with the force applied to the rim of the wheel is illustrated in Figure 5–6.

Most of the examples of the wheel and axle in the body, like anatomic levers, are arranged for gaining distance and speed at the expense of force. Both kinds, however, are represented in the body. All rotatory movements in the body involve a wheel-and-axle type of

**Fig. 5–6. The wheel-and-axle machine.**

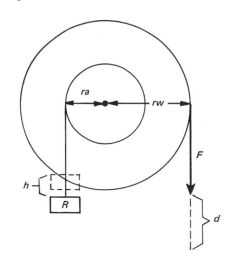

arrangement. Shaking the head, twisting the trunk, and inward and outward rotations of the arm and thigh are good examples of movements produced by wheel-and-axle arrangements. A cross section of the rib cage, for instance, shows that the ribs serve as a wheel and the vertebral column as an axle in a wheel-and-axle system. Some muscles act upon the wheel furnished by the ribs (oblique abdominal muscles); others (deep spinal muscles) act upon the axle represented by the vertebrae in producing rotation of the trunk. A cross section of the arm or the thigh likewise presents the characteristics of a wheel and axle. Here the center of the shaft of the long bones serves as the axle, and the surrounding tissues serve as the wheel. The rotation both of the trunk and of the limbs around their longitudinal mechanical axis constitutes the movements of a wheel and axle.

The action of a pulley is the same as that of a first-class lever with equal arms. Of the several types of pulleys, only the *fixed pulley* is represented in the human anatomy. Its function is to change the direction of a muscle's line of pull.

Although a mechanical advantage of unity obtained with a fixed pulley may be looked upon as no mechanical advantage at all, it often happens that a change in a muscle's line of pull, such as increasing the angle of its action on a bone, will increase its effectiveness as a mover. This is illustrated in Figure 5-7, which shows how the position of the knee cap increases the angle of pull of the quadriceps muscle. Figure 5-8 shows the external malleolus of the ankle serving as a pulley to change the direction of the line of pull of the peroneus longus. This pulley arrangement allows the peroneus longus to perform a more useful function than would be possible otherwise.

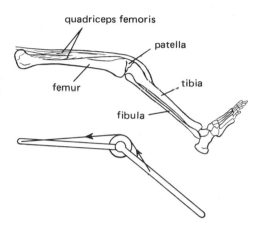

Fig. 5-7. The patella functions as a pulley.

quadriceps femoris

patella

femur

tibia

fibula

### 5.14 The Pulley

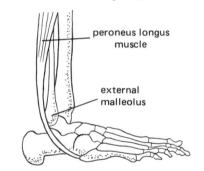

Fig. 5-8. The external malleolus functions as a pulley.

peroneus longus muscle

external malleolus

## 5.21 The Machine Function of Bones

A. Specific Student Objectives

1. Describe a machine.
2. Define mechanical energy.
3. List and describe the three components of a machine system.
4. Illustrate a machine system in the human body.
5. List the three types of machines in the body.

## 5.20 Study Guidelines

### 5.22  The Lever

A.  Specific Student Objectives

1.  Define a lever.
2.  Identify and describe the three important points on a lever.
3.  Identify and describe the three types of levers.
4.  Define lever arm.
5.  List the three functions of levers.
6.  Give an example of the three lever functions and of the three types of levers as found in everyday life.
7.  Define torque.
8.  Given the magnitude of a force and the length of a lever arm, calculate the produced torque.
9.  State the law of the lever.
10.  Explain the mechanical advantage (MA) of a lever.
11.  Differentiate between the magnification of force and the magnification of displacement as lever functions.
12.  State the law of the conservation of energy.
13.  Define mechanical work.
14.  Define the mechanical work done *on* a machine.
15.  Define the mechanical work done *by* a machine.
16.  State the relationship between the law of the lever and the law of conservation of energy.

### 5.23  The Wheel and Axle

A.  Specific Student Objectives

1.  Describe a wheel-and-axle machine.
2.  Identify the two locations where the force can be applied to a wheel-and-axle machine and give an example of each.
3.  State the two primary functions of a wheel and axle.
4.  Define the mechanical advantage of a wheel and axle.
5.  Give an example of a wheel-and-axle arrangement in the human body.

### 5.24  The Pulley

A.  Specific Student Objectives

1.  Describe a pulley.
2.  List examples of human body pulleys and state their functions.

### 5.30  Recommended Supplementary Readings

The student should consult any recent general physics text for supplementary readings on levers, wheel and axles, and pulleys.  A list of selected physics texts is given in Appendix B.

# 6

# The Mechanical Function
# of Muscles

**General Student Objective**

*In his study of the basic concepts of this chapter the student should become familiar with:*

**6.11   Muscles as Sources of Mechanical Energy**

Without doubt one of the most fundamental concepts in all nature is that of energy. Energy is defined simply as the capacity for doing work and overcoming resistance. It should be remembered that there are many forms of energy. For example, there are mechanical energy, electrical energy, chemical energy, and thermal energy. All these forms of energy are involved in one way or another in human physiology.

The muscles of the body are actually chemical motors that convert fuel into heat and mechanical energy. In discussions of the energy production of muscles, heat is often referred to as "wasted" or "lost" energy. This is true only from a mechanical standpoint, which does not consider heat a part of mechanical work. It is "lost," therefore, in the same sense that heat produced by an automobile engine during the performance of its work is lost. Heat in the right amount, however, is absolutely essential to various physiological functions of the body.

It is mechanical energy that gives the muscle the capacity to perform mechanical work. The lifting of a weight by the body is no less a manifestation of mechanical work than is the lifting of a weight by a diesel-driven crane. Its measurement involves the same physical principles, and it is defined in the same terms: work equals force multiplied by the distance through which the force is applied:

$$\text{Work} = \text{force} \times \text{distance} \quad \text{or} \quad W = F \times D$$

If a muscle lifts a 10-lb weight through a distance of 2 ft, the mechanical work done is 10 lb × 2 ft, or 20 ft-lb.

The term force used in reference to muscle contractions is synonymous with strength. The terms force and strength, however, should not be confused with the term power. Force is the energy tending to produce motion or to produce mechanical work, whereas power is the rate at which the work is being done:

$$\text{Power} = \frac{\text{work}}{\text{time}} \quad \text{or} \quad P = \frac{F \times D}{t}$$

In other words, the faster a given amount of work is done the greater is the power. In the engineering system, with work measured in foot-pounds (ft-lb), power is expressed in foot-pounds per second (ft-lb/sec) and in horsepower (1 hp = 550 ft-lb/sec).

When a muscle applies force, it can shorten (concentric contraction), lengthen (eccentric contraction), or remain at the same length (isometric contraction). When a muscle shortens, it is said to be producing *positive work. Negative work* results when an external force overcomes the force developed by muscle contraction, and thus the muscle lengthens during contraction. When a muscle contracts against an immovable load and the distance that the load is moved is zero, the work is also zero even though great force may be applied. Therefore, by definition, positive work is performed when a weight is lifted, negative work is performed when the weight is lowered to its original position, and zero work is performed when the weight is simply held without being either lifted or lowered.

The ability of a muscle to produce mechanical work is dependent upon its ability to produce force. The factors affecting the ability of muscles to apply force will be discussed in Chapter 8. The present discussion, therefore, is limited to the relationship of force to motion.

## 6.12 The Definition and Description of Force

When we push or pull on a body, we are said to exert a *force* on it. Forces can also be exerted by inanimate objects; a stretched rubber band exerts forces on the bodies to which its ends are attached; the compressed air in an automobile tire exerts a force on the walls of the tire; a locomotive exerts a force on the train it is drawing. The force of which we are most aware in our daily lives, of course, is the force of gravitational attraction exerted on every body by the earth—the force called the *weight* of the body.

By definition, force is anything that tends to produce motion or change of motion, and its magnitude is measured in terms of gravitational units, i.e., pounds or kilograms. The force with which the earth attracts a body at some specified point on the earth's surface is a perfectly definite, reproducible force and is called a force of one pound (approximately 0.454 of a standard kilogram). In order that an unknown force can be compared with the force unit, and thereby measured, some measurable effect produced by the force must be used. One such effect is to alter the dimensions or shape of a body on which the force is exerted; another is to alter the state of motion of the body. Both these effects are used in the measurement of muscle strength as will be discussed in Chapter 8.

## Graphic Representation of Forces

A graphic representation of a force is called a vector. It consists of a straight line, drawn to scale, with an arrow indicating its direction. As an example we shall consider weight as both a force and as a vector.

The instrument most commonly used to measure forces is the spring scale represented in Figure 6–1A by a bathroom scale. Everyone knows that when he weighs himself he is measuring the downward force he exerts on the footboard of the scale, and that this force causes some mechanism within the scale to indicate his weight. We are not interested here in how the scale works, but rather with the downward force we call our *weight*.

As illustrated in Figure 6–1B, gravitational forces always act in the direction of a line joining the body and the center of the earth and, therefore, act perpendicular to the earth's surface. Every object on the surface of the earth has a *center of gravity*, which is defined as an imaginary point representing the weight center of the body. At this point all the parts of the body exactly balance each other. Since the center of gravity can be considered the point in the body at which its weight is concentrated, the force of gravity can be represented by an imaginary line which passes through this point and is perpendicular to the surface of the earth. This imaginary vertical line is called the *line of gravity*.

Figure 6–1C can be used to illustrate the above concepts. The point C represents the center of gravity of the object, and the line CW represents the line of gravity drawn as a vector to represent the weight of the object. We can assume that the weight of the object has been determined to be 10 lb. It is clear that simply to write "10 lb" on the diagram would not completely describe the force, since it would not indicate the direction in which the force is acting. All the necessary information about a force may be conveyed conveniently by adopting the convention of representing a force by an arrow. The length of the arrow, drawn to some chosen scale, indicates the size or magnitude of the force, and the direction in which the arrow points indicates the direction of the force.

Force is not the only physical quantity that requires the specification of direction as well as magnitude. For example, the velocity of an aircraft is not completely specified by stating that it is 300 miles per hour; the direction must also be given. The concept of volume, on the other hand, has no direction associated with it.

Quantities, such as volume, that involve a magnitude only are called *scalars*. Those, such as force and velocity, that involve both magnitude and direction are called *vector quantities*.

Shown in Figure 6–2A is a box with its center of gravity at C. The dotted line passing vertically through C is the line of gravity. Two separate forces are shown acting on the box: a vertical force $F_1$ acting parallel to the line of gravity and a horizontal force $F_2$ acting perpendicular to the gravitational line. It is obvious that $F_1$ will

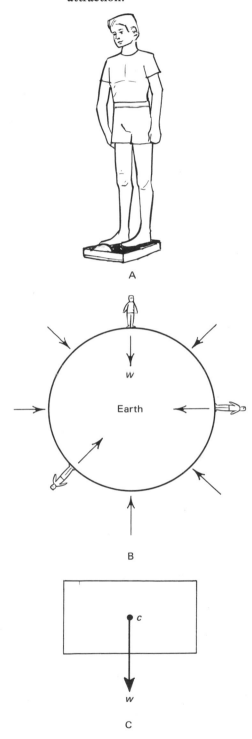

**Fig. 6–1. Weight is a downward force produced by gravitational attraction.**

A

B

C

## 6.13 The Components of a Force

**Fig. 6–2. The components of a force.**

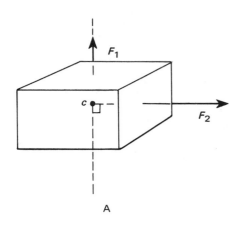

A

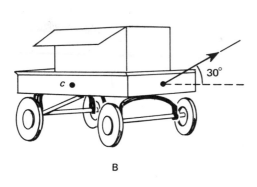

B

**Fig. 6–3. The coordinate system.**

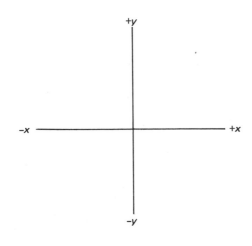

tend to move the box vertically and that $F_2$ will tend to move the box horizontally.

In Figure 6–2B is shown a wagon on which a force is being applied through a rope at a 30° angle from the horizontal. It will be noticed that this force will tend to produce two simultaneous actions. One action will be to lift the front end of the wagon, and the other will be to roll the wagon forward. Therefore, the force has two tendencies: one forward and the other upward, known as the vertical and horizontal components of the force.

The coordinate system shown in Figure 6–3 is used to designate the components of a force. The vertical component is designated $y$ and the horizontal component is designated $x$. By convention, a horizontal component acting to the right of the vertical is positive; to the left, negative. Likewise, a vertical component acting above the horizontal is positive; below negative.

## Resolution of a Force into Components

The resolution of a force into its vertical and horizontal components can be accomplished by either a graphic method or trigonometry.

*The Graphic Method of Resolving a Force into Its Two Components.* The graphic method is illustrated in Figure 6–4A. In this illustration the known force $F$ is applied at point $O$ at an angle of $\theta$ (theta) degrees with the $x$ axis. Perpendicular lines are drawn from point $A$ to the $x$ and $y$ axes. If the known force $F$ has been drawn to scale, the vertical component $F_y$ (read $F$ sub $y$) is given by the length of the line $AB$, and the horizontal component $F_x$ is given by the length of the line $AC$. With $F_x$ and $F_y$ perpendicular to each other, triangles $OAB$ and $OAC$ are equivalent right triangles with corresponding sides equal, i.e., lines $AC$ and $BO$ are both equal to $F_x$ and lines $AB$ and $CO$ are both equal to $F_y$.

*The Trigonometric Method of Resolving a Force into Its Two Components.* This method involves the solving of a right triangle and, therefore, the use of the three most common functions in trigonometry, *sine, cosine,* and *tangent.*

A right triangle is shown in Figure 6–4B, with the lower case letters $a$, $b$, and $c$ representing the lengths of the three sides of the triangle and the capital letters $A$, $B$, and $C$ representing the corresponding angles. Angle $C$ equals 90°, and angle $A$ is $\theta$ or the angle under consideration. Side $c$ is called the hypotenuse, side $a$ is the side opposite $\theta$, and side $b$ is the side adjacent (Figure 6–4C). The following definitions of the relationships of a right triangle are important:

I. The sine of an angle is the ratio of the "side opposite" to the hypotenuse, or

$$\text{sine of } \theta = \frac{\text{side opposite}}{\text{hypotenuse}} \quad \text{or} \quad \sin \theta = \frac{O}{H}$$

II.  The cosine of an angle is the ratio of the "side adjacent" to the hypotenuse, or

$$\text{cosine of } \theta = \frac{\text{side adjacent}}{\text{hypotenuse}} \quad \text{or} \quad \cos \theta = \frac{A}{H}$$

III.  The tangent of an angle is the ratio of the "side opposite" to the "side adjacent," or

$$\text{tangent of } \theta = \frac{\text{side opposite}}{\text{side adjacent}} \quad \text{or} \quad \tan \theta = \frac{O}{A}$$

If we now refer again to Figure 6-4A we see the following elationships:

hypotenuse $H$ = known force $F$

side adjacent $A$ = horizontal component $F_x$

side opposite $O$ = vertical component $F_y$

Therefore, we have the following equivalents:

$$\sin \theta = \frac{O}{H} = \frac{F_y}{F} \quad \text{and} \quad \cos \theta = \frac{A}{H} = \frac{F_x}{F}$$

Transposing, we obtain

$$F_y = F \sin \theta \quad \text{and} \quad F_x = F \cos \theta$$

Suppose we have a force of 100 lb acting on a body at an angle of 30°. The two components $F_y$ and $F_x$ can be calculated by direct substitution into the equations.

$$F_y = F \sin \theta = 100 \text{ lb} \times \sin \theta$$
$$F_x = F \cos \theta = 100 \text{ lb} \times \cos \theta$$

A table of sines, cosines, and tangents, given in Appendix A, shows for a 30° angle a sine of .500 and a cosine of .866. Substitution of values in the equations gives

$$F_y = 100 \times .500 = 50.0 \text{ lb}$$
$$F_x = 100 \times .866 = 86.6 \text{ lb}$$

Thus, 86.6 lb of force will be acting on the body in the horizontal direction, and 50 lb of force will be acting in the vertical direction.

Since the trigonometric method is by far the most convenient for the resolution of a force into components, it will be adopted for standard use in this book. Perhaps it should be mentioned here that the concept of components applies not only to forces, but equally well to all vectors and is used often in relation to velocities. A ball, for instance, projected at an angle from the horizontal has an upward

Fig. 6-4. (A) The graphic method of resolving a force into its two components. (B and C) The angles and sides of a right triangle.

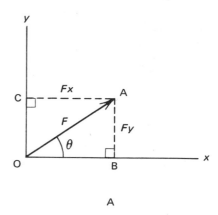

A

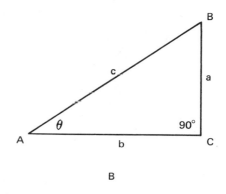

B

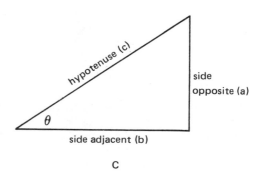

C

Fig. 6–5. The biceps brachii muscle pulling at a 30° angle to the forearm.

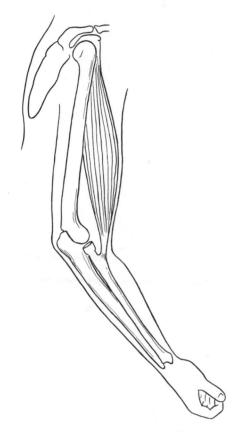

velocity $V_y$ and a forward velocity $V_x$. Technically, it is the resolution of vectors into components that has been the topic of the preceding discussion.

## The Components of a Muscle Force

When a muscle contracts, it applies force to the bones to which it is attached. Figure 6–5 shows the location of the biceps brachii muscle in the arm and its attachments on the shoulder and on the forearm. Let us assume that the angle of pull of the biceps on the forearm is 30°. It should be clear that the action of the biceps will cause rotation of the forearm at the elbow (flexion), but it will also cause the forearm to be pulled into the elbow joint which tends to stabilize this joint. Thus, the force of biceps contraction at this angle has two components: one causing rotation and the other causing stabilization of the elbow joint. These components are the same as the horizontal and vertical components that were discussed before, but are given different names here because of the nature of their actions.

The rotatory component $F_r$ is the same as the vertical component $F_y$ that was studied before and is given by the equation $F_r = F \sin \theta$. The stabilization component $F_s$ is the same as the horizontal component $F_x$ and is given by the equation $F_s = F \cos \theta$. To illustrate these effects it can be assumed that the biceps brachii in Figure 6–5 produces 100 lb of force at its forearm attachment. Thus, the magnitudes of the two components, remembering that a 30° angle has a sine of .500 and a cosine of .866, are

$$F_r = F \sin \theta = 100 \text{ lb} \times .500 = 50.0 \text{ lb}$$
$$F_s = F \sin \theta = 100 \text{ lb} \times .866 = 86.6 \text{ lb}$$

Therefore, only one half the total force exerted through biceps brachii contraction is actually used to produce rotation of the elbow when the line of pull of the muscle is 30°. At 30°, 86.6 lb of force pulls the arm and forearm bones into closer contact at the elbow and thus tends to stabilize the joint.

## The Components of a Muscle Force and the Law of the Lever

In Chapter 5 the law of the lever ($F \times f = R \times r$) was discussed. It should be obvious now that the law of the lever holds only when the force and the resistance are applied perpendicular to the lever. This is true because the rotatory component force applied at a 90° angle to the lever will be equal to the original force itself. That is, the sine of a 90° angle equals 1.00, and the cosine of a 90° angle equals 0.00. Therefore, when a force is applied at a 90° angle to a lever, the rotatory component of the force will equal the force ($F_r = F \times \sin \theta = F \times 1 = F$), and the stabilizing component will equal zero ($F_s = F \times \cos \theta = F \times 0 = 0$). This illustrates that the rotatory component of a force increases with an increase in the angle of application of the force from 0 to 90°.

Since the ($F \times f$) part of the law of the lever equation is the same as the torque for that force, and since the ($R \times r$) part of the law of the lever equation is the same as the torque produced by the resistance, the law of the lever can be changed to read: a lever will be in a state of rotatory equilibrium when the sum of the torques tending to produce clockwise rotation is equal to the sum of the torques tending to produce counterclockwise rotation. It should be remembered, however, that the law of the lever deals only with rotatory equilibrium and, therefore, is concerned only with the rotatory component of a force. Thus, when only one force and one resistance are acting on a lever and these forces are acting at an angle other than 90°, the formula for the law of the lever becomes

$$(F \sin \theta) \times f = (R \sin \theta) \times r$$

Some students might wonder how a force of 100 lb can be resolved into two components with magnitudes of 50 and 86.6 lb. The sum of the two components does not equal the original force because we are dealing with vectors not scalars. Scalars that involve magnitude only can be added in the traditional manner, but vector addition is entirely different in that direction as well as magnitude must be considered.

In problems concerned with the composition of a single force in which the solution of a right triangle is involved, the *pythagorean theorem* can be used for vector addition. This theorem states that for any right triangle the square of the hypotenuse is equal to the sum of the squares of the other two sides ($H^2 = O^2 + A^2$). Thus, we find that the sum of the squares of the two components of the muscle force discussed in the preceding section, which were 50 and 86.6 lb, equals the square of the original force, which was 100 lb, i.e., $100^2 = (50)^2 + (86.6)^2 = 10,000$.

Seldom do we find in anatomical kinesiology a body movement produced by a single muscle, but rather we find movements produced by groups of muscles acting together either simultaneously or in sequence. To determine the combined effects of these muscles requires vector addition.

Should two or more forces be applied at the same point in identical directions (Figure 6–6A), the sum of their effects is obtained through simple addition, e.g., 2 lb plus 4 lb equals 6 lb. An example of this type of action is the psoas and iliacus muscles acting at the hip joint simultaneously through a common tendon. Sometimes two or more forces with identical lines of action are applied to the same point in sequence, e.g., 2 lb of force starts the object moving, and immediately afterward another force of 4 lb is added to give a total of 6 lb of effective force.

When forces are applied in sequence which do not have the same line of action, the resultant effects are obtained through a triangle method. As an example of this method, consider Figure 6–6B and C. Here we have a force of 5 lb applied horizontally; at its termination another force of 3 lb is added at a 60° angle to the horizontal. The sum of these two vectors is not found to be 8 lb but 7 lb. The triangle method requires that the two forces be drawn to scale at the proper angles as they are in Figure 6–6B. The ends of the two lines

### 6.14 Vector Addition

Fig. 6–6. Illustration of the triangle method of vector addition.

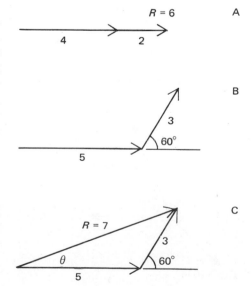

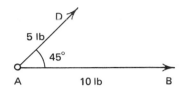

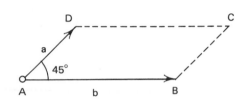

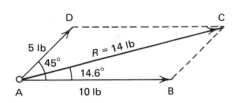

are then connected to form a triangle as in Figure 6–6C. The line drawn to connect the two ends is called the resultant and is simply measured with a ruler to determine its magnitude, and the angle θ is measured with a protractor. This method can be used regardless of the number of forces that are brought into play sequentially.

The *sequential summation of forces* is a very important factor in many motor performances. For example, in lifting a heavy object from the floor we start the object moving through the use of our large thigh muscles, then the forces of hip and back extension and shoulder and elbow flexion are added in sequence to produce the total movement.

Rarely in human anatomy do we find two or more muscle forces being applied to a bone at the same point and in identical directions. More usually the muscles producing a joint action attach to different points on a bone and/or have different lines of action. The problem of adding muscle forces that have different points of attachment on a bone is solved by adding the torques that the muscles produce.

When two or more forces are applied at the same point simultaneously but have different lines of action, their resultant effects can be determined by the method of components already discussed. The parallelogram method may be used when there are only two forces involved.

The parallelogram method of vector addition of two forces is illustrated in Figure 6–7. As shown at the top in Figure 6–7A, the vectors are first drawn outward from the same origin A. From D a dotted line is next drawn parallel to vector b, and from B a dotted line is drawn parallel to vector a, as in the middle diagram. From point C, where these two lines cross, the diagonal line AC is drawn and labeled with an arrowhead as the resultant R.

As an illustration of the *method of components*, consider the example of three forces shown graphically in Figure 6–8; $F_1$ = 120 lb at 0°, $F_2$ = 200 lb at 60°, and $F_3$ = 150 lb at 225°. The problem here is to find the resultant force equivalent to all three forces together. The operations involved in this procedure (Fig. 6–9) are

A. Each force is resolved into $x$ and $y$ components.
B. A sum of the $x$ components ($\Sigma x$) is obtained to give a resultant $R_x$ component.
C. A sum of the $y$ components ($\Sigma y$) is obtained to give a resultant $R_y$ component.
D. The resultant $R_x$ and $R_y$ components are combined at right angles to obtain their resultant $R$.

The first step is carried out by using the equations for the $x$ and $y$ components given before. Thus, for $F_1$ the $x$ component is 120 cos 0° = 120 lb, and the $y$ component is 120 sin 0° = 0. Likewise, the $x$ component for $F_2$ is 200 cos 60° = 100 lb, and the $y$ component is 200 sin 60° = 173 lb. For $F_3$ the $x$ component is 150 cos 225° = 106 lb. Perhaps it should be noted here that when using the table of trigonometric functions in Appendix A with angles greater than 90° the following rules should be used:

A. If the angle is greater than 90 but less than 180°, the value of the angle should be subtracted from 180°. For example, 180° – 120° = 60°; therefore, the cos of 120° equals the cos of 60°.

**Fig. 6–8. A graphic representation of three forces.**

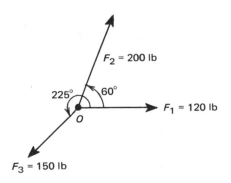

B. If the angle is greater than 180° but less than 270°, 180 should be subtracted from the value of the angle. For example, the sin of 190° equals the sin of 10°, i.e., 190° − 180° = 10°.

C. If the angle is greater than 270°, the value of the angle should be subtracted from 360°. Thus, the tan of 290° equals the tan of 70°, i.e., 360° − 290° = 70°.

*Note:* These rules are designed to always make the "side opposite" of a right triangle equal to the vertical component.

As was discussed in relation to Figure 6-3, components with directions to the right and up are positive in sign and components to the left and down are negative in sign. The second and third steps of adding $x$ and $y$ components separately are tabulated below:

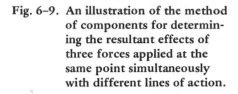

Fig. 6-9. An illustration of the method of components for determining the resultant effects of three forces applied at the same point simultaneously with different lines of action.

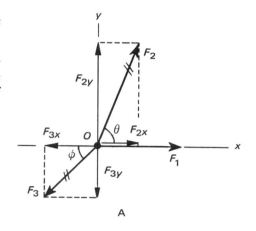

A

| Force | Angle | $x$ Component | $y$ Component |
|-------|-------|---------------|---------------|
| $F_1$ = 120 lb | 0 | 120 lb | 0 |
| $F_2$ = 200 lb | 60 | 100 lb | 173 lb |
| $F_3$ = 150 lb | 45 | −106 lb | −106 lb |
| | | $\Sigma x = R_x$ = 114 lb | $\Sigma y = R_y$ = 67 lb |

Since $R_x$ and $R_y$ are at right angles to each other (Fig. 6-8C), we are dealing again with a right triangle and the resultant $R$ is the hypotenuse, which is given by the pythagorean theorem as

$$R^2 = (114)^2 + (67)^2 = 17495$$

By taking the square root of 17495, we finally obtain $R$ = 132 lb. The angle $\theta$ of the resultant is obtained from the tangent relation, i.e., $\tan \theta = O/A = R_y/R_x = 67 \text{ lb}/114 \text{ lb} = 0.588$; therefore, in Appendix A we find that the angle $\theta = 30.4°$.

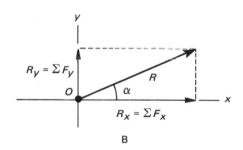

B

## 6.21  Muscles as Sources of Mechanical Energy

### 6.20  Study Guidelines

A. Specific Student Objectives

1. Define energy.
2. Define mechanical work.
3. Differentiate between muscle strength and muscle power.
4. Define horsepower.
5. Differentiate between negative, positive, and zero work.

## 6.22  The Definition and Description of Force

A. Specific Student Objectives

1. Define force.
2. Identify the force unit.
3. Define a vector.

4. Describe the graphic representation of a force.
5. Define center of gravity.
6. Define gravitational line.

## 6.23 The Components of a Force

A. Specific Student Objectives

1. Identify the two components of a force.
2. Describe the graphic method of resolving a force into its two components.
3. Describe the trigonometric method of resolving a force into its two components.
4. Differentiate between the sine, cosine, and tangent of a right triangle.
5. Identify the hypotenuse, side opposite, and side adjacent of a right triangle.
6. State the formula for finding the vertical component of a force.
7. State the formula for finding the horizontal component of a force.
8. Identify the two components of a muscle force.
9. State the modification of the law of the lever required by knowledge of the components of a muscle force.

## 6.24 Vector Addition

A. Specific Student Objectives

1. Differentiate between scalar and vector quantities.
2. State the pythagorean theorem.
3. State how forces applied at the same point at the same time in identical directions are added.
4. State how two or more forces with identical lines of action that are applied to the same point in sequence are added.
5. State how muscle forces that have different points of application on a bone are added.
6. Describe the parallelogram method of vector addition.
7. Describe the method of components for vector addition.

## 6.30 Recommended Supplementary Readings

The student should consult any recent physics text for supplementary readings on force components and vector addition. A list of selected physics texts is given in Appendix B.

# 7

# The Mechanical Function
# of Joints

**General Student Objective**

*In his study of the basic concepts of this chapter the student should become familiar with:*

*7.11    The Mechanics of Joint Actions*
*7.12    The Kinematics of Joint Actions*
*7.13    The Dynamics of Joint Actions*

The primary mechanical function of diarthrodial joints in the production of human movements is to serve as the fulcrums for bony levers. The bony levers, of course, rotate at these joints and thereby produce the movements of the human body.

Because of the foundational nature of joint actions in the total picture of human movement, this chapter will be used to present briefly the basic principles concerned with the kinematics and dynamics of joint actions and, therefore, of human motion. *Kinematics* is generally defined as that branch of mechanics which deals with the *description* of motion, whereas *dynamics* is that branch which deals with the *causes* for any changes in the states of motion of a body.

**7.11    The Mechanics of Joint Actions**

When a muscle contracts and applies its force to a lever, the rate of change of position of the muscle and of the lever are both described in terms of velocity. The rate of muscle shortening, however, is expressed in terms of linear velocity, whereas the rate of rotation of a lever is expressed in terms of angular velocity.

**7.12    The Kinematics of Joint Actions**

**Fig. 7–1.** Displacement as illustrated through the contraction of a muscle. (*A*) The resting length of the muscle. (*B*) The shortened position. The change in length of the muscle, displacement is represented by *d,* which in this example is 6 in.

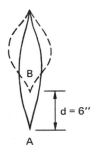

## Linear Velocity

Velocity is the rate of change of position. Since linear change in position is measured in terms of length or distance, the definition of linear velocity can be written as

$$\text{Linear velocity} = \frac{\text{distance}}{\text{time}} \quad \text{or} \quad v = \frac{d}{t}$$

Change in the length of a muscle called displacement is illustrated in Figure 7–1. Point *A* denotes the resting position of the muscle, point *B* denotes the shortened position, and *d* is the distance between *A* and *B*. If the distance that the muscle shortens is 6 in. and the time during which shortening occurred is 2 sec, the velocity is $d/t =$ 6 in./2 sec = 3 in./sec (read as 3 in. per second). This measure is often referred to as the speed or velocity of muscle contraction. The terms speed and velocity are used synonymously in this instance. Strictly speaking, however, speed is a scalar quantity as defined in the last chapter and velocity is a vector quantity. The term speed, therefore, is used when we are concerned with magnitude only, and the term velocity is used when we are concerned with both magnitude and direction.

## Angular Velocity

The rotation of a hypothetical bony lever at a joint is illustrated in Figure 7–2*A*. In this illustration the lever is moved by a muscle

**Fig. 7–2.** The rotation of the forearm lever at the elbow joint.

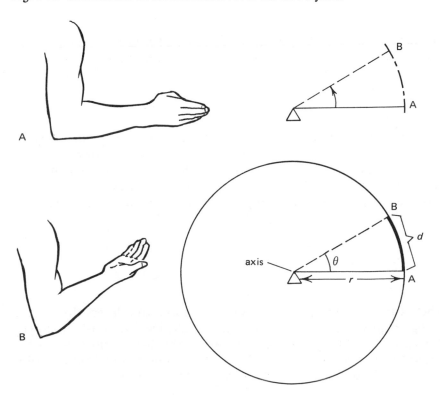

from position $A$ to position $B$. As shown in Figure 7–2B, the length of the lever can be considered the radius of a circle, the difference in positions $A$ and $B$ can be measured by the angle turned through $\theta$, and the actual distance $d$ that the end of the lever travels is given by the arc of the circle cut by the angle.

For formulating the laws of mechanics it has been found necessary to express the angle turned through $\theta$ in *radians* and not in degrees or revolutions. The radian is a unit of angular measure just as the inch is a unit of linear measure.

A radian is defined as the ratio of the arc length $d$ to the length of the radius $r$. Therefore, the angle turned through $\theta$ in radians can be obtained by the formula $\theta = d/r$. Evidently an angle of one radian (abbreviated 1 rad) has an arc that is of the same length as the radius.

It is easy to find the conversion factor between degrees and radians by remembering the following relationships.

A. There are $360°$ in a complete circle.
B. The circumference $d$ of a circle of a given radius $r$ is $2\pi r$.
C. The number of radians $\theta$ in a complete circle is 6.283, i.e., $\theta = d/r = 2\pi r/r = 2\pi$. Since $1\pi$ equals 3.1416, $2\pi$ equals 6.283.
D. From the above relationship it can be seen that $360° = 2\pi$ radians. Therefore, 1 rad $= 360°/6.283 = 57.3°$, or $1° = 6.283/360° = 0.01745$ rad.

Often it is useful to express angles in radians measured in terms of $\pi$ itself. For example, if 1 revolution equals $2\pi$ radians, 2 revolutions equals $2 \times 2\pi$ rad. Also an angle of $90°$ is 1/4 of a complete circle, 1/4 of a revolution equals $1/4 \times 2\pi$ rad. Of course, this has the same numerical value as $90 \times 0.01745 = 1.571$ rad.

The angular velocity $\omega$ (omega) of a motion is defined as the angle turned through $\theta$ (in radians) divided by the elapsed time $t$. That is,

$$\text{Angular velocity} = \frac{\text{angle turned through}}{\text{time}} \quad \text{or} \quad \omega = \frac{\theta}{t}$$

This is comparable to the corresponding definition of linear velocity, $v = d/t$, and angular displacement $\theta$ corresponds to linear displacement $d$.

*Relationship of Angular Velocity to Linear Velocity.* From the definition of a radian, it is known that the angle $\theta$ in radians between any two points on the circumference of a circle is given by $d$, the length of arc between the two points, divided by the radius $r$. In words, angle in radians = arc length/radius, or in algebraic symbols $\theta = d/r$. By rearranging this formula it can be seen that the arc length is given by $d = r\theta$. By substituting $r\theta$ for $d$ in the linear velocity formula $v = d/t$, we obtain $v = r\theta/t = r(\theta/t)$. Since $\omega = \theta/t$, we can replace $\theta/t$ by $\omega$ to obtain $v = r\omega$. Therefore, we see that the linear velocity of an object at the end of a lever is the product of the angular velocity and the length of the lever. Hence, the greater the angular velocity, and the greater the length of the lever, the greater the linear velocity at the end of the lever. This is illustrated in Figure 7–3, which shows two levers, one of length $A$ and the other of length $B$. It is obvious that the arc length of lever $B$ is greater than

**Fig. 7–3.** An illustration of two levers of unequal lengths turning the same number of radians per unit of time, i.e., $\omega = \theta/t$ is identical for both levers.

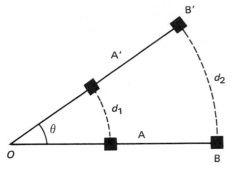

$d_2 > d_1$, therefore $v_2 > v_1$

that of lever $A$. Therefore, for a given angular velocity, the end of lever $B$ will travel a greater distance $d$ per unit of time $t$ than will the end of lever $A$; hence, linear velocity $d/t$ for lever $B$ is greater.

Even though greater velocity is obtained from lever $B$, it also takes greater force to move it. This is true because the torque exerted by an object at the end of the lever is the product of its weight and the length of the resistance arm, which in this case is the length of the lever. For this reason mention was made in Chapter 5 that a lever with a resistance arm longer than its force arm is designed to gain distance and speed at the expense of force.

## Acceleration

Whenever the speed or velocity of a movement changes, the motion is described as an acceleration. Acceleration is defined as the rate of change of velocity. An object "picking up speed" has a *positive acceleration*, whereas one slowing down has a *negative acceleration* also known as a *deceleration*.

Consider as an example of accelerated motion the sprinter shown in Figure 7–4. Due to a constantly acting force exerted by his muscles, the sprinter is constantly accelerated as he moves along the straight line $AB$. As he passes $A$, he has a relatively low velocity $v_o$ (called the original velocity), whereas farther along the track at point $B$ he is moving faster and has a velocity $v_f$ (called the final velocity).

If the time required for the sprinter to go from $A$ to $B$ is $t$, the acceleration by the definition given above is schematically written as

$$\text{acceleration} = \frac{\text{final velocity} - \text{original velocity}}{\text{time}} \quad \text{or} \quad a = \frac{v_f - v_o}{t}$$

Suppose that in Figure 7–4 the velocity of the sprinter at $A$ is 10 ft/sec, that at $B$ it has increased to 20 ft/sec, and that it takes 2 sec to go from $A$ to $B$. Then the acceleration of the sprinter would be (20 ft/sec – 10 ft/sec)/2 sec, or 5 ft/sec² (read five feet per second per second; this means the velocity increases at an average rate of 5 ft/sec every second of time).

**Fig. 7–4. The movement of a sprinter as an example of linear acceleration.**

| Instantaneous velocity: | $V_o$ | | $V_f$ | velocity change | $= V_f - V_o$ |
| Time: | $t_1$ | | $t_2$ | time required | $(t) = t_2 - t_1$ |

## Angular Acceleration

A rotating body need not have a uniform angular velocity $\omega$, just as a body in linear motion need not have a uniform velocity $v$. If the angular velocity of a body changes from some original value $\omega_o$ to a new value $\omega_f$ in a time interval $t$, the angular acceleration $\alpha$ (alpha) of the body is $\alpha = (\omega_f - \omega_o)/t$.

The acceleration, both positive and negative, of joint actions is foundational to all movement performances. The linear acceleration of the body as a whole during a run, for example, is produced partially by the increased angular velocity (angular acceleration) of the limbs.

## Relationship of Angular Acceleration to Linear Acceleration

Remembering that linear velocity $v$ equals the product of the radius $r$ and the angular velocity $\omega$, $v = r\omega$, we can obtain the relationship of linear acceleration to angular acceleration by substituting $r\omega$ for $v$ in the linear acceleration equation:

$$a = \frac{v_f - v_o}{t} = \frac{r\omega_f - r\omega_o}{t} = \frac{r(\omega_f - \omega_o)}{t} = r\alpha$$

Thus, linear acceleration equals the product of the radius $r$ and the angular acceleration $\alpha$.

---

In the preceding section on kinematics the discussion centered on *how* motion is described mathematically. But the answer to the question of *why* an object moves the way it does has not been given. This question is central to that branch of mechanics called *dynamics*, which deals with the causes for changes in the states of motion of an object.

To Isaac Newton goes credit for being the first to formulate the fundamental laws governing all motion. These laws constitute the fundamental principles of dynamics and resolve themselves into three laws commonly referred to as "Newton's Laws of Motion."

**7.13 The Dynamics of Joint Actions**

### Newton's Laws of Motion

*Newton's first law* is also known as the law of *inertia* because it deals with the resistance of an object to any change in its state of motion. That is, the law states that an object at rest has a tendency to remain at rest and that an object in motion tends to remain in motion and to travel in a straight line with uniform velocity unless some external force is applied to it. *Newton's second law* is also known as the law of *acceleration* in that it deals with the factors affecting the acceleration of an object. This law states that when a body is acted upon by a force, its resulting acceleration is directly proportional to the force and inversely proportional to its mass and takes place in the direction of the acting force. *Newton's third law*, known as the law of *reaction*, states that for every action force there is an equal and opposite reaction force. This law emphasizes that when a force is applied upon an object, the object pushes back with a force equal and opposite to the original force.

### Implications of Newton's Laws

Newton's first law states that an object moves because a force greater than its inertia has been applied to it. This law clears up many ambiguities about the concept of force by defining it simply as any influence that can cause a body to be accelerated. It also introduces the concept of *net force*. A body at rest, for example, can have many forces acting upon it, but if this is the case, their magnitudes and directions are such that they cancel one another out to leave no *net force*. In other words, in the parlance of vector addition, the *resultant* sum of all the forces acting upon the object equals zero, a condition known as equilibrium. On the other hand, when one or more forces act upon a body at rest, and their resultant sum is not zero, the body will be set into motion. Under such conditions there is an *unbalanced force* acting and this force alone accounts for the motion. The branch of dynamics dealing with bodies in a state of equilibrium, a condition brought about by balanced forces, is called *statics*. *Kinetics* on the other hand is the branch of dynamics that deals with changes in motion brought about by one or more unbalanced forces.

*Statics.* Newton's first law, from the standpoint of statics, can be turned around to state that any object remaining at rest, or moving with uniform motion, is in equilibrium and the resultant of all forces acting upon it is zero.

Some students might object to Newton's first law in that although everyday experience does indicate that bodies in motion *tend* to remain in motion along a straight line at constant speed, sooner or later they invariably come to a stop and, often, deviate from a straight path as well. A bowling ball, for instance, rolling along a smooth, perfectly level alley will not continue forever owing to the resistance of air and to friction between it and the alley. But we are at liberty to imagine what would happen if the air were to be removed and the friction were to vanish as would happen should the ball be moving in outer space far removed from the gravitational field of the earth. In this case, what would *cause* the ball to change its state of motion? The answer according to Newton's first law is that since *no force* would be acting on the ball it would continue to move in a straight line with uniform velocity.

On the earth, however, we do have air resistance and we do have frictional forces which tend to decrease the velocity of moving objects. Therefore, in order to maintain uniform velocity we must have a constantly acting propelling force which will counteract the resistive forces.

Newton's third law is also involved in problems of equilibrium. In Figure 7–5 a 2-lb book is shown lying stationary on a table, pressing down on the table with a force of 2 lb. The table pushes upward on the book with a reaction force of 2 lb. Why does the book not fly upward into the air? The answer is that the upward force of 2 lb on the book merely balances its weight of 2 lb which acts downward. If the table were not there to cancel out the latter 2-lb force, the book would, of course, be accelerated downward. This situation also exists when we try to push or lift an immovable object, i.e., the weight of the object is greater than we have the strength to move. Say that we apply 100 lb of force against the object. Since the object pushes back against us with an equal and opposite reaction force of 100 lb, the resultant sum of the two forces equals zero and the object remains stationary in equilibrium.

As another example of equilibrium, let us consider the game of tug-of-war, and assume that two opposing teams are pulling on the ends of a rope with equal and opposite forces of 500 lb. That is, team *A* is pulling on the rope with a force of 500 lb, and team *B* is pulling on the rope in the opposite direction with a force of 500 lb. It should be noted here that the tension in the rope is 500 lb and not 1,000 lb. This apparent paradox can be explained by supposing that one team gets tired and ties their end of the rope to a post. The other team still pulling with their 500 lb maintains the same equilibrium condition as before and in so doing maintains the tension of 500 lb. One team can be looked upon as holding the rope so the other team can pull. Therefore, the force of one team is offset by the reaction force of the other team. If the two forces, however, become unequal, as might occur when one team begins to fatigue, equilibrium will no longer exist and the rope will move in the direction of the greater force.

The principles of statics can be summarized by stating the two conditions of equilibrium. The first condition specifies that in order for an object to be in *linear* equilibrium the sum of all the rectangular components of the forces acting upon it must equal zero. That is, the sum of all the $x$ components must equal zero, and the sum of all the $y$ components must equal zero ($\Sigma F_x = 0$, and $\Sigma F_y = 0$). The second condition of equilibrium specifies that in order for an object to be in *rotatory* equilibrium the sum of all the torques tending to produce clockwise rotation must be counterbalanced by the sum of all the torques tending to produce counterclockwise rotation.

The problem of balanced and unbalanced forces certainly occurs in the human anatomy. A muscle, for example, will be able to move a body segment only when its rotatory component is greater than the resistive force of the segment.

*Kinetics.* As mentioned before, Newton's first law defines force as any influence that can cause a body to be accelerated. When an object at rest, for instance, is set into motion, its velocity is changed from zero to a positive value and is, therefore, accelerated. Likewise, when the velocity of an object in motion is either increased or decreased, it is, by definition, being accelerated.

Newton's second law provides a method for analyzing and comparing forces in terms of the accelerations they produce. Thus, a force that causes a body to have twice the acceleration another force produces must be twice as great. Newton's first law is clearly a special case of the second; when the net applied force (resultant sum of a force) is zero, the acceleration is also zero.

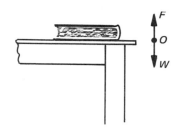

**Fig. 7-5. A book lying on a table is in equilibrium.**

Newton's first law of motion imputes to material bodies the property of tending to resist changes in their state of rest or uniform motion, a property that is known as *inertia*. We can specify inertia in a precise way with the help of the second law of motion. Since the response of a body to a net force $F$ is an acceleration $a$ proportional to $F$, we can write the equation $F = m \times a$. In this equation $m$ is a constant of proportionality characteristic of the particular body being subjected to the force. The larger the value of $m$, the smaller will be the acceleration produced by a given applied force. Thus, $m$ is a measure of the inertia of a body.

Upon what properties of a body does $m$ depend? From everyday experiences we know that such external characteristics of an object as color and shape are not involved in $m$, but what we might loosely call the *amount of matter* in the object is involved. The quantity $m$ is called the *mass* of the body.

The second law of motion provides a method for measuring what is called the *inertial mass* of a body. All that is necessary is to apply the same force, in turn, to a standard mass and to an unknown mass and then to compare their accelerations. This comparison can be made anywhere in the universe with the same results. No matter where we are, we can always tell a wooden ball from a lead ball of the same size by throwing them. The difference in the inertial masses of the two balls would make the balls feel very different to us even though we might be isolated in interstellar space where sensations of weight would be absent.

On the earth's surface, however, the inertial mass of an object is considered to be the same as its gravitational mass. In this case we use as a standard the *force* of gravity and the *acceleration* of gravity that results when a suspended object is allowed to fall. At a given place on the earth we measure the acceleration $g$ resulting from the earth's gravity at that point. This acceleration has been found to average around 32 ft/sec$^2$. We might also measure the force of gravity $W$, called weight, on any object at that place.

In the British system, weight, being a force, is expressed in pounds. According to the second law of motion $F = m \times a$, and so with $F = W$ and $a = g$ we have $W = m \times g$. By transposing, we have $m = W/g$. That is, the gravitational mass of a body is equal to the weight of the body divided by the acceleration of gravity. In the British system with weight $W$ expressed in pounds and with the acceleration of gravity averaging 32 ft/sec$^2$, mass $m$ is expressed in *slugs*. Thus the weight of a 1-slug mass is 32 lb, and the mass of a 1-lb weight is $\frac{1}{32}$ slug.

With mass now defined, we can express Newton's second law in a different way. Remembering that acceleration is the rate of change of velocity and is written algebraically as $a = (v_f - v_o)/t$, we can replace $(v_f - v_o)/t$ for $a$ in the force equation $F = m \times a$ and obtain $F = m \times [(v_f - v_o)/t]$. When this equation is multiplied out, we obtain $F = (mv_f - mv_o)/t$. This equation introduces us to the concept of *momentum*. Momentum is defined as the product of mass times velocity ($mv$). According to this definition, all moving bodies have momentum.

By using momentum rather than velocity, Newton's second law can be changed to state that the rate of change of momentum of a body is proportional to the applied force and takes place in the direction of the force. The relationship $mv_f - mv_o$ is defined as the change in momentum. By transposing the force equation expressed in terms of momentum with the time $t$ being moved to the left side of the equation, we obtain $F \times t = mv_f - mv_o$. This is called the *impulse* equation with $F \times t$ being the impulse and $mv_f - mv_o$ being the change in momentum. From this new equation we can see that the change in the momentum of an object is a product of the force and the time during which the force is applied. Therefore, the greater the force and the greater the time during which the force acts, the greater is the change in momentum.

## Dynamics of Rotation

The principles of dynamics already discussed are as applicable to rotatory movements as they are to linear movements. However, the application of these principles does require the introduction of a few additional concepts.

Perhaps we should first change the force equation $F = m \times a$ into a form applicable to rotatory motion. This is done by multiplying both sides by the radius of the circle $r$ to obtain $F \times r = ma \times r$. The product on the left side of the equation represents the applied torque $T$. Remembering from our discussion on kinematics that linear acceleration $a$ equals the product of the radius $r$ and the angular acceleration $\alpha$, $a = r\alpha$, we can replace the acceleration $a$ on the right side of the above equation by its equal $r\alpha$ and thus obtain $T = mr^2\alpha$. Since $m$ and $r$ for a given body are both constants, they may be replaced by a single constant $I$ and the equation written $T = I\alpha$, where $I = mr^2$ and is called the *moment of inertia*. The moment of inertia in rotatory motion is analogous to $m$ in linear motion, i.e., the resistive force opposing changes in the state of motion of the object.

With these relationships in mind we can now make the following comparisons:

| Linear Motion | Angular Motion |
|---|---|
| Linear momentum = $mv$ | Angular momentum = $I\omega$ |
| Linear impulse = $F \times t$ | Angular impulse = $T \times t$ |
| $Ft = mv_f - mv_o$ | $Tt = I\omega_f - I\omega_o$ |

With these changes the principles of dynamics can be applied to problems of rotatory motion in the same manner they are applied to problems of linear motion.

## 7.21  The Mechanics of Joint Actions

7.20  Study Guidelines

A. Specific Student Objectives

1. State the primary mechanical function of diarthrodial joints.
2. Define kinematics.
3. Define dynamics.

## 7.22   The Kinematics of Joint Actions

A.  Specific Student Objectives

1.  Define velocity.
2.  Define and give the formula for linear velocity.
3.  Define and give the formula for angular velocity.
4.  Define a radian.
5.  State the relationship of radians to degrees in describing angular displacement.
6.  State the relationship of angular velocity to linear velocity.
7.  Define acceleration.
8.  Differentiate between positive and negative acceleration.
9.  Define and give the formula for linear acceleration.
10.  Define and give the formula for angular acceleration.
11.  State the relationship of angular acceleration to linear acceleration.

## 7.23   The Dynamics of Joint Actions

A.  Specific Student Objectives

1.  State Newton's three laws.
2.  State the definition of force derived from Newton's first law.
3.  State what is meant by "net force."
4.  Differentiate between statics and kinetics.
5.  Give the two conditions of equilibrium.
6.  Define mass in terms of Newton's second law.
7.  Define momentum and impulse.
8.  Define moment of inertia.

**7.30   Recommended Supplementary Readings**

The student should consult any recent physics text for supplementary readings on the principles of kinematics and dynamics discussed in this chapter. A list of selected physics texts is given in Appendix B.

# Part III

# Motor Ability Factors

# 8

# Muscle Strength, Power,
# and Endurance

**General Student Objective**

*In his study of the basic concepts of this chapter the student should become familiar with:*

    *8.11    The Concept of Muscle Strength, Power, and Endurance*
    *8.12    Key Concepts of Muscle Strength*
    *8.13    The Measurement of Muscle Strength, Power, and Endurance*
    *8.14    The Prescription of Exercises*

The function of skeletal muscles in the body is to produce mechanical work through isotonic contractions and/or to prevent mechanical work from being performed on the body through isometric contractions. The key concepts related to these functions are those concerned with the term *force*, which is often called muscle strength in the kinesiology literature.

Muscle *strength*, as defined before, is the ability of a muscle or muscle group to apply force; muscle *power* is the ability of a muscle or muscle group to apply force rapidly. Muscle *endurance*, on the other hand, is the ability of a muscle or muscle group to continue applying force over a period of time.

Power, as defined in Chapter 6, is the rate at which work is performed, where work is defined as the product of the force and the distance over which the force is applied. Thus, power is $P = (F \times d)/t$. Since $d/t$ equals velocity $V$, another expression of the power equation is $P = FV$. Therefore, all motor performances that involve the element of velocity are "power" events. Hence, it is evident that the only "nonpower" events are those that involve muscle contractions of the isometric type.

According to McCloy and Young,[1] the velocity of muscle contraction is limited by the resistance of muscular tissue and by the fact

[1] C. H. McCloy and N. D. Young: *Tests and Measurements in Health and Physical Education*, 3rd ed. (New York, Appleton-Century-Crofts, Inc., 1954) p. 66.

that the speed of relaxation of muscles functioning antagonistically is less than the speed of contraction of muscles functioning agonistically. Thus, up to the limit imposed by these restraining factors, increases in strength result in increases in velocity. Beyond this limit, an increase in strength results in little or no increase in velocity. It is because most performers have not attained their maximum velocity, that new records in power events are constantly being made by people involved in weight-training or strength-building programs.

Since muscle endurance is basically a physiological rather than an anatomical or mechanical problem, the current discussion will be mostly limited to muscle strength and power. It is not intended, however, to underemphasize the important interrelationships that exist between muscle strength, power, and endurance. Many of the principles of muscle strength and power discussed in this chapter are also applicable to muscle endurance.

## 8.12 Key Concepts of Muscle Strength

Some of the key concepts involved with muscle strength are

1. *Skeletal muscles contract according to the graded strength principle.* Skeletal muscles are able to match the force of a movement to the demands of a task. Therefore, skeletal muscles operate according to the graded strength principle and not according to the all-or-none principle, as do the individual muscle fibers composing them. Graded strength contractions enable one to lift a pencil, for example, with the same velocity as a book even though it is obvious that a different amount of force is required in the two tasks.

2. *The strength of a skeletal muscle contraction is affected by the number of motor units employed.* Graded strength contractions are partially accomplished by "summing" the contractions of varying numbers of muscle fibers at once. Since all the fibers composing a motor unit contract in unison and to their maximum, if they contract at all, the variations in strength applications are partly due to the number of motor units employed. This type of summation, in which a varying number of motor units are brought into play simultaneously to produce gradations, is called *multiple motor unit summation.* In this type of summation, when a weak contraction is desired, only a few motor units are contracted simultaneously; when a strong contraction is desired, a great number of motor units are contracted at the same time. Should all the motor units contract at the same time, the contraction would be maximal. The strength of a muscle contraction, therefore, can be varied by varying the number of motor units contracting at the same time.

3. *The strength of a skeletal muscle fiber contraction is affected by its frequency of stimulation.* When a muscle fiber is stimulated many times in succession with the contractions occurring closely enough together so that a new contraction occurs before the previous one is over, each succeeding contraction adds to the force of the preceding one, increasing the overall strength of the contraction. This type of summation, in which gradations in strength applications are produced by variations in the frequency of stimulation of the fiber, is called *wave summation.* In wave summation, a weak contraction is produced when the fiber is stimulated only a few times per second,

and a strong contraction is produced when the fiber is stimulated many times per second. A maximum contraction is produced when all the individual muscle twitches become fused into a smooth, continuous contraction. This type of contraction is called a tetanized contraction, and the process of producing it is called *tetanization*.

4. *In submaximal efforts the force of a muscle contraction is attained by utilizing a combination of multiple motor unit summation and wave summation*. The force of a submaximal muscle contraction is attained by contracting the different motor units of a muscle a few at a time, but in rapid succession so that the muscle tension is always of a tetanic rather than a twitching type. In a weak contraction, perhaps only one or two motor units contract at only two or three times per second, but the contractions are spread one after another among the different motor units to achieve the tetanized state. In this way some motor units are always contracting to produce the observed force. When a stronger contraction is desired, more motor units are employed simultaneously and contract more frequently. This combination of multiple motor unit summation and wave summation is called *asynchronous summation*.

5. *The strength of a muscle contraction is controlled by the central nervous system*. The asynchronous summation of muscle forces, as discussed above, is controlled by neuronal circuits in the spinal cord that automatically distribute neuronal impulses evenly and sequentially among the different nerve fibers to a muscle. The spinal circuits, in turn, are controlled by centers in the brain so that movements may be produced in accordance with the wishes of the individual.

6. *Variations in maximal strength applications are affected by variations in the psychological state of the individual*. It is well known that variations in the emotional state of an individual markedly affect his ability to apply maximal muscle force. In states of excitement, for example, an individual can apply much more force than he can in a calmer state. This is due to an alteration in the facilitation of the nervous system, which affects the effectiveness of neural pathways and impulses.

7. *The force of a muscle-fiber contraction is affected by the number of myofibrils that it contains*. Since the myofibril is the contractile unit of the fiber and the contraction of a fiber follows the all-or-none principle, the strength of the fiber is affected by the number of myofibrils that it contains. One of the purposes of strength-building exercises is to stimulate the formation of new and thus additional myofibrils in the fibers.

8. *The force of a muscle-fiber contraction is affected by the metabolic state of the fiber*. It is a common observation that rested muscles can apply greater force than fatigued muscles.

9. *The force of a muscle contraction is affected by the initial length of the muscle*. A muscle at its most elongated position in the body is in its optimal position for a maximal strength of contraction. In other words, a muscle at its normal full length contracts with greatest force; as the muscle progressively shortens, its strength of contraction decreases.

10. *The force of a muscle contraction is affected by its speed of shortening*. In the human body, the force of a muscle contraction varies inversely with its speed of shortening. Thus, a muscle con-

tracts extremely rapidly when it contracts to a maximum extent against no load. However, the velocity of contraction becomes progressively less as the load increases. When the load equals the maximum force the muscle can exert, the velocity of contraction is zero, and no shortening occurs despite maximal activation of the muscle fibers. Therefore, isometric contractions produce higher force values than do isotonic contractions. As the velocity of shortening increases above zero, there is a corresponding decrease in the force of the contraction.

11. *The effective force of a muscle contraction is affected by mechanical factors.* As discussed in the last chapter, the effective force of a muscle contraction is affected by the following factors:

A. The muscle torque (torque = force x force arm) which depends upon

   1. The magnitude of the rotatory component of the muscle force, which depends upon (a) the magnitude of the muscle contraction and (b) the angle at which the muscle is applying the force to the bony lever.
   2. The force arm of the muscle, which is the perpendicular distance from the axis of motion to the line of action of the muscle.

   Therefore, it can be stated that the greater the magnitude of the rotatory component of the muscle force and the longer the force arm of the muscle, the greater is the effective force of a muscle contraction.

B. The length of the resistance arm of the lever system upon which the muscle torque is being applied. The effectiveness of a muscle torque is inversely related to the length of the resistance arm of the lever system, which is the perpendicular distance from the axis of motion to the line of action of the resistance. As the length of the resistance arm increases, the effective force of a muscle contraction decreases.

12. *The effective force of a muscle contraction is affected by the extent of development of the bony projections to which the muscle is attached.* There is strong evidence that the tensile stresses placed on bones through muscle contractions increase the size of the trochanters, tuberosities, and other projections on bones. When a muscle contracts, it transmits a tensile force through its tendon to the periosteum of the bone to which it is attached. This tensile force has a tendency to lift the periosteum a short distance from the bone, and this stress stimulates osteoblastic activity of the osteogenic layer of the periosteum. Thus, bone is deposited under the periosteum causing the area to be elevated. This increase in the elevation of the bony projections increases the angle of pull of the muscle on the bone, which increases the rotatory component of the muscle force. Therefore, one of the factors important in muscle-strength performances is the extent of development of the bony projections to which the muscles are attached.

13. *The torque of a muscle contraction is affected by an interaction of mechanical and physiological factors.* At each position of a joint, the result of maximal isometric muscle contraction in terms of torque depends in part upon such mechanical conditions as the

leverage of the muscle at that particular joint angle and in part upon physiological conditions such as the relative length of the muscle since the tension that a muscle can develop decreases with a decrease in its length. During joint movement, furthermore, the speed of contraction must be taken into consideration, since the tension that a muscle can develop decreases with increasing rate of shortening of the muscle.

The strength of a voluntary muscle contraction can be measured either isometrically or isotonically. The isometric method is the most common, because, as mentioned above, a measure of the maximum force of a muscle contraction can be obtained only when the velocity of contraction is zero. In the isotonic method an individual is required to move a weight through a given distance. The many dynamometers, spirometers, and tensiometers that have been devised to measure the strength of isometric and isotonic contractions and the directions for their use are described in detail in most test and measurement books in physical education.

The use of isometric and isotonic strength tests in conjunction with the study of the various muscles of the body discussed in the myology sections of this book has been found to be quite valuable. These tests enable the student to visualize the location and the function of the different muscles in producing joint movements. They also demonstrate dramatically the effects of mechanical and physiological variables upon muscle function.

Muscle power can be measured by performing any isotonic movement as rapidly as possible. The force, in this case, would be the weight of the body moved. The distance and the time of movement would be measured directly during the performance of the movement. For example, to obtain the power involved in performing the "bench press" exercise often used in weight training, the amount of weight pressed is multiplied by the distance through which it is moved divided by the elapsed time.

Power is most often measured, however, through projection-type activities, that is, activities in which the body as a whole or some external object is projected into the air, and the distance that it travels is the criterion measure. For example, the vertical jump is often used to measure the power of the legs. In this task, the performer, starting from a crouched position, rapidly does enough work to extend the body completely and develops enough momentum to project the body upward in space. The criterion measure here would be the vertical displacement of the body. The throwing of medicine balls and shot puts has also been used to measure the power of the body and its parts, and the horizontal displacement of these objects is the criterion measure.

Muscle endurance, like muscle strength, can be measured either isometrically or isotonically. The isometric method requires the subject to hold a certain force of isometric contraction for as long as he can. The criterion measure here would be the duration of the effort.

## 8.13 The Measurement of Muscle Strength, Power, and Endurance

There are two types of isotonic endurance measurements. One method has the time element held constant; the other method has the time element as a variable. For example, we can have a subject perform as many "push-ups" in a certain time interval as he can, or we can see how long he can continue performing "push-ups" at a certain rate.

## 8.14 The Prescription of Exercises

The problem of prescribing exercises for the development of particular muscles, from an anatomical standpoint, is one of (1) determining the joint actions in which the muscles have the strongest participation and (2) determining the position that the body must be in for the maximum resistance to be placed upon the joint action and, therefore, upon the muscles.

The solution of the problem of determining the joint actions in which the muscles have the strongest participation was given partially in the preceding chapters, and the problem will continue to be discussed in the myology sections that follow. However, a few hints that relate to this problem should be given now.

1. It should be remembered that some movements are produced by concentric contractions of muscles, whereas other movements are controlled by eccentric contractions. For example, some physical educators have been known to recommend the standing toe-touch exercise as being of value in the development of the abdominal muscles. This exercise is performed by the individual standing erect, bending forward to touch his toes, followed by a return to the erect position. In this movement, the lowering of the trunk forward to touch the toes is performed through eccentric contractions of the trunk extensors, whereas the raising of the trunk to the erect position is performed by the concentric contraction of these same muscles. Therefore, the exercise is a very poor one for the abdominal muscles in that these muscles are trunk flexors.

2. Muscles are often brought into action just as strongly through accessory actions as they are through their prime-mover actions. For example, the abdominal muscles are strongly involved in the supine leg-raising exercise in which the individual is resting on his back, hands behind his head, and the legs are raised from the floor. The movement is hip flexion, but the abdominal muscles are involved in the stabilization of the pelvis so as to give a stable base for the pull of the hip flexors. This is often considered an undesirable exercise primarily because most people do not have the abdominal strength to properly stabilize the pelvis.

3. Some muscles are brought into play only when the joint action in which they could be involved is strongly resisted, whereas other muscles are activated the strongest only during certain ranges of the total movement.

4. A muscle can receive a maximum stimulation while it is engaged in either an isometric or an isotonic contraction.

The problem of determining the position that the body must be in for the maximum resistance to be placed upon the joint action and, therefore, upon the muscle is one of anatomical mechanics. The difficulty of an exercise can be varied by (1) changing the magnitude of the muscle torque, or (2) changing the magnitude of the resistance torque.

Since very little can be done to change the length of the force arm of a muscle, the variations in the muscle torque are accomplished primarily by varying the magnitude of the rotatory component of the muscle force, which can be accomplished as follows:

1. Changing the line of pull of the muscle. For example, it is common knowledge that the difficulty of the pull-up (chins) exercise can be increased by assuming a pronated grip on the horizontal bar (palms forward) rather than a supinated grip (palms toward the performer). The flexors of the elbow have a much better line of pull in the supinated position than they do in the pronated position.

2. Changing the length of the muscle. The strength of a muscle contraction, as mentioned before, is affected by the initial length of the muscle.

3. Changing the velocity of a muscle contraction. The difficulty of an exercise can be increased by performing it faster, since the strength of a muscle contraction is inversely affected by its velocity of shortening.

4. Changing the angle of pull of the muscle. The rotatory component of a muscle force is equal to the total force produced by the muscle only when the muscle is pulling on its bony lever at a 90° angle.

The magnitude of the resistance torque can be varied by (1) varying the magnitude of the rotatory component of the resistance force and (2) varying the length of the resistance arm of the lever system. Therefore, the resistance can be increased not only by increasing its load, but also by holding or lifting a weight farther away from the axis of motion of the joint. The greater the perpendicular distance of the line of gravity of the weight being held or lifted to the center of the joint the greater is the resistance torque. Also, the closer the line of action of the resistance to the bony lever approximates a 90° angle the greater is the rotatory component of the resistance force.

**8.21 The Concept of Muscle Strength, Power, and Endurance**

**8.20 Study Guidelines**

A. Specific Student Objectives

1. Differentiate between muscle strength, power, and endurance.
2. State the relationship between muscle strength and the velocity of muscle contraction.

**8.22 Key Concepts of Muscle Strength**

A. Specific Student Objectives

1. Identify the thirteen key concepts of muscle strength.
2. Differentiate between the graded strength principle and the all-or-none principle.
3. Describe multiple motor unit summation.

4. Describe wave summation.
5. Define tetanization.
6. Describe asynchronous summation.
7. Describe the role of the nervous system in muscle-strength performances.
8. Describe the relationship of muscle strength and the number of myofibrils contained in the muscle fibers.
9. State how muscle strength is affected by the metabolic state of the fiber.
10. State how muscle strength is affected by the initial length of the muscle.
11. State how muscle strength is affected by the speed of muscle shortening.
12. Give the mechanical factors that affect the effective force of a muscle contraction.
13. State how muscle strength is affected by the extent of development of the bony projections to which the muscle is attached.
14. Describe how the torque of a muscle contraction is affected by an interaction of mechanical and physiological factors.

### 8.23  The Measurement of Muscle Strength, Power, and Endurance

A. Specific Student Objectives

1. Describe the isometric and isotonic methods of measuring muscle strength.
2. Describe the measurement of muscle power.
3. Describe the isometric and isotonic methods of measuring muscle endurance.

### 8.24  The Prescription of Exercises

A. Specific Student Objectives

1. Describe the problem of prescribing exercises from an anatomical standpoint.
2. State the four factors involved in determining the joint actions in which the muscles participate the strongest.
3. State the two ways that the difficulty of an exercise can be varied.
4. State the four ways that the magnitude of the rotatory component of a muscle force can be varied.
5. State the two ways that the magnitude of the resistance torque can be varied.

### 8.30  Recommended Supplementary Readings

The student should do additional reading in the areas of muscle strength, power, and endurance. A list of selected kinesiology texts is given in Appendix B.

# 9

# The Mobility and Stability of Joints

## 9.11 The Concept of Joint Mobility and Stability

The key concepts in structural kinesiology are those concerned with the factors affecting the mobility and the stability of joints. The mobility of a joint is expressed in terms of the range of motion possible at the joint, often called its *flexibility*. Joint stability, on the other hand, is the resistance of a joint to displacement.

The study of joint mobility, as discussed in Chapter 7, is largely concerned with the description and recording of body angles. This is true because human motion is basically angular in nature. The apparent linear movement of the body as a whole from one place to another is largely a product of a sequence of rotatory movements of the limbs. Since the angular movements of the body are produced by bony levers rotating at diarthrodial joints, the problem of movement analysis resolves itself into one of analyzing joint angles and actions.

Joint angles are also involved in problems of body equilibrium, both at rest and in motion, in which the objective is to prevent the undesired displacements of the body and its parts. Therefore, the stability of the joints, which is the opposite of joint mobility, is just as important in some activities as is the production of movement in other activities.

**9.12 The Recording of Joint Positions and Movements**

The recording of body positions and movements can employ either a three-dimensional or a two-dimensional system. The three-dimensional system employs coordinates and requires that three planes perpendicular to each other be laid through either the center of gravity of the body, or through the center of a joint. As defined in Chapter 3, a plane laid through the center of gravity of a body is called a *cardinal plane*. Planes drawn through the center of gravity of a body segment or through the center of a joint, as is often the case, are called *secondary planes*. In review, the three cardinal planes, which correspond to the three dimensions of space, as defined in Chapter 3, are

A. *Sagittal plane*: This is a vertical plane that passes through the body from front to back and divides it into right and left sections.
B. *Frontal plane*: This is a vertical plane that passes through the body from side to side and divides it into front and back sections.
C. *Transverse plane*: This is a horizontal plane that passes through the body and divides it into upper and lower sections.

When a two-dimensional system is used to describe and to record body movements, only one of the three planes is utilized. This system is typically used when movements are recorded by photographs or described by line drawings. A still- or motion-picture camera, for instance, can only record a movement in two dimensions. When the movement is photographed in the frontal plane, we obtain either a front or a back view. Likewise, in the sagittal plane, we obtain a side view; in the transverse plane, we obtain either a top or a bottom view. Since standard photographic procedures give only a two-dimensional view, a three-dimensional recording is obtained by the simultaneous utilization of three synchronized cameras in each of the three planes.

**The Axes of Motion**

The angular motion of a body part, as discussed in Chapter 3, occurs around a center of rotation or *axis*. The three axes of motion, called X, Y, and Z, are located at the intersection between the three planes of space as was shown in Figure 3–2. Each of these axes is perpendicular to the plane in which the motion occurs. They are defined as follows:

A. *Frontal or X axis*: This axis passes horizontally from side to side perpendicular to the sagittal plane.
B. *Vertical or Y axis*: This axis passes perpendicular to the ground and to the transverse plane.
C. *Sagittal or Z axis*: This axis passes horizontally from front to back and is perpendicular to the frontal plane.

When the *anatomical position*, which has the individual upright with his arms at his sides and palms forward, is used as a frame of reference, we can see that the fundamental joint movements, as mentioned in Chapter 3, occur in a definite plane and around a definite axis. Flexion and extension, for instance, occur in the sagittal plane about a frontal axis. Likewise, abduction and adduction occur in the frontal plane about a sagittal axis, and rotation occurs in the transverse plane about a vertical axis. Since circumduction involves flexion, abduction, adduction, and extension performed in sequence, it occurs in both the sagittal and frontal planes.

By convention, negative and positive signs are given to movements around the three axes according to the following system:

A. *Frontal or X axis:* Movements toward the right side of the subject are positive; those to the left are negative.
B. *Vertical or Y axis:* Upward movements are positive; downward movements are negative.
C. *Sagittal or Z axis:* Forward movements are positive; backward movements are negative.

### The Three-Coordinate System

When recording the position of body parts, the X, Y, and Z axes are considered coordinates in a three-coordinate system. By convention, negative and positive signs are given to body positions in relation to the three coordinates and to the center of gravity of the body as follows:

A. *Frontal or X axis:* Distance to the right of the center of gravity are positive; those to the left are negative.
B. *Vertical or Y axis:* Distances above the center of gravity are positive; those below are negative.
C. *Sagittal or Z axis:* Distances that lie in front of the center of gravity are positive; those that lie behind it are negative.

Through the use of the three coordinates, any point in space can be determined precisely. For instance, we might specify the location of the center of a subject's left knee joint in the anatomical position as follows: X = − 8.5 cm, Y = −52 cm, and Z = 0.

The coordinate system is also applicable to two-dimensional analysis. For instance, when analyzing a photograph made in the frontal plane, the X and the Y coordinates are used. Likewise, in the sagittal plane the Y and Z coordinates are used, whereas the X and Z coordinates are used in the transverse plane.

Like the recording of body positions and movements, the mobility of a joint can be measured either in two or three dimensions.

Two-dimensional measures of joint mobility in a single plane involve the use either of an instrument called a goniometer, which measures the range of motion at a joint in terms of the degrees of a circle, or of a yardstick-type instrument, which measures the linear displacement of body parts. These two types of measurements are illustrated in Figure 9–1.

There are many types of goniometers currently in use. The simplest type is illustrated in Figure 9–1A. This instrument consists of a 180° protractor with extended plexiglas arms. One arm is movable,

**9.13  The Measurement of Joint Mobility**

**Fig. 9–1. Measures of flexibility. A goniometer is shown in *A*, and the Scott-French standing, bending, and reach test is shown in *B*.**

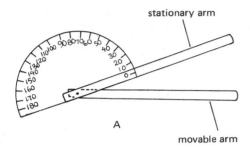

stationary arm

A

movable arm

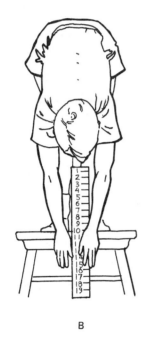

B

and the other is fixed at the zero line of the protractor. The application of this goniometer is simple. Let us assume we wish to measure the range of motion possible at the knee joint of a subject. The arms of the goniometer are placed parallel with the thigh and leg of the subject with the center of motion at the knee joint. Readings are taken with the knee fully flexed and with the joint fully extended. The difference between the two readings represents the range of motion.

The linear method illustrated in Figure 9–1*B* is the type most often used in school situations, because of its economy in terms of time and effort. Even though the measure can be obtained simply and fast, it is still regarded as only a "rough" estimate of general body flexibility. The specific test illustrated is called the *Scott and French standing, bending, reach test.*[1] In this test a 20-in. scale, marked in 1/2 in. units, is attached to a stable bench. In taking the test, the subject stands with toes even with the front edge of the bench and touching the edges of the scale. The subject then bends slowly downward as far as possible reaching equally with the fingers of both hands. The knees must be kept straight. The score is the lowest point reached on the scale by the finger tips.

There are, of course, many types of goniometers and many types of flexibility tests as may be found in most test and measurement books in physical education. An interesting innovation, however, is the electrogoniometer developed by Karpovich at Springfield College.[2] This electronic device can be used to continuously measure changes in joint angles during the performance of various body movements, and it has proven a most valuable aid in the study of human movement.

The two-dimensional methods identified above are useful for recording joint movements occurring in a single plane. To measure motion in a joint that has more than one axis of motion and is capable of moving in two or three planes, a three-dimensional approach is required. In this approach the subject is conceived of as standing inside a globe as illustrated in Figure 9–2. The joint movements of the subject are recorded on the surface of the globe. Abduction and adduction are measured by the meridians, whereas flexion and extension are measured by the parallels of the globe. In this way the *excursion field* subscribed by a joint can be traced upon the surface of the globe as shown in Figure 9–3.

## 9.14 Limiting Factors in Joint Mobility

Some factors that limit the flexibility of an individual are (1) bony structures, (2) soft tissue bulk, (3) ligaments, (4) muscle connective tissue, (5) muscle tonus, (6) the skin, and (7) viscosity of the synovial fluid.

The range of motion in some joints is very definitely limited by the surrounding bony structures. Extension of the elbow, for instance,

---

[1] M. Gladys Scott and Esther French: *Measurement and Evaluation in Physical Education* (Dubuque, Iowa, Wm. C. Brown Company Publishers, 1959), p. 312.
[2] Peter V. Karpovich and Wayne E. Sinning: *Physiology of Muscular Activity*, 7th ed. (Philadelphia, W. B. Saunders Co., 1971), p. 63.

is limited by the length of the olecranon process and the depth of the olecranon fossa. Also, for example, flexion of the neck is limited when the chin comes into contact with the chest, and movements of the thorax are limited by the presence of the ribs.

Not only do the surrounding bony structures interfere with movement, but so do the surrounding soft tissues. This is evidenced by the inability of some fat people to tie their shoes. It is also likely that the muscle bulk of heavily muscled men limit, for example, the range of elbow and knee flexion.

The tautness of ligaments is a limiting factor as evidenced by the restricted hyperextension of the hip joint due to the presence of the iliofemoral ligament. The connective-tissue framework, tendons, and fascial sheaths of muscles tend to resist stretch and therefore to limit the range of motion in the joints. This effect can be experienced by attempting to place the palm of the hand on the floor from the standing position with the knees straight. Probably everyone has experienced the resulting strain in his posterior thigh and calf muscles when attempting this exercise. It has been found that the resistance of a muscle to stretch is primarily due to its connective tissue and not to its contractile elements. It is possible, however, that a muscle being stretched is not completely relaxed in which case the muscle tonus tends to oppose the attempted joint movement. Likewise, it has been found that the skin offers a certain amount of resistance to being stretched, and that the synovial fluid of a joint varies in its viscosity and its resistance to movement.

Fig. 9-2. In three-dimensional measures of flexibility, the subject is conceived as standing inside a globe.

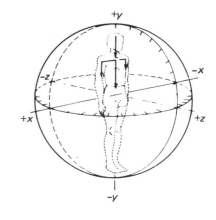

Joint stability is the resistance of a joint to displacement and is, therefore, the opposite of joint mobility. The two main factors affecting joint stability, within the scope of this book, are (1) anatomical and (2) mechanical.

Some of the anatomical factors that affect joint stability are (1) the shape of the articular surfaces, (2) ligamentous structures, (3) viscosity of the synovial fluid, (4) atmospheric pressure, (5) fascial structures, and (6) the location and action of muscles.

The shape of the articular surfaces is an important factor in the stability of some joints. In the elbow joint, for example, the surfaces are so engaged that a bond of union is formed. This is also true in the knee joint, where, when the individual is in the standing position with the knees straight, the large rounded condyles of the femur rest firmly on the concave surfaces of the tibia and the intervening articular disks making for a secure articulation.

Since the primary function of ligaments is to hold the bones of a joint together, their importance in joint stability is obvious. Atmospheric pressure (760 mm Hg) has been found to be important as it presses the many structures of a joint closer together. Fascia, as mentioned before, has a tendency to contract and to resist being stretched and thereby tends to secure the joints. Very viscous synovial fluid resists the displacement of the joints. Probably one of the most important factors is muscle tension produced by the stabilizing component of a muscle force, which is usually greater than the rotatory component.

## 9.15 Anatomical Factors Affecting Joint Stability

Fig. 9-3. The excursion field subscribed by a joint can be traced upon the surface of a globe.

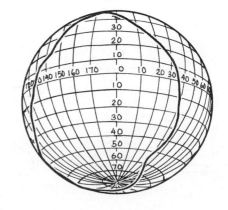

## 9.16 Mechanical Factors Affecting Joint Stability

In addition to the anatomical factors are certain mechanical principles (factors) which interact with the anatomical factors to determine the degree of stability of the joints. These principles are only special applications of Newton's three laws of motion.

According to Newton's first law, a body is in equilibrium when there is no *net* force acting upon it. This effect is explained by Newton's third law, which states that a body is in equilibrium when all forces acting upon it mutually neutralize each other in magnitude and in direction so that the resulting *net* force is zero. Newton's second law states that a net force acting upon a body imparts to it an acceleration proportional to the force both in magnitude and direction and inversely proportional to the mass of the body. Therefore, it can be seen that one factor that affects the stability of a body is its mass. The larger the mass of a body, the greater is its stability as measured by the amount of force required to move (accelerate) it.

The mass of a body is considered to be concentrated at one point called the *center of gravity*. An imaginary line passing through the center of gravity to the center of the earth is called the *line of gravity*. This line represents the *line of action* of gravity, which is the one force always acting upon the body during activities on the earth.

For a body to be in *gravitational* equilibrium, according to Newton's third law, all gravitational forces must be completely neutralized by counterforces. These counterforces are supplied by (1) the resistance of the supporting surface upon which the body rests, or by (2) some additional restraining force such as that applied in the anatomy by muscles and ligaments. As long, however, as all gravitational forces fall within the area of the supporting surface, the force of gravity is neutralized and the body will remain in equilibrium. Therefore, one of the requirements of stability for a body otherwise unrestrained is that the *line of gravity fall within the area of the support base.*

Should the line of gravity of a body fall outside its support base, or should the support base be removed entirely, then, of course, gravitational stability will have been upset and the body will be accelerated by the force of gravity. With no support, the acceleration will be linear. When the gravitational line of a body falls outside its support base, the resulting acceleration will be rotatory.

The resistance of a body to rotatory displacement is based upon three factors in addition to its mass. These factors are (1) the size of its support base, (2) the horizontal distance of its line of gravity to its axis of rotation, and (3) the height of its center of gravity above its support base.

Shown in Figure 9–4 are two wooden blocks of the same size and weight with the center of gravity $C$ of each located at the same height above the support base. As shown in Figure 9–5, in order to upset the gravitational stability of these blocks it is necessary to rotate them so that their lines of gravity fall outside their support bases. The magnitude of the resistive torque ($T = F \times f$) that each block in Figure 9–4 offers to rotatory displacement is determined by their weights $F$ and the perpendicular distance $f$ from their axes of rotation, point $D$, to their lines of gravity. This distance in block A is 5 in., and in block B it is 10 in. Therefore, remembering that the weights of the two blocks are the same, the difference in the resistive torques of the blocks is solely determined by the difference in the

**Fig. 9–4.** The gravitational stability of an object is affected by the size of its base of support.

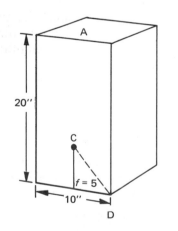

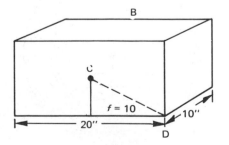

lengths of the two resistance arms $f$. This difference in the lengths of the resistance arms can be accounted for, in the present example, solely by the difference in the sizes of the two support bases. Thus, one of the factors affecting the gravitational stability of an object is *the size of its support base.*

Another factor affecting gravitational stability is illustrated in Figure 9–6, which shows two blocks of equal size, weight, support bases, but with different horizontal locations of their centers of gravity. The center of gravity of block B is located farther to the right than is that of block A; i.e., block A is symmetrical with its center of gravity at its center, whereas block B is heavier on the right side than it is on the left. The axis of rotation of each block is indicated as point $D$. Therefore, it can be seen that the length of the resistance arm $f$ of block B is greater than that of block A, which means that block B has a correspondingly greater stability than does block A. Thus, one of the factors affecting the gravitational stability of a body is *the horizontal distance from its line of gravity to its axis of rotation.*

The third factor affecting the gravitational stability of a body is the height of its center of gravity above its support base as illustrated in Figure 9–7. Shown here are two blocks of equal size and weight. The sizes of their support bases and the horizontal distance of their lines of gravity to the axes of rotation are identical. But the height of the center of gravity in block A is greater than that in block B, and for this reason much greater force is required to upset block B than is required to upset block A. This is because the lower the center of gravity is located in a body the greater is the angular displacement $\theta$ required before its gravitational line falls outside of its support base. The greater the angle $\theta$ the greater is the rotatory component of the resistance ($R \sin \theta$) and the greater is the amount of mechanical work that must be performed and the amount of force that must be applied. Also, as can be observed in Figure 9–7, only a small tipping of the blocks results in a much greater *decrease* in the length of the resistance arm in block A than in block B. Thus, it can be seen that another factor affecting the stability of a body is *the height of its center of gravity above its support base.* The lower the center of gravity the greater is the stability of a body.

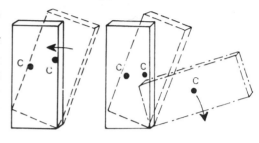

**Fig. 9–5.** To upset the gravitational stability of an object, it is necessary to rotate it so that its line of gravity falls outside its support base.

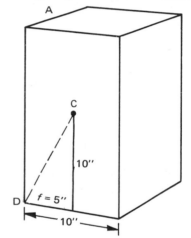

**Fig. 9–6.** The gravitational stability of an object is affected by the horizontal distance from its line of gravity to its axis of rotation.

**Fig. 9–7.** The gravitational stability of an object is affected by the height of its center of gravity above its support base.

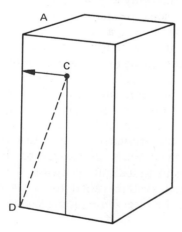

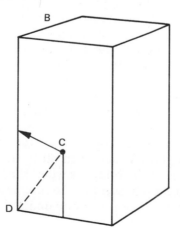

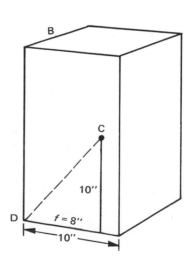

## Stable and Unstable Equilibrium

When a body in equilibrium is displaced slightly, the magnitudes, directions, and lines of action of the forces acting on it may all change. If the forces in the displaced position are such as to return the body to its original position, the equilibrium is *stable*. If the forces act to increase the displacement still further, the equilibrium is *unstable*. If the body is still in equilibrium in the displaced position, the equilibrium is *neutral*. Whether a given equilibrium state is stable, unstable, or neutral can only be determined by considering other states slightly displaced from the first.

The position of a circular cone on a level surface affords an example of the three types of equilibrium. When the cone rests on its base, as in Figure 9–8A the equilibrium is stable. When balanced on its apex, as in B, the equilibrium is unstable. When resting on its side, as in C, the equilibrium is neutral.

Whether a person desires stable or unstable equilibrium depends upon his purpose, i.e., whether he wishes to produce or to resist motion. A sprinter in the "set" position obviously desires an unstable position so that he can produce the movement of his body down the track as rapidly as possible. On the other hand, a defensive lineman in football may desire a stable position so that he can better resist the blocks of offensive linemen attempting to move him.

Whether a person is in a stable or unstable body position is determined by his joint angles and the segmental alignment of his body parts.

**Fig. 9–8.** (*A*) Stable, (*B*) unstable, and (*C*) neutral equilibrium.

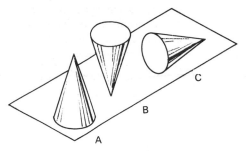

### 9.17 Principles of Stable Segmental Alignments

The human body is not a rigid structure, but a complicated, segmented unit composed of many parts joined together at joints. The stability of the body, therefore, is dependent upon the stability of its individual segments, and the gravitational forces that act upon the segments must be neutralized individually in order for the body as a whole to be in gravitational equilibrium.

The part of the total equilibrium of the body contributed by the equilibrium of a segment is called the *partial equilibrium* of that segment. Likewise, each segment has a partial center of gravity and a *partial* gravitational line. The location of the *common* center of gravity, which is the center of gravity of the body as a whole, is determined by the vector addition of the separate partial centers of gravity. Since the common gravitational line is a vertical line that passes through the common center of gravity to the center of the earth, its location is determined by the location of the common center of gravity. Thus, any relocation of a partial center of gravity will cause a corresponding relocation of the common center of gravity and the common gravitational line. For instance, swinging the arms forward shifts the common center of gravity forward, and raising the arms raises the common center of gravity. Similarly, the position of the segments may even shift the common center of gravity to the outside of the body, as when the body is in a jackknife position.

Since each segment in the articulated system called the human body rests upon the one underneath it, the intervening joint surfaces are the support bases of the separate segments. Therefore, by remembering the principles of stability from previous discussions, it can be seen that joint stability is partially dependent upon (1) the sizes of the joint surfaces, (2) the horizontal distance of the common gravitational line to the center of the joint, and (3) the height of the partial centers of gravity above the joint surfaces.

Body positions that require muscle forces for maintenance are said to be in *active* equilibrium, whereas those positions not requiring muscle contractions for maintenance are said to be in *passive* equilibrium.

The condition of passive equilibrium requires that all the partial centers of gravity of the individual segments and the centers of all the joints fall within the line of gravity of the body as a whole, and that this common line of gravity fall within the area of the support base of the whole system. Only when these conditions are met can the system be kept in passive equilibrium. That is, only when all the linear and rotatory components of the gravitational force are neutralized by the joint surfaces and the support base of the body can the body as a whole be in passive equilibrium. These conditions are met only when the body is lying horizontally on a flat surface; with the body in the upright position such a passive equilibrium is impossible.

In the upright position, neither all the centers of gravity of the different parts nor all the axes of motion between the different parts can be brought to coincide with the common line of gravity. Most of the joint centers are, in fact, at a considerable distance from the common line of gravity. Thus, in the upright standing position the force of gravity develops active rotatory torques in many of the joints. These rotatory torques must be neutralized by active opposing muscle forces, if an equilibrium is to be established and the parts are to be maintained in their relative positions. The muscles supplying these resistive forces are often referred to as antigravity muscles and are illustrated in Figure 9–9.

The center of gravity of the body in the erect standing position in the adult is located approximately in the region of the first sacral vertebra near the plane of the pelvic inlet. This location, of course, is never static, but always varies due to the normal swaying of the body over its small support base and to the constant changing of position of the body segments.

The term posture is often used to describe the various segmental alignments of the body. *Good posture*, however, is a *model* that describes the most efficient way in which the muscles can be used to ensure the most effective alignment of body parts for the position and movements desired. Some positions, for instance, are desired for effective force application, others are desired for force absorption, still others for energy conservation. Because of differences in purposes and in body builds there are, in fact, many models of good posture, both static and kinetic.

The average position for the erect standing posture that best meets the conditions of equilibrium discussed previously and that has proven to be most efficient for most people is one in which the partial centers of gravity of the head, upper trunk, lower trunk, and legs are in a straight line parallel with the gravitational line of the body. In this model the individual is in the upright position with the gravitational line falling within the base of support formed by the

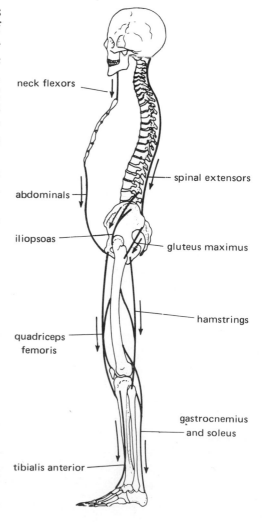

**Fig. 9–9. The chief antigravity muscles responsible for maintaining the erect position.**

feet. From a side view of the subject, a plumb line dropped even with the lobe of the ear would pass through the middle of the shoulder, through the middle of the hip joint, to the side and slightly behind the patella, and fall in front of the lateral malleolus (Fig. 9–10). As seen from the back, the line representing the line of gravity would bisect the head and neck and follow the vertebral column down between the cleft of the buttocks. Also, in this model the vertebral column should be straight and the shoulders and hips level.

The more the body deviates from the model alignment, the greater is the energy usually required to hold the body erect. This is true because the antigravity muscles will usually have to overcome a greater rotatory torque produced by the force of gravity. However, in certain cases the structure of the body may be such that more energy will be expended in forcing the body to maintain the alignment described above than would be required in a less ideal position. Caution should be taken, therefore, not to try to fit this model to everyone.

**9.20   Study Guidelines**

**9.21   The Concept of Joint Mobility and Stability**

A.  Specific Student Objectives

1.   Differentiate between joint mobility and stability.
2.   Describe the role of joint angles in determining the mobility and the stability of joints.

**9.22   The Recording of Joint Positions and Movements**

A.  Specific Student Objectives

1.   Differentiate between cardinal and secondary planes.
2.   Identify and define the three planes of space.
3.   Identify and define the three axes of motion.
4.   State how negative and positive signs are given to movements around the three axes.
5.   Identify and define the three coordinates used in the recording the position of body parts.
6.   State how the coordinate system is used in the three-dimensional analysis of human movements.
7.   State how the coordinate system is used in the two-dimensional analysis of human movements.

**9.23   The Measurement of Joint Mobility**

A.  Specific Student Objectives

1.   Describe the two-dimensional measures of joint stability.
2.   Describe the three-dimensional measures of joint mobility.
3.   Define electrogoniometry.

## 9.24 Limiting Factors in Joint Mobility

A. Specific Student Objectives

1. Identify the seven factors that limit joint mobility.
2. Describe how each of the seven factors acts to limit joint mobility.

## 9.25 Anatomical Factors Affecting Joint Stability

A. Specific Student Objectives

1. Identify the six factors that affect joint stability.
2. Describe how each of the six factors affects joint stability.

## 9.26 Mechanical Factors Affecting Joint Stability

A. Specific Student Objectives

1. State how the mass of a body affects its stability.
2. State the conditions of gravitational equilibrium.
3. Identify the three mechanical factors in addition to mass that affect the stability of a body.
4. Differentiate between stable, unstable, and neutral equilibrium.
5. Give an example of a motor performance situation in which unstable equilibrium is desired.
6. Give an example of a motor performance situation in which stable equilibrium is desired.

## 9.27 Principles of Stable Segmental Alignments

A. Specific Student Objectives

1. Differentiate between partial and common center of gravity.
2. Differentiate between active and passive equilibrium.
3. State the conditions of passive equilibrium.
4. Describe the model for "good posture."

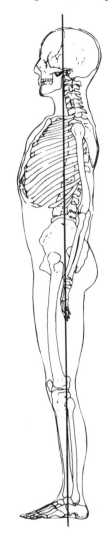

Fig. 9–10. The skeletal form of a person with good standing posture.

The student should do additional reading in the areas of joint mobility and stability. A list of selected kinesiology texts is given in Appendix B.

9.30 Recommended Supplementary Reading

# Part IV

# Anthropometry

Chapter 10

Introduction to
Anthropometry

# 10

# Introduction to Anthropometry

## 10.11 The Divisions of Anthropometry

Anthropometry (an″thro-pom′e-tre) is the science that deals with the measurement of the weight, size, and proportions of the human body and its parts. The measurement of the body as a whole is called *general* anthropometry; measurement of body parts is called *regional* anthropometry. General and regional anthropometry are highly interrelated as will be seen in this chapter.

The three main types of anthropometric measures are those concerned with (1) the *weight*, (2) the *size*, and (3) the *proportions* of the human body and its parts. The various methods of obtaining these measures will not be discussed in detail, but examples will be given and the implications of these measures as structural and mechanical variables in human movement will be considered.

## 10.12 Body Weight

Body weight is a structural variable of great mechanical significance in human movement, because it represents the force of gravity acting upon the body. The weight of a body can be obtained by any instrument that will measure the magnitude of the attractive force between the body and the earth. The most common instrument used for this purpose is the standard spring scale found in most bathrooms.

The weight of the body can be divided into two main components: a fat component and a fat-free component. The fat-free component is often referred to as the *lean body mass*. The relative proportion of the body weight that is fat and fat-free can be determined either through skinfold measures or through body fluid measures.

Instruments used to obtain skinfold measures of the amount of subcutaneous tissue and fat in different parts of the body are generally known as fat calipers. Pascale, Grossman, and Sloane[1] report the following regression equation for the estimation of body density from fat caliper measurements.

$$Y = 1.088468 - .007123X_1 - .004834X_2 - .005513X_3$$

where $Y$ is the estimated body density, $X_1$ the skinfold measurement on the chest on the midaxillary line at the level of the ziphoid, $X_2$ the skinfold measurement for the chest at the juxta-nipple position, and $X_3$ the dorsum of the arm, midway between the tip of the acromion and olecranon processes.

Keys and Brozek[2] report that the following equation will give the proportion of the body weight that is fat from the measure of body density:

$$F = \frac{4.201}{D} - 3.813$$

where $F$ is the proportion of the body weight that is fat, and $D$ is the measure of body density.

Morehouse and Miller[3] report that a measure of the fat content of the body can be calculated from a knowledge of the total amount of water in the body and give methods of measuring the total body water volume. The body fluid measure of the fat content of the body is based on the fact that fat is simply added to the body without the addition of a corresponding amount of water, and that the fat-free portion of the body has a reasonably constant 72% water content. If the measured water content of an individual is 54% and if $X$ = % fat, the proportion of the body weight that is fat can be calculated as follows:

$$(100)(0.54) = (100 - X)(0.72) + (X)(0)$$

$X$ = 0.25 or the fat content is 25% of the body weight

### The Importance of Body Weight in Human Movement

The importance of body weight as a variable in human movement can be explained by referring once again to Newton's second law,

[1] L. R. Pascale, M. I. Grossman, and H. S. Sloane: "Correlation between skinfolds and body density in eighty-eight soldiers," *Med. Nutrition Lab.*, 162, 1955.
[2] A. Keys and J. Brozek: "Body fat in adult man," *Physiol. Rev.*, 33:245, 1953.
[3] L. E. Morehouse and A. T. Miller: *Physiology of Exercise*, 4th ed. (St. Louis, The C. V. Mosby Company, 1963), p. 129.

which states that a *net* force acting upon a body imparts to it an acceleration proportional to the force both in magnitude and direction and inversely proportional to the mass of the body. Therefore, it can be seen that one of the most important factors affecting the equilibrium and acceleration of a body is its *mass*. The mass of a body is given by its weight divided by the gravitational constant (32 ft/sec$^2$), $m = W/g$. Therefore, the greater the mass (weight) of a body, the greater is its equilibrium as measured by the amount of force required to either positively or negatively accelerate it.

Whether body mass is to the advantage or disadvantage of a performer depends upon his movement objectives. Should he desire to maintain his body in a state of *equilibrium*, either static or kinetic, a greater body mass, other things being equal, is to his advantage. However, should he desire to produce an *acceleration* of his body, a greater body mass, other things being equal, would be to his disadvantage. These relationships of body mass to performance are well known from everyday and sports experience. In matters of static equilibrium, for instance, we know that it is much more difficult to *move* a heavy object than it is to move a lighter one. Therefore, heavy football linemen and wrestlers usually have an advantage over lighter players. Also, in matters of kinetic equilibrium, we know that it is much more difficult to *stop* the movement of a heavy object than it is to stop the movement of a lighter one. Therefore, the heavy running backs in football usually have an advantage over the lighter players.

On the other hand, should the movement objective of a performer be to *accelerate* his body, we know from Newton's second law ($a = F/m$) that the mass of the body as such is an encumbrance. Therefore, performers in acceleration and endurance activities usually attempt to reduce to a minimum any *dead weight* that might be present in their body masses.

Dead weight is defined as the weight of all body parts not directly involved in the production of a movement. This weight is accounted for by the weight of the skeleton, the skin, the viscera, the blood vessels, and especially the weight of the inactive muscles and the body fat. Heavy inactive muscles are just as much dead weight in movement activities as is the body fat. Therefore, resistive exercises that develop muscle strength without a great increase in muscle bulk are preferred for performance in acceleration and endurance activities.

The fat content of the body, like body weight in general, can be to either the advantage or disadvantage of the performer. Football players, especially linemen, employ the fat portion of their mass in achieving momentum (mass × velocity) and also as a cushion to absorb the shocks of repeated contact. In acceleration and endurance activities, however, body fat is simply dead weight and it is desirable to reduce it to an absolute minimum.

The fat-free component of the body weight is, of course, mostly composed of the weight of the muscles and of the skeleton. Since muscle strength is roughly proportional to the amount of muscle that an individual has, it should be easy to understand the importance of lean body mass as a variable in human movement.

According to McCloy and Young,[4] the muscles in an adult male of good muscular development constitute approximately 40 to 45 per cent of his body weight; in an adult female, 35 to 40 per cent. McCloy and Young give the following illustration of the importance of muscle weight and muscle development in motor performance: If a man who weighs 150 lb has 40 per cent of his weight comprised of muscle, he has 60 lb muscle. If he increased in weight to 180 lb, and if all this increase were in muscular weight, his increase in muscular weight would be 30 lb (180 – 150), an increase of 50 per cent (60 + 30). The increase in the load would also be 30 lb (i.e., 150 to 180), or an increase of only 20 per cent. Hence the increase in muscle strength would be proportionately greater than that represented by the increased load. In other words, the undesirable effects of increasing the mass of the body is compensated for by the greater increase in the force available for the production of movements.

## 10.13  Body Size

The anthropometric measures of body size are those concerned with (1) the linear dimensions of the body, (2) the girth (circumference) of body parts, and (3) the body surface area.

### The Linear Dimensions of the Body

The linear measures of the body are those concerned with the length (height), width, and depth of body parts. These measures can be obtained either by photographs or by the use of calipers on a live subject.

The height of an individual is an important variable in many types of motor activities simply because tall performers usually have longer limbs and, therefore, longer levers. Body height, however, is also a pure factor that in and of itself is important in many activities. In basketball, for example, the tall player has such an advantage at the basket that he can completely dominate the game. This is true because the goal (basket) in basketball is above the heads of the performers and, therefore, the tall player is simply closer to the basket than is a shorter player.

Because of height, tall players are able to move their hands through a wider range (reach), which gives them an advantage in catching activities. For instance, the tall football receiver and the tall first baseman in baseball obviously have a greater reach, which enables them to catch many high and/or wide throws beyond the reach of a shorter player. Thus, when we consider the total range in which a tall player can reach the ball, it becomes obvious that he also affords a much larger target for the thrower than does a shorter player.

Height is also directly advantageous in such events as the high jump and the high-hurdle race in track and field. This advantage exists because the center of gravity of a tall performer is higher from the

[4]C. H. McCloy and N. D. Young: *Tests and Measurements in Health and Physical Education*, 3rd ed. (New York, Appleton-Century-Crofts, Inc., 1954), p. 52.

ground than is that of a shorter person, and all the tall performer has to do to gain this advantage is to lift his legs out of the way. In events like the shot-put, height is an advantage because the shot in the hands of a tall performer starts from a higher point above the ground than does the shot in the hands of a shorter person. Therefore, the shot thrown by the taller performer travels farther than the shot thrown by a shorter performer before it reaches the ground, even if no other factors are involved.

Body height can also be to the disadvantage of the performer, because of the leverage problems involved. The tall performer, for example, is poorly designed for weight lifting in that he is built more for speed than for strength. Tall players are also lacking in the static and kinetic stability necessary for equilibrium during (1) physical contact activities and (2) activities requiring abrupt changes of direction. The primary reason for this lack of stability is the high center of gravity of tall individuals, which makes it difficult for them to maintain their balance. Many tall basketball players, for example, do not like to leave the floor in rough play because a comparatively light force against the lower parts of their legs while they are in the air could cause them to crash to the floor. For the same reason, excessive height is a disadvantage in such activities as wrestling and judo.

The *linear measures of body parts* are of importance in the study of human movement because they describe the various lever components of the body. These measures are highly affected by the bony framework of the body. The length of the forearm, for example, *cannot* be any shorter or any longer than the length of the radius and ulna. Therefore, the anthropometric measure of forearm length is a *direct* measure of the length of the two forearm bones. The same is true of arm length (humerus), leg length (tibia and fibula), thigh length (femur), etc.

Since most of the levers of the body are of the third class in which the lever arm of the resistance equals the entire length of the lever, long limbs would be an advantage in those activities in which emphasis is upon velocity and range of motion and a disadvantage in those activities in which strength and equilibrium are emphasized. A long arm, therefore, should be an aid to the javelin thrower or the discus thrower, since greater velocity can be developed at the end of this longer lever. Likewise, long legs should be to the advantage of the runner, since this would increase the possible length of his stride. Long-legged men, however, often find these third-class levers awkward to manipulate in such sports as soccer and speedball, and their high centers of gravity make abrupt changes of direction more difficult. Likewise, long limbs are to the disadvantage of the weight lifter in that the long resistance arms of these third-class levers increase the magnitude of the resistance torques that must be overcome.

Linear measures of the width and depth of body parts are important in the study of human movement in that they represent the relative sizes and masses of body segments. Broad feet and hands, for example, are important to the swimmer in that they give him better paddles with which to propel his body through the water. Large hands also might be to the advantage of the basketball player in giving him greater control of the ball.

### Girth and Surface Area Measures of the Body

Girth and surface area measures of the body and its parts are important in determining the body build of an individual. For example, such measures as the girth and surface area of the shoulders, chest, waist, and hips are important in determining the shape and contours of the body.

Girth measures are made by anthropometric tape measures. Body surface area (volume), on the other hand, can be estimated through either body height and weight measures or submersion of the body in water and measurement of the water displaced.

## 10.14 Body Proportions

The primary measures of body proportions are those concerned with (1) location of the center of gravity and (2) the body build of an individual.

### Location of the Center of Gravity in Man

The various methods of locating the common center of gravity in man are described in detail in most test and measurement textbooks in physical education. There are also several methods for determining the masses and locating the centers of gravity of body segments. Figure 10-1 illustrates a simple method of locating the common center of gravity of an individual in the transverse plane. In this method, a board long enough for the individual to lie on is placed on two triangular blocks of wood (knife edges), one of which is located at each end. One end of the board rests on a platform scale and the other on a block. The weight of the board can be read from the scale and must be subtracted from subsequent readings made during the measurement. In the illustration, a man weighing 150 lb is shown lying on the board, the distance between the two knife edges is 60 in., and the corrected reading on the scale is 80 lb.

Since the individual in the illustration is in rotatory equilibrium, we can use the law of the lever ($F \times f = R \times r$) to locate the center of gravity as follows:

$$150 \text{ lb} \times f = 80 \text{ lb} \times 60 \text{ in.} \quad \text{thus} \quad f = \frac{4800 \text{ lb-in.}}{150 \text{ lb}} = 32.0 \text{ in.}$$

Since in the illustration the man's head is even with the knife edge, his center of gravity in the transverse plane is 32 in. from the top of his head. This same method can be used to locate the center of gravity in the frontal and sagittal planes, except the individual is standing erect with his body facing either straight ahead (frontal plane) or to one side (sagittal plane).

A simple method of determining the weight of body segments and locating the centers of gravity of each segment was devised by Cleaveland[5] in 1955. In this method, marks are made on the body

**Fig. 10-1.** Method of locating the body's center of gravity in the transverse plane.

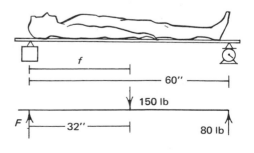

[5] Henry G. Cleaveland: "The Determination of the Center of Gravity in Segments of the Human Body," thesis, University of California, 1955.

to indicate the limits of each segment, and the body is lowered into a tank of water to each mark in succession. The weight of each segment is calculated by the amount of weight lost and water displaced at each stage of submersion. The center of gravity of each segment is located at the point at which half of the amount of weight is lost.

The importance of the location of a performer's center of gravity was discussed in Chapter 9 and previously in this chapter. The key concept presented in these discussions is that the location of the common center of gravity of an individual greatly affects his static and kinetic equilibrium in the performance of motor activities. The segmental centers of gravity are also important in human movements because their locations are the points at which the gravitational resistances to segmental movements are concentrated.

**Fig. 10–2. Three types of physique as classified by Sheldon: (A) endomorph, (B) mesomorph, and (C) ectomorph.**

### Body Build

The most widely used method of classifying body builds, often referred to as somatotyping, is that associated with the work of W. H. Sheldon[6] and his collaborators. According to Sheldon, bodies can be classified into three main types: endomorphic, mesomorphic, and ectomorphic (Fig. 10–2). The following characteristics, determined through methods previously discussed in this chapter, are associated with each of the three body types:

*Endomorphy* is characterized by roundness and softness of body. The head is large and round, bones are small, neck is short, central concentration of mass with a predominance of abdomen over thorax, and high narrow shoulders. The chest is broad with fatty breasts, short arms, heavy fat buttocks, short heavy legs, and broad hips. In this type of physique, the digestive system dominates the body economy.

*Mesomorphy* is characterized by a heavy, hard, rectangular outline with prominent muscular development. The bones are large and heavy, the thorax is larger than the waist, the shoulders are broad, and the neck is usually fairly long. This type of physique is well adapted for most types of motor performances.

*Ectomorphy* is characterized by a slender, frail body structure with small bones and thin segments. The limbs are relatively long, but the trunk is usually short which prevents the individual from being tall. The neck is long and slender, the shoulders round, and the buttocks are inconspicuous. This type of physique is associated with linearity, delicacy, and fragility of the body.

In Sheldon's technique, the somatotype of an individual consists of three numbers to represent the combination of the above characteristics. The first number represents the endomorphy component; the second, mesomorphy; and the third, ectomorphy. The numeral one represents the lowest amount of a component, and the numeral seven represents the highest amount. Therefore, a somatotype of 711 would represent an extreme endomorph; 171 an extreme mesomorph; and 117 an extreme ectomorph.

[6] W. H. Sheldon: *Atlas of Men* (New York, Harper & Brothers, 1954).

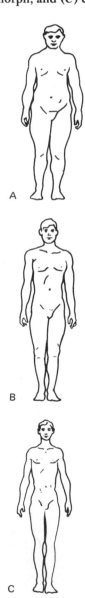

A

B

C

The one component that seems to be involved in all physiques in which some degree of success in motor activities is found is mesomorphy. Extreme mesomorphs, because of their great lean body mass, muscular development, and streamlined build are usually excellent in their general motor abilities. They usually make good football backs, sprinters in track, middleweight wrestlers, and boxers. However, in activities requiring greater mass and greater cushions against repeated contact in sports, the performers tend toward higher endomorphic components. For example, football linemen tend to be endomorphic mesomorphs. On the other hand, performers in speed and endurance activities, because of the need for height, long limbs, and less mass, tend toward higher ectomorphic components. For example, tennis players and endurance runners tend to be ectomorphic mesomorphs.

Since weight and linear and girth dimensions of the body and its parts largely determine the somatotype, all the discussions of this chapter are directly applicable to the study of body builds and the roles that they play in the successful performance of motor tasks. In addition, however, the aesthetic appeal of well-proportioned bodies should not be overlooked as an important factor in physical education.

## 10.20 Study Guidelines

### 10.21 The Divisions of Anthropometry

A. Specific Student Objectives

1. Define anthropometry.
2. Differentiate between general and regional anthropometry.
3. Identify the three main types of anthropometric measures.

### 10.22 Body Weight

A. Specific Student Objectives

1. State the mechanical significance of body weight.
2. Define lean body mass.
3. Identify the two methods of measuring the lean body mass of an individual.
4. Give an example of a motor performance situation in which a greater body weight would be desirable.
5. Give an example of a motor performance situation in which a lesser body weight would be desirable.
6. Define dead weight.
7. Give an example of a motor performance situation in which greater body fat would be desirable.
8. Give an example of a motor performance situation in which lesser body fat would be desirable.
9. State the importance of muscle weight and muscle development in motor performance.

## 10.23  Body Size

A. Specific Student Objectives

1. Identify the three types of anthropometric measures of body size.
2. Give an example of a motor performance situation in which greater body height would be desirable.
3. Give an example of a motor performance situation in which lesser body height would be desirable.
4. Give an example of a motor performance situation in which greater length of the body limbs would be desirable.
5. Give an example of a motor performance situation in which lesser length of the body limbs would be desirable.
6. State how linear measures of the width and depth of body parts are important in the study of human movement.
7. State how girth and surface area measures of the body are important in the study of human movement.

## 10.24  Body Proportions

A. Specific Student Objectives

1. Describe a method of locating the center of gravity of an individual in each of the three planes.
2. Describe a method of locating the centers of gravity of body segments.
3. State the importance of the location of a performer's center of gravity.
4. Differentiate between endomorphic, mesomorphic, and ectomorphic types of body build.
5. Define somatotype.
6. Identify the one component of body build that seems to be involved in all physiques which find some degree of success in motor performances.
7. State the type of activity in which mesomorphs usually excel.
8. State the type of activity in which endomorphic mesomorphs usually excel.
9. State the type of activity in which ectomorphic mesomorphs usually excel.

The student should do additional reading in the area of anthropometry. A list of selected kinesiology texts is given in Appendix B. The following are especially recommended.

10.30  Recommended
Supplementary
Readings

Morehouse, Laurence E., and Philip J. Rash: *Sports Medicine for Trainers*, 2nd ed. Philadelphia, W. B. Saunders Co., 1963, Ch. 2.

Sills, Frank D.: "Anthropometry in Relation to Physical Performance," in *Science and Medicine of Exercise and Sports*, edited by Warren R. Johnson. New York, Harper & Brothers Publishers, 1960, Ch. 3.

Willgoose, Carl E.: *Evaluation in Health Education and Physical Education*. New York, McGraw-Hill Book Company, Inc., 1961, Ch. 13.

# Part V

# Structural Kinesiology of the Foot and Leg

# 11

# Structure
# of the Foot

**General Student Objective**

*In his study of the basic concepts of this chapter the student should
become familiar with:*

   *11.11   Bones of the Foot*
   *11.12   Joints of the Foot*
   *11.13   Muscles of the Foot*

The bones of the foot (Figs. 11-1 and 11-2) are 26 in number:
14 phalanges, 5 metatarsals, and 7 tarsal bones.

**11.11   Bones of the Foot**

## The Phalanges

The five toes of the foot are called digits, a general term that
applies also to the fingers of the upper extremity.  The digits are
numbered from the medial to the lateral side with the big toe being
number one.  The big toe is also called the hallux, and the little toe
is also called the digitus minimus (littlest toe), or digitus quintus
(fifth toe). The bones of the toes are called *phalanges*.  There are two
phalanges in the big toe and three in each of the other toes, which
are indicated as the first or proximal, the second or middle, and the
third or distal.  Each phalanx (fa''lanks) consists of a *shaft* and two
*extremities*.  The proximal extremity is called the *base*; the distal
extremity is called the *head*.  The distal extremity of the distal phalanx is expanded and flattened forming the *ungual* (ung'gwal)
*tuberosity*, which supports the nail.  The shafts of the phalanges are
longer in the proximal row than in the middle row, and the shafts
in the middle row are longer than in the distal row.  The distal phalanges of the toes, with the exception of the big toe, are rather in-
significant bones.  In fact, the phalanges of the toes as a whole are
not nearly as well developed as are those in the hand.

Fig. 11-1. Dorsal view of the bones of the left foot.

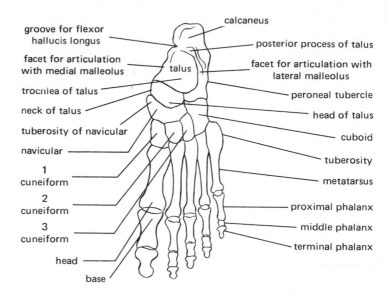

## The Metatarsal Bones

The *metatarsus* is the sole and lower instep of the foot and is composed of five bones called the *metatarsal* bones. These are numbered, like the digits, from the medial to the lateral side. Like the phalanges, each metatarsal bone consists of a *shaft* and two *extremities*. Also, like the phalanges, the proximal extremity is called the *base*, and the distal extremity is called the *head*. Each metatarsal bone has two surfaces as does the foot as a whole, which are indicated as the plantar (plan'tar) (or bottom of the foot) and the dorsal (or top of the foot). The shaft of each metatarsal bone is slightly arched presenting a concavity on the plantar surface. Prominent

Fig. 11-2. Plantar view of the bones of the left foot.

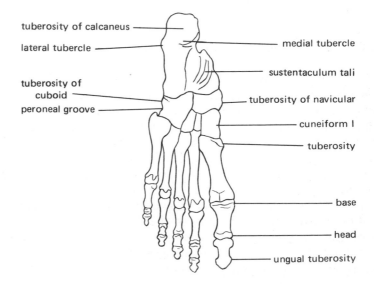

*tuberosities* are found on the bases of the first and fifth metatarsals. The first metatarsal bone is the most massive because it serves as the main support of the body weight when the foot is plantar flexed as in walking or jumping.

## The Tarsal Bones

The *tarsus* or ankle is composed of seven bones known as the tarsal bones. These bones, important in bodily support and locomotion, are known as the calcaneus, the talus, the navicular, the cuboid, and the three cuneiform bones.

The *calcaneus* is the largest of the tarsal bones. Its *posterior extremity* projects backward behind the ankle and forms the *heel* of the foot. The expanded portion of the posterior extremity is called the *tuberosity of the calcaneus*. The *lateral* and *medial tubercles*, located on the inferolateral and inferomedial surfaces of the tuberosity, are the only parts of the bone that normally touch the ground and bear all the weight that falls upon the heel. The upper surface of the bone has *articular facets* (fas'ets) for the talus, the largest surface being borne by the *sustentaculum tali* (sus″ten-tak'u-lum tal'i), which is an overhanging projection, grooved inferiorly, located on the medial surface of the bone. Located on the lateral surface of the bone is the *peroneal* (per″o-ne'al) *tubercle*, which separates two grooves, an upper and a lower, for the passage of the tendons of the peroneus brevis and longus, respectively.

The *talus* is the most superior of the tarsal bones and rests upon the upper surface of the calcaneus. It consists of a *head, neck*, and *body*. Located on the superior surface of the body is a pulleylike articular surface called the *trochlea* (trok'le-ah). The upper part of the trochlea articulates with the end of the tibia, the medial part with the medial *malleolus* (mal-e″o-lus or mah-le'o-lus) of the tibia, and the lateral part with the lateral malleolus of the fibula. It is broader anteriorly than posteriorly, which is important in preventing its forward displacement during locomotion. The anterior end of the talus is called the *head*, and it articulates anteriorly with the navicular bone. The chief articulations between the talus and calcaneus are behind the head. The *neck* separates the head and body of the bone. Located on the superior surface of the neck is a slight depression that receives the anterior margin of the distal extremity of the tibia during extreme flexion of the ankle joint.

The remaining bones of the foot are both smaller and simpler. The *navicular* lies anterior to the talus on the medial side of the foot and is, as its name implies, somewhat boat shaped. Anteriorly it articulates with the three cuneiform bones. Medially it presents a prominent projection called the *tuberosity of the navicular*, which may be felt on the medial surface of the foot about the width of two fingers below and to the front of the medial malleolus. The lateral surface of the navicular is attached to the cuboid by a heavy ligament.

The *cuboid* is located on the lateral side of the foot, where it articulates posteriorly with the calcaneus. It is, as its name implies, roughly cuboidal in shape. It has a proximal articular surface for the calcaneus, a distal one for the two lateral metatarsals, and a small medial one for the lateral cuneiform. The *peroneal groove* is an

Fig. 11-3. The two arches of the foot: (A) The longitudinal arch and (B) the transverse arch.

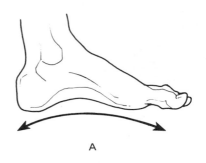

A

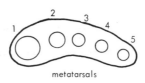

metatarsals

B

oblique groove located on the plantar surface of the bone through which passes the tendon of the peroneus longus muscle.

The three *cuneiforms* are located between the navicular and the bases of the first three metatarsals on the medial to the lateral side of the foot. The first or *medial cuneiform*, the largest of the three bones, articulates anteriorly with the base of the first metatarsal. The *second* or *middle cuneiform*, the smallest of the three, articulates anteriorly with the base of the second metatarsal. The *third* or *lateral cuneiform* articulates anteriorly with the base of the third metatarsal.

### The Two Arches of the Foot

The bones of the foot are arranged to form two arches: an antero-posterior, or longitudinal, and a transverse (Fig. 11-3). These two arches form the hollow associated with the sole of the foot. The *longitudinal arch* is the principal of the two arches. Its anterior pillar is formed by the heads of the metatarsals, and its posterior pillar is formed by the calcaneus. The keystone of the arch is the talus. The arch is sometimes described as having an inner and an outer component. The inner or medial component is higher and more elastic than the lateral or outer component and is made up of the calcaneus, the talus, the navicular, the three cuneiforms, and the first three metatarsals. The outer component is composed of the calcaneus, the cuboid, and the fourth and fifth metatarsals.

The *transverse arch* is the side-to-side concavity on the underside of the foot formed by the metatarsals anteriorly and the three cuneiforms and cuboid posteriorly. The medial pillar of this arch is formed by the first cuneiform and first metatarsal: the lateral pillar by the cuboid and fourth and fifth metatarsals. The second and third cuneiforms and the second and third metatarsals occupy the highest plane and may therefore be considered the keystone.

The functions of the two arches are (1) to support the weight of the body while standing, (2) to give elasticity to the step and therefore to absorb the shocks of locomotion, and (3) to provide a space for the plantar blood vessels, nerves, tendons, and muscles, the pressure on which produces the discomforts characteristic of flat feet or fallen arches.

Since the outer component of the longitudinal arch has a nearly flat contour and lacks mobility, it is better adapted to the function of support, than the inner component, with its greater flexibility and its curving arch, which is adapted to the function of shock absorption. The transverse arch also contributes to shock absorption, since it too is capable of a certain amount of flattening when weight is placed upon it.

### 11.12  Joints of the Foot

The five major joints of the foot are the interphalangeal, the metatarsophalangeal, the intermetatarsal, the tarsometatarsal, and the intertarsal. The names of these joints, obviously, are derived from the names of the bones involved with the proximal bones being named first.

## The Interphalangeal Joints

The interphalangeal joints are the articulations between the heads or distal extremities of the proximal and middle phalanges and the adjacent bases of the middle and terminal phalanges, respectively.

*Movements.* These joints being of the *hinge* type permit only *flexion* and *extension*. Extension is drawing the toes dorsally or upward; flexion is drawing them downward.

*Ligaments* (Fig. 11-4). Each interphalangeal joint is reinforced on its medial and lateral sides by collateral ligaments. Located in the intervals between the collateral ligaments on the plantar and dorsal surfaces of each joint are the plantar and dorsal interphalangeal ligaments, respectively.

**Fig. 11-4. Plantar ligaments of the foot.**

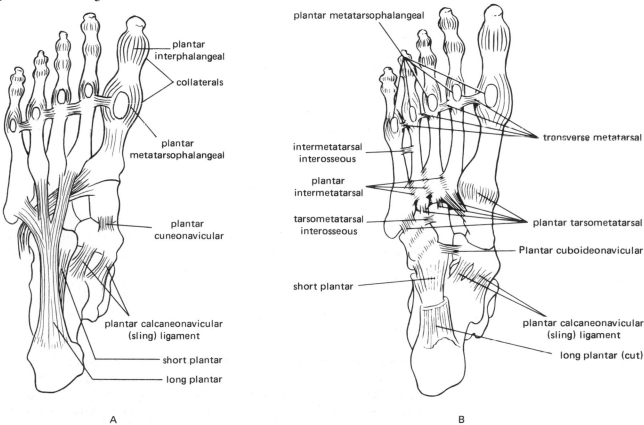

A

B

## The Metatarsophalangeal Joints

These *condyloid* joints are formed by the articulation of the distal extremities or heads of the metatarsals with the posterior concave articular facets of the proximal phalanges.

*Movements.* In addition to *flexion* and *extension*, these joints permit limited *abduction* and *adduction*. Abduction is drawing the first and second toes, and the fourth and fifth toes away from the middle or third toe. Adduction is the movement of these toes toward the middle toe. Movement of the middle toe laterally is abduction, and movement of this toe medially is adduction.

*Ligaments* (Fig. 11-4). Each metatarsophalangeal joint is reinforced on its medial and lateral sides by collateral ligaments. Located in the intervals between the collateral ligaments on the plantar and dorsal surfaces of each joint are the plantar and dorsal metatarsophalangeal ligaments.

## The Intermetatarsal Joints

The intermetatarsal joints are sliding joints, and they include two sets of articulations. One set is formed by the adjacent sides of the bases of the metatarsal bones, and the other is formed by the adjacent sides of the heads.

*Movements.* Since these are nonaxial joints, they permit only slight gliding movements.

*Ligaments* (Fig. 11-4). The *bases* of the metatarsal bones are connected on their dorsal and plantar surfaces by the dorsal and plantar intermetatarsal ligaments, respectively. The shafts are connected by interosseous ligaments, and the *heads* are connected by the transverse metatarsal ligament. All these ligaments pass transversely between the bones.

## The Tarsometatarsal Joints

The tarsometatarsal joints are sliding joints formed by the articulation of the bases of the metatarsal bones with the adjacent tarsal bones.

*Movements.* These are all nonaxial joints, with the possible exception of the first, which presents a slightly saddle-shaped appearance. The movements are of a gliding nature and resemble a restricted form of flexion, extension, abduction, and adduction.

*Ligaments* (Fig. 11-4). The tarsal bones are connected to the metatarsal bones on their dorsal and plantar surfaces by the dorsal and plantar tarsometatarsal ligaments, respectively. Interosseous ligaments join the first cuneiform to the second metatarsal, the third cuneiform to the second metatarsal, and the third cuneiform to the third metatarsal.

## The Intertarsal Joints

The intertarsal joints are sliding joints formed by the articulations between the individual tarsal bones. These include

    A. *The subtalar joint*: articulation between the talus and calcaneus.

B. *The transverse tarsal or midtarsal joint*: two articulations: the lateral one the calcaneocuboid joint and the medial one the talonavicular joint. These two joints stretch across the foot almost transversely and combined they form a horizontal letter S.

C. *The anterior intertarsal or cuneonavicular joint*: the articulation between the navicular and the cuneiforms. This joint also extends slightly between cuneiforms and between the cuboid and the lateral cuneiform.

*Movements.* The movements of the intertarsal articulations are gliding, flexion, extension, abduction, adduction, inversion, and eversion. *Gliding movements* occur mainly at the anterior intertarsal articulations and are produced by the weight of the body on the anterior pillar of the longitudinal arch. These movements tend, therefore, to increase the elasticity of the foot and to dampen shocks.

The six fundamental movements produced by muscles occur mainly in the posterior intertarsal joints, i.e., in the subtalar and transverse tarsal joints. *Flexion* and *extension* may occur to a slight extent at the transverse tarsal joint, particularly at the talonavicular joint. Here these movements occur in conjunction with those of the ankle except that they are reversed, i.e., flexion and extension at these joints are simultaneous with extension and flexion of the ankle, respectively. Slight *abduction* and *adduction* of the front part of the foot on the rear occurs mostly at the talonavicular joint. *Inversion* and *eversion* occur at both the subtalar and transverse tarsal articulations. Inversion is turning the sole of the foot medially, whereas eversion is turning the sole of the foot laterally. The combined movements of abduction and eversion is called *pronation*, and the combined movements of adduction and inversion is called *supination*.

**Ligaments of the Subtalar Joint.** The locations of the anterior, posterior, lateral, and medial talocalcaneal ligaments, and the talocalcaneal interosseus ligament are given by their names (Fig. 11-5). These ligaments serve to reinforce the joint and to permit slight forward, backward, and sideward gliding. They also allow very slight inversion and eversion.

The *plantar calcaneonavicular* or *spring ligament* forms an inherent part of the subtalar joint (Figs. 11-4 and 11-5). This ligament passes from the sustentaculum tail of the calcaneus to the lower surface of the navicular and in so doing forms a sling on which the lower surfaces of the head of the talus rests. It resists the downward movement of the head of the talus and thus helps to support the highest part of the arch. This ligament contains a considerable amount of elastic fibers to give elasticity to the arch and spring to the foot; hence, it is sometimes called the "spring" ligament. The importance of this ligament as a shock absorber can readily be seen when one remembers that the talus receives the weight of the entire body during locomotion, and that the talus is in turn supported largely by the spring ligament. Excessive prolonged pressure on this ligament can result in permanently stretched fibers and a lowered arch.

Fig. 11-5. Ligaments of the subtalar joint.

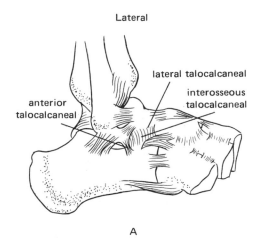

Lateral

lateral talocalcaneal

interosseous talocalcaneal

anterior talocalcaneal

A

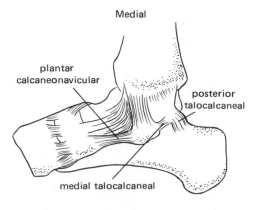

Medial

plantar calcaneonavicular

posterior talocalcaneal

medial talocalcaneal

B

*Ligaments of the Transverse Tarsal Joint.* This joint is reinforced dorsally by three dorsal ligaments, namely: (1) the dorsal talonavicular ligament, (2) the bifurcate ligament, and (3) the dorsal calcaneocuboid ligament (Fig. 11–6).

Fig. 11–6. **Ligaments of the transverse and anterior tarsal joints.**

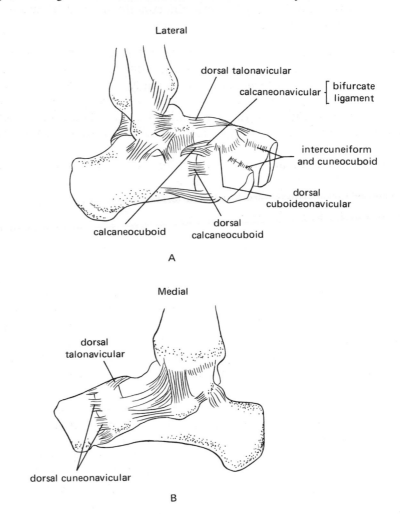

The transverse tarsal joint is reinforced on its plantar surface by the long and short plantar ligaments (Fig. 11–4). The *long plantar ligament* is the longest of all the ligaments of the foot. It extends from the plantar surface of the calcaneus in front of the tuberosity to the plantar surface of the cuboid, with prolongations to the bases of the second, third, fourth, and medial half of the fifth metatarsal bones. This ligament, therefore, extends for most of the length of the lateral part of the arch and is the chief support of this side.

*The short plantar ligament*, also called the plantar calcaneocuboid ligament, lies nearer to the bones than does the long plantar ligament. It is a short but wide band of great strength, which extends from the tubercle of the calcaneus to the plantar surface of the cuboid.

*Ligaments of the Anterior Tarsal Joints.* The primary ligaments which reinforce the anterior tarsal joints are

    A. Cuneonavicular joint

        1. The dorsal and plantar cuneonavicular ligaments (Figs. 11-4 and 11-6).

    B. Cuboideonavicular joint

        1. The dorsal and plantar cuboideonavicular ligaments (Figs. 11-4 and 11-6).
        2. The cuboideonavicular interosseous ligament.

    C. Intercuneiform and cuneocuboid joints (Fig. 11-6)

        1. The dorsal and plantar intercuneiform ligaments.
        2. The intercuneiform interosseous ligaments.

        *Note:* The dorsal and plantar intercuneiform ligaments each consist of three transverse bands; one connects the first with the second cuneiform, another the second with the third cuneiform, and another the third cuneiform with the cuboid.

The intrinsic muscles of the foot are those that are located entirely in the foot and do not cross the ankle joint. They include one muscle located on the dorsal surface of the foot, the extensor digitorum brevis, and ten muscles located on the plantar surface.

## 11.13 Muscles of the Foot

### The Dorsal Muscle of the Foot

*The extensor digitorum brevis* (Fig. 11-7) is the only intrinsic muscle located on the dorsal surface of the foot. It is located beneath the tendons of the extensor digitorum longus. Its proximal attachment is on the lateral and upper portion of the calcaneus. It divides into four tendons, which attach distally to the lateral sides of the long extensor tendons of the second, third, and fourth toes and into the base of the proximal phalanx of the big toe. As its name implies, this muscle extends the medial four toes. Perhaps it should be noted that the most medial portion of the muscle is sometimes named separately as the *extensor hallucis brevis.*

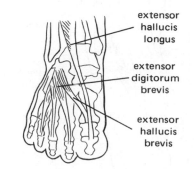

Fig. 11-7. **The extensor digitorum brevis—the only intrinsic muscle located on the dorsal surface of the foot.**

extensor
hallucis
longus

extensor
digitorum
brevis

extensor
hallucis
brevis

### The Plantar Muscles of the Foot

The plantar muscles of the foot are divided into four layers and consist of the following muscles:

    A. The first or superficial layer (Fig. 11-8)

        1. Abductor hallucis (hal′lucis)
        2. Abductor digiti minimi
        3. Flexor digitorum brevis

**Fig. 11-8.** The first layer of plantar muscles of the foot.

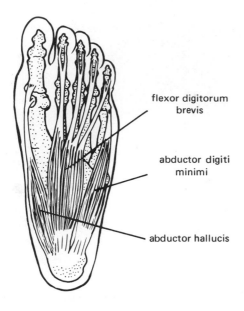

flexor digitorum brevis

abductor digiti minimi

abductor hallucis

**Fig. 11-9.** The second layer of plantar muscles of the foot.

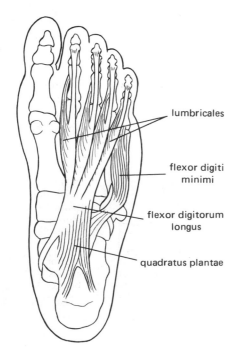

lumbricales

flexor digiti minimi

flexor digitorum longus

quadratus plantae

B. The second layer (Fig. 11-9)

1. Quadratus plantae
2. Flexor digiti minimi
3. Lumbricales (lum″bre-ka′les)

C. The third layer (Fig. 11-10)

1. Adductor hallucis
2. Flexor hallucis brevis

D. The fourth or deep layer (Fig. 11-11)

1. Plantar interossei (in″ter-os′e-i)
2. Dorsal interossei

*The First Layer of Plantar Muscles* (Fig. 11-8). All the muscles of this layer have their proximal attachments on the calcaneus. The *abductor hallucis* attaches distally to the medial side of the base of the proximal phalanx of the big toe. It abducts and flexes this toe. The *abductor digiti minimi* has its distal attachment on the lateral side of the base of the proximal phalanx of the fifth toe. It abducts and flexes the little toe. The *flexor digitorum brevis* attaches distally to the base of the second phalanx of the four lateral toes. It flexes the four lateral toes.

*The Second Layer of Plantar Muscles* (Fig. 11-9). The *quadratus plantae* has its proximal attachment on the calcaneus and attaches distally to the tendon of the flexor digitorum longus. It aids in flexion of the lateral four toes. The *flexor digiti minimi* has its proximal attachment on the base of the fifth metatarsal and attaches distally on the lateral side of the base of the proximal phalanx of the little toe. It flexes and tends to abduct the little toe. The *lumbricales* arise from the tendons of the flexor digitorum longus and attach distally to the expansion of the tendons of the extensor digitorum longus on the dorsal surfaces of the four lateral toes. They, therefore, aid in flexion of the proximal row of phalanges and, at least theoretically, in extension of the third row. They also move the four lateral toes toward the big toe.

*The Third Layer of Plantar Muscles* (Fig. 11-10). The *adductor hallucis* muscle has two heads. An oblique head arises from the long plantar ligament (some books substitute the sheath of the tendon of the peroneus longus muscle for the long plantar ligament, because of the close proximity of the two in the foot) and from the bases of the second, third, and fourth metatarsals. A transverse head arises from the ligaments of the lateral four metatarsophalangeal joints. The two heads fuse and are attached, in common with the lateral tendon of the flexor hallucis brevis, to the lateral side of the base of the proximal phalanx of the big toe. It adducts and flexes the big toe. The *flexor hallucis brevis* has its proximal attachment on the cuboid and the lateral cuneiform and attaches distally by two heads to the medial and lateral sides of the proximal phalanx of the big toe. It flexes the big toe.

*The Fourth Layer of Plantar Muscles* (Fig. 11-11). The *plantar interossei* arise from the medial sides of the shafts of the third, fourth, and fifth metatarsal bones and attach distally to the medial sides of the proximal phalanges of the same toes from which they originated. When acting alone, they adduct the toes. When acting with the dorsal interossei, they flex the toes. Each muscle of the *dorsal interossei* originates by two heads from the sides of the adjacent metatarsal bones. Their distal attachments are as follows: the first on the medial side of the base of the proximal phalanx of the second toe, and the remaining ones on the lateral side of the bases of the proximal row of phalanges of the second, third, and fourth toes. When acting with the plantar interossei, they flex the toes. When acting alone, the first interosseus draws the second toe toward the big toe. The second, third, and fourth draw the second, third, and fourth toes away from the big toe.

Certain generalizations should now be evident. First, all the intrinsic muscles of the foot act upon the toes. Second, because of their location on the bottom of the foot, all the plantar muscles are involved in flexing the toes. Third, by remembering that the term digitorum refers to the toes, the term digiti minimi to the little toe, and the term hallucis to the big toe, the actions of the following muscles can be known by their names:

Abductor hallucis: abducts the big toe
Abductor digiti minimi: abducts the little toe
Adductor hallucis: adducts the big toe
Flexor digitorum brevis: flexes the four lateral toes

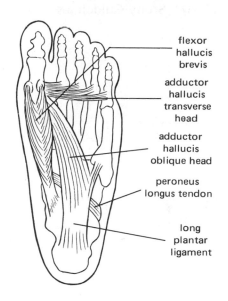

Fig. 11-10. The third layer of plantar muscles of the foot.

flexor hallucis brevis

adductor hallucis transverse head

adductor hallucis oblique head

peroneus longus tendon

long plantar ligament

Fig. 11-11. The fourth layer of plantar muscles of the foot.

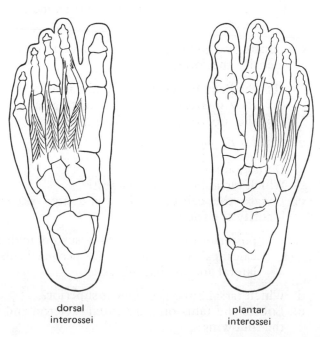

dorsal interossei

plantar interossei

| 11.20   Study Guidelines | 11.21   Bones of the Foot |
|---|---|

A.  Specific Student Objective

1.  *The Phalanges*

   a.  Define digit.
   b.  How are the digits numbered?
   c.  Define hallux, digitus minimus, and digitus quintus.
   d.  How many phalanges are found in the big toe?  How many are found in each of the four lateral toes?
   e.  Locate the phalanges on a mounted skeleton and identify the following:

        shaft           head
        base           ungual tuberosity

   f.  Locate the phalanges in your own foot and identify the following:

      (1)  the head of the distal phalanx of the third digit
      (2)  the middle phalanx of the fifth digit
      (3)  the base of the proximal phalanx of the hallux

2.  *The Metatarsal Bones*

   a.  Define metatarsus.
   b.  How many metatarsals are located in each foot?
   c.  How are the metatarsal bones numbered?
   d.  Locate the metatarsal bones on a mounted skeleton and identify the following:

        shaft       tuberosity of the first metatarsal
        base        tuberosity of the fifth metatarsal
        head

   e.  Locate the metatarsal bones in your own foot and identify the following:

      (1)  the head of the second metatarsal
      (2)  the tuberosity of the first metatarsal
      (3)  the tuberosity of the fifth metatarsal

3.  *The Tarsal Bones*

   a.  Define tarsus.
   b.  Which tarsal bone is the largest?
   c.  Locate the calcaneus on a mounted skeleton and identify the following:

        posterior extremity       sustentaculum tali
        calcaneal tuberosity      peroneal tubercle
        lateral and medial tubercles

   d.  Which tarsal bone is the most superior?
   e.  Locate the talus on a mounted skeleton and identify the following:

        head           body
        neck           trochlea

f. Locate the navicular, the cuboid, and the three cunei-forms on a mounted skeleton and identify the following:

> tuberosity of the navicular
> peroneal groove on the cuboid

g. With what bones does the talus articulate? Describe these articulations.
h. With what bones does the calcaneus articulate? Describe these articulations.
i. With what bones does the cuboid articulate? Describe these articulations.
j. With what bones does the navicular articulate? Describe these articulations.
k. How are the cuneiforms named?
l. With what bones does the first cuneiform articulate? Describe these articulations.
m. With what bones does the second cuneiform articulate?
n. With what bones does the third cuneiform articulate?
o. Locate the following bony landmarks in your own foot by palpation.

> posterior extremity of the calcaneus
> tuberosity of the navicular

4. *The Two Arches of the Foot*

a. Identify the anterior pillar, posterior pillar, and the keystone of the longitudinal arch.
b. Describe the two components of the longitudinal arch.
c. Which component is the highest?
d. Describe the transverse arch.
e. Identify the medial pillar, lateral pillar, and keystone of the transverse arch.
f. What are the functions of the two arches in the foot?
g. What is the primary function of the outer component of the longitudinal arch?
h. What is the primary function of the inner component of the longitudinal arch?
i. What is the primary function of the transverse arch?

B. Study Hints

1. The use of actual bones is quite beneficial in the study of specific osteology, and there is no substitute for independent study of a mounted skeleton in learning the specific markings on a bone.
2. Locating bony landmarks in the student's body is also a valuable aid to learning.

## 11.22 Joints of the Foot

A. Specific Student Objectives

1. *The Interphalangeal Joints*

a. What type of joints are these?

      b. Describe the bony articulations involved in these joints.

      c. What movements are allowed in these joints? Describe these movements.

      d. Describe the ligamentous reinforcements of these joints.

2. *The Metatarsophalangeal Joints*

      a. What type of joints are these?

      b. Describe the bony articulations involved in these joints.

      c. What movements are allowed in these joints? Describe these movements.

      d. Describe the ligamentous reinforcements of these joints.

3. *The Intermetatarsal Joints*

      a. What type of joints are these?

      b. How many sets of articulations are involved?

      c. Describe the bony articulations involved in these joints.

      d. What movements are allowed in these joints?

      e. Describe the ligamentous reinforcements of these joints.

4. *The Intertarsal Joints*

      a. What type of joints are these?

      b. Identify the three sets of joints involved.

      c. Describe the bony articulations involved in these joints.

      d. What movements are allowed in these joints? Describe these movements.

      e. Describe the ligamentous reinforcements of these joints.

B. Study Hints

1. The student should study each joint on a mounted skeleton, where he can visualize the bony articulations and ligamentous reinforcements involved in the joint.

2. The student should also identify each joint in his foot and perform the movements of that joint according to the descriptions presented in the text. It is important that he learn to identify the movements by their proper names whenever he sees them performed.

## 11.23 Muscles of the Foot

A. Specific Student Objectives

1. *The Dorsal Muscles of the Foot*

      a. Define an intrinsic muscle of the foot.

      b. What does the word brevis mean?

      c. What is the proximal attachment of the extensor digitorum brevis?

  d. What is the distal attachment of this muscle?

  e. From its location on the dorsal surface of the foot and from its name we know that it performs what action on the toes?

  f. What specific toes are extended by this muscle?

  g. The most medial portion of the muscle is sometimes known by what other name.

  h. Locate the muscle in your foot.

   *Note:* this muscle can be felt during contraction on the dorsal surface of the foot just anterior to the lateral malleolus.

 2. *The Plantar Muscles of the Foot*

  a. Identify the muscles located in each of the four layers of plantar muscles.

  b. Give the proximal and distal attachments of each of the ten plantar muscles.

  c. Give the joint actions produced by the contraction of each of the ten plantar muscles.

  d. Locate in your foot the abductor hallucis and the abductor digiti minimi, which can be felt on the medial and lateral borders, respectively.

B. Study Hints

 1. Table 11-1 is presented here to aid in the mastery of specific muscle actions and attachments.

Table 11-1. **The Attachments and Actions of the Intrinsic Muscles of the Foot.**

| Location | Name | Proximal Attachment | Illustration | Distal Attachment | Action |
|---|---|---|---|---|---|
| Dorsal surface | Extensor digitorum brevis | Anterior and lateral portion of the calcaneus | Fig. 11-7 | Divides into four tendons. One tendon attaches to the base of the proximal phalanx of the big toe. The other three tendons attach to the long extensor tendons of the middle three toes | Extension of the four medial toes |
| Plantar surface 1st layer | Abductor hallucis | Medial tubercle of the calcaneus | Fig. 11-8 | Medial side of the base of the proximal phalanx of the big toe | Abduction and flexion of the big toe |
| | Abductor digiti minimi | Lateral tubercle of the calcaneus | Fig. 11-8 | Lateral side of the base of the proximal phalanx of the little toe | Abduction and flexion of the little toe |
| | Flexor digitorum brevis | Medial tubercle of the calcaneus | Fig. 11-8 | Divides into four tendons. Each tendon also divides and attaches to the sides of the middle phalanges of the lateral four toes | Flexion of the four lateral toes |

**Table 11-1.  The Attachments and Actions of the Intrinsic Muscles of the Foot (continued)**

| Location | Name | Proximal Attachment | Illustration | Distal Attachment | Action |
|---|---|---|---|---|---|
| 2nd layer | Quadratus plantae | Two heads: one from the lateral side and the other from the medial side of the calcaneus | Fig. 11-9 | Fuses with the tendon of the flexor digitorum longus | Flexion of the four lateral toes |
| | Flexor digiti minimi | Base of the fifth metatarsal bone | Fig. 11-9 | Lateral side of the base of the proximal phalanx of the little toe | Flexion and abduction of the little toe |
| | Lumbricales | The tendons of the flexor digitorum longus | Fig. 11-9 | Passes around medial sides of the bases of the proximal phalanges of the lateral four toes and to the tendons of the extensor digitorum longus | Flexion of the proximal and extension of the distal phalanges of the lateral four toes, abduction of second toe, and adduction of lateral three toes. |
| 3rd layer | Adductor hallucis | Two heads.  The *oblique* head arises from the long plantar ligament, and from the bases of the middle three metatarsals.  The *transverse* head arises from the ligaments of the lateral four metatarsophalangeal joints | Fig. 11-10 | Lateral side of the base of the proximal phalanx of the big toe | Adduction and flexion of the big toe |
| | Flexor hallucis brevis | Medial part of the cuboid, and lateral cuneiform | Fig. 11-10 | By two heads to the medial and lateral sides of the proximal phalanx of the big toe | Flexion of the big toe |
| 4th layer | Plantar interossei | Medial sides of the shafts of the lateral three metatarsal bones | Fig. 11-11 | Medial sides of the proximal phalanges of the same toes from which they originated | Adduction of the lateral three toes. Flexion of these toes when acting with the dorsal interossei |
| | Dorsal interossei | By two heads from the sides of the adjacent metatarsal bones | Fig. 11-11 | First: medial side of the base of the proximal phalanx of the second toe. Second, third, and fourth: lateral side of the bases of the proximal row of phalanges of the middle three toes | Second: adduction of the second toe. First, third, and fourth: abduction of the middle three toes. Flexion of these toes when acting with the plantar interossei |

**11.30  Recommended Supplementary Readings**

The student should consult any recent basic anatomy text for supplementary readings on the structure of the foot.  A list of selected anatomy texts is given in Appendix B.

# 12

# Structure of the Leg

**General Student Objective**

*In his study of the basic concepts of this chapter the student should become familiar with*

12.11 *Bones of the Leg*
12.12 *The Ankle and Tibiofibular Joints*
12.13 *Muscles of the Leg*

The two bones of the leg are the tibia and fibula. These bones lie side by side connected by an interosseous membrane and articulate with each other at the superior and inferior tibiofibular joints. Distally, the tibia and fibula form an arch or mortise to accommodate the talus, the highest of the tarsal bones, and the strong hinge so formed is the ankle joint.

**12.11 Bones of the Leg**

### The Tibia

The tibia (Figs. 12–1 and 12–2) is the medial of the two bones of the leg, and it is commonly referred to as the shinbone. It is a long bone consisting of a shaft and two extremities. Some of the important markings on the tibia are

A. *The superior extremity or head*

1. *Medial and lateral condyles*: surfaces that articulate with the condyles of the femur to form the knee joint.
2. *Intercondyloid eminence*: projection located between the condyles.
3. *Intercondyloid tubercles*: projections surmounting the intercondyloid eminence.
4. *Anterior intercondyloid fossa*: depression anterior to the intercondyloid tubercles.
5. *Posterior intercondyloid fossa*: depression posterior to the intercondyloid tubercles.

**Fig. 12-1. Anterior view of left tibia and fibula.**

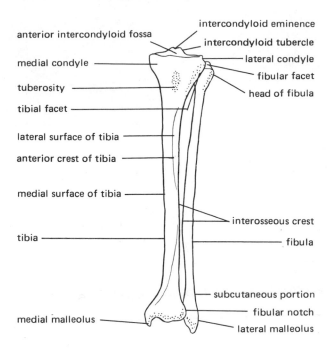

6. *Tuberosity of the tibia*: a roughened prominence located inferior to the condyles on the anterior aspect of the tibia.
7. *Fibular facet*: a depression for articulation with the head of the fibula located inferior to the lateral condyle on the posteriolateral aspect of the head.

B. *The shaft*

1. *Three borders*

   a. *Anterior border* is sharp and is known as the crest.
   b. *Lateral border* or *interosseous* (in″ter-os′e-us) *crest* is directed toward the interosseous crest of the fibula, the two being connected by the interosseous membrane.
   c. *Medial border* is continuous inferiorly with a marked projection called the *medial malleolus* (mal-e′o-lus).

2. *Three surfaces*

   a. *Medial surface* is convex and is largely subcutaneous. Since it is so exposed to injury and is so unprotected, it has been popularly called the *shin*.
   b. *Posterior surface*

      (1) *Popliteal* (pop-lit′e-al) *line*: a slight oblique line located on the upper part of the posterior surface where it extends from the lateral to the medial borders.

   c. *Lateral surface* is largely covered by muscles.

**Fig. 12-2. Posterior view of left tibia and fibula.**

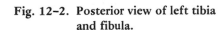
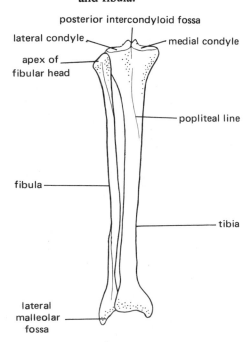

C. *Distal extremity*

1. *Fibula notch*: receives the lateral malleolus or distal extremity of the fibula and is located on the lateral border of the distal extremity.
2. The inferior surface of the distal extremity is marked by an *articular surface* which articulates with the trochlea or superior surface of the talus.

## The Fibula

The fibula (Figs. 12–1 and 12–2) is the lateral of the two bones of the leg. It does not sustain any of the weight of the body because it does not articulate with the femur at the knee joint, but it does enter into the formation of the ankle joint and serves to secure it on its lateral side. The fibula is primarily important, however, as the site of muscle attachments. Like the tibia, it is a long bone consisting of a shaft and two extremities. Some of the important markings on the fibula are

A. *The superior extremity or head*

1. The tibia facet: a somewhat rounded facet on the superomedial surface of the head, which articulates with the fibula facet on the lateral aspect of the tibial head.

B. *The shaft* is so twisted and so marked by the attachments of muscles that its surfaces and borders are difficult to follow. Its sharp edge, however, is its interosseous border, which is directed medially.

C. *The distal extremity or lateral malleolus* articulates with the fibula notch of the tibia and with the lateral side of the trochlea of the talus.

## The Ankle Joint

12.12 The Ankle and Tibiofibular Joints

The ankle joint or talocrural articulation is a *hinge* joint formed by (1) the articular facet on the distal extremity of the tibia, which articulates with the superior articular surface (trochlea) of the talus, (2) the medial malleolus, which articulates with the medial surface of the trochlea of the talus, and (3) the lateral malleolus, which articulates with the lateral surface of the trochlea.

*Movements.* Because it is a hinge joint, the movements of the ankle joint are only *flexion*, also called *dorsal flexion*, and *extension*, also called *plantar flexion*. Flexion is a movement of the dorsal surface of the foot toward the anterior surface of the leg, and extension is the reverse action.

*Ligaments* (Fig. 12–3). The ligaments of the ankle joint consist of (1) the articular capsule, (2) the medial or deltoid ligament, and

**Fig. 12-3. Ligaments of the ankle joint.**

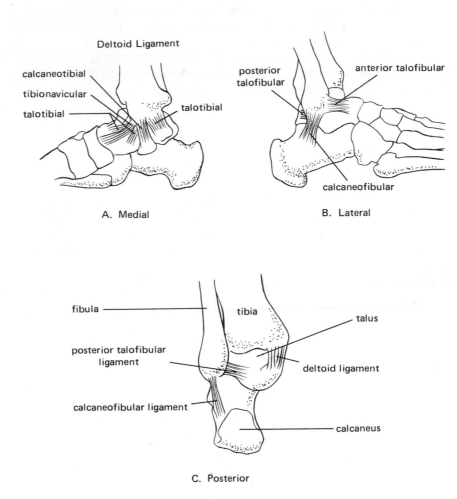

(3) the three lateral ligaments. These ligaments are described as follows:

A. *The articular capsule*: surrounds the joint and is attached, above, to the borders of the articular surfaces of the tibia and malleoli and, below, to the talus around its upper articular surface.

B. *The medial or deltoid ligament*: a triangular ligament. It is attached superiorly to the borders of the medial malleolus. Its inferior attachments are to the medial surface of the body of the talus, to the sustentaculum tali of the calcaneus, and to the posterior margin of the navicular. This important ligament resists extreme eversion of the foot. Weakness of it is believed to be a cause of flatfoot in that this would allow eversion and would therefore throw a greater weight than usual on the medial side of the arch.

C. *Three lateral ligaments*

1. *The anterior talofibular ligament*: the most anterior of three bandlike ligaments situated on the lateral aspect of the ankle. It is attached superiorly to the anterior

border of the lateral malleolus and inferiorly to the anterior margin of the lateral malleolar facet on the trochlea of the talus.

2. *The posterior talofibular ligament*: the most posterior of the lateral ligaments. It extends almost horizontally from its attachment on the lateral malleolus to its medial attachment on the posterior surface of the talus.

3. *The calcaneofibular ligament*: the middle of the three lateral ligaments. It is attached superiorly to the anterior border of the lateral malleolus and inferiorly to a tubercle near the middle of the lateral surface of the calcaneus.

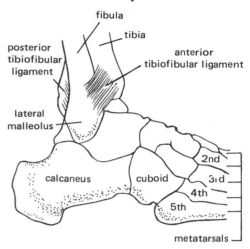

**Fig. 12-4.** Ligaments of the inferior tibiofibular joint.

## The Tibiofibular Joints

The tibiofibular joints include three separate articulations, namely, the inferior tibiofibular joint, the tibiofibular union, and the superior tibiofibular joint. *The inferior tibiofibular articulation* (sliding joint) is the articulation between the lateral malleolus and the fibular notch of the tibia. *The tibiofibular union* (syndesmosis) is the union of the shafts of the tibia and fibula by an interosseous membrane that consists of numerous short fibers, which pass transversely from one articular surface to the other. *The superior tibiofibular articulation* (sliding joint) is the articulation between the head of the fibula and the fibular facet of the tibia.

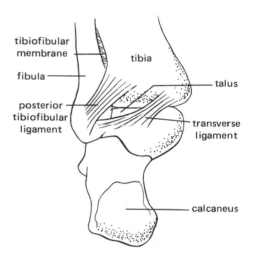

*Movements.* The movements of the tibiofibular joints consist merely of gliding movements, which are passive in character in that they complement the movements of the ankle joint. Thus, during flexion of the ankle, the fibula tends to be displaced upward; during extension, it is displaced downward. These movements are resisted by the interosseous membrane.

*Ligaments.* The primary ligaments of the tibiofibular joints are as follows:

A. *The inferior tibiofibular articulation* (Fig. 12-4)

1. The anterior inferior tibiofibular ligament.
2. The posterior inferior tibiofibular ligament.
3. The inferior transverse ligament: a strong band attached laterally to the lateral malleolus and posterior talus and medially to the posterior surface of the distal extremity of the tibia.

B. *The tibiofibular union* (Fig. 12-4)

1. The interosseous ligament or membrane.

C. *The superior tibiofibular articulation* (Fig. 12-5)

1. The articular capsule.
2. The anterior superior tibiofibular ligament.
3. The posterior superior tibiofibular ligament.

**Fig. 12-5.** Ligaments of the superior tibiofibular joint.

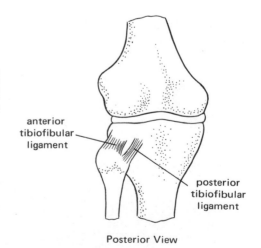

Posterior View

**12.13  Muscles of the Leg**

The musculature of the leg can be divided into three groups: anterior, lateral, and posterior. The muscles included in each of these groups are

A.  Anterior group (Fig. 12-6)

1.  Tibialis (tib"e-a'lis) anterior
2.  Extensor digitorum longus
3.  Peroneus tertius (ter'she-us)
4.  Extensor hallucis longus

B.  Lateral group (Fig. 12-7)

1.  Peroneus (per"o-ne'us) longus
2.  Peroneus brevis

C.  Posterior group

1.  Superficial layer (Fig. 12-8)

   a.  Gastrocnemius (gas"trok-ne'me-us)

2.  Middle layer (Fig. 12-9)

   a.  Soleus (so'le-us)
   b.  Plantaris (plan-ta'ris)

3.  Deep layer (Fig. 12-10)

   a.  Tibialis posterior
   b.  Flexor digitorum longus
   c.  Flexor hallucis longus

The functions of these muscles are described in terms of their actions at the ankle and upon the foot and toes. In studying the actions of the leg muscles, it is convenient to think of the malleolus (mal-e'olus or mah-le'o-lus) as a pulley that changes the direction of the muscle's line of pull. A muscle that has a tendon passing posterior to the pulley will plantar flex the foot. A muscle that has a tendon passing anterior to the malleolus will dorsiflex the foot.

Lifting the medial border of the foot is called inversion, and moving the forefoot medially is adduction. The combined movement of inversion and adduction is supination. As a general rule, supination, and either inversion or adduction alone, is caused by muscles with tendons located on the medial side of the foot. Opposite to inversion is eversion, or the lifting of the lateral border of the foot, and the lateral movement of the forefoot is abduction. The combined movement of eversion and abduction is pronation. Pronation, and either eversion or abduction alone, is generally caused by muscles with tendons located along the lateral side of the foot. A muscle, therefore, passing *posterior* to the lateral malleolus will probably cause plantar flexion of the ankle and pronation of the foot.

It can also be generalized that the anterior muscles serve to dorsiflex (flex) the foot and to extend the toes; the posterior muscles to plantar flex (extend) the foot and to flex the toes; the lateral muscles serve primarily to evert the foot, but assist also in plantar flexing it.

**The Anterior Leg Muscles** (Fig. 12-6)

Since all four anterior leg muscles pass anterior to the malleoli, they are involved in dorsiflexion. The tibialis anterior is the only one that passes in front of the medial malleolus and is, therefore, an inverter of the foot. The extensor digitorum longus and the peroneus tertius pass in front of the lateral malleolus and serve to evert the foot. The extensor hallucis longus passes anterior to the center line of the ankle, but because of its attachment on the medial side of the foot, it assists in inversion in addition to its role as dorsiflexor of the foot and extensor of the big toe. The extensor digitorum longus, as its name implies, is an extensor of the lateral four toes in addition to its role as a dorsiflexor and evertor of the foot. These muscles are important in such movements as walking, in that they elevate the front part of the foot preventing it from scraping the ground as the foot leaves the ground, thus preventing "foot drop."

Fig. 12-6. The anterior muscles of the leg.

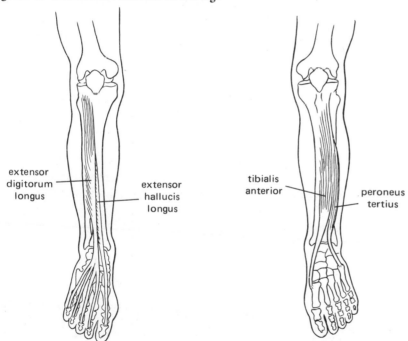

extensor digitorum longus  
extensor hallucis longus  
tibialis anterior  
peroneus tertius

The *tibialis anterior* lies along the lateral surface of the head and the shaft of the tibia and is subcutaneous. It is responsible for the roundness of the leg anteriorly. Because it is superficial throughout its course, it may be palpated all the way from its proximal to its distal attachments. It has its distal attachment on the first cuneiform and base of the first metatarsal. Its actions are dorsiflexion of the ankle and supination of the foot (adduction and inversion).

The *extensor digitorum longus* is a flat, penniform muscle that lies lateral to and partly under cover of the tibialis anterior and borders laterally with the peronei muscles. The *peroneus tertius* is a separate portion of the extensor digitorum longus on its lateral side and may be considered its fifth tendon. The extensor digitorum longus attaches proximally to the head of the tibia and the upper two thirds of the fibula. In the region of the ankle it gives off four tendons that traverse the dorsum of the foot. Its distal attachment is on the dorsal surface of the phalanges of the lateral four toes. The peroneus tertius arises from the distal third of the fibula and passes to the base of the fifth metatarsal. The extensor digitorum longus, as its name implies, is an extensor of the lateral four toes. Both the extensor digitorum longus and peroneus tertius are dorsiflexors of the ankle and pronators (abductors and evertors) of the foot.

The *extensor hallucis longus* is the long or proper extensor of the big toe and lies between the tibialis anterior and the extensor digitorum longus. It arises from the middle portion of the fibula and passes to the base of the distal phalanx of the big toe. Its actions are dorsiflexion of the ankle, supination (adduction and inversion) of the foot, and extension of the big toe.

### The Lateral Leg Muscles (Fig. 12–7)

The lateral group of leg muscles consist of the peroneus longus and brevis. Both of these muscles have their proximal attachments on the fibula. The peroneus longus, however, attaches to the head and the upper two thirds of the fibula, whereas the peroneus brevis attaches to the lower two thirds of the fibula shaft.

The *peroneus longus* is the most superficial of the two muscles. Its long tendon passes behind the lateral malleolus, curves around the lateral border of the foot following the peroneal grooves of the calcaneus and cuboid bones, and passes obliquely forward across the plantar surface to its distal attachment on the plantar aspect of the first cuneiform and base of the first metatarsal.

The *peroneus brevis*, as its name suggests, is shorter and smaller than the peroneus longus under which it lies. Its tendon descends anterior to the tendon of the peroneus longus and, with it, passes

Fig. 12–7. The lateral muscles of the leg.

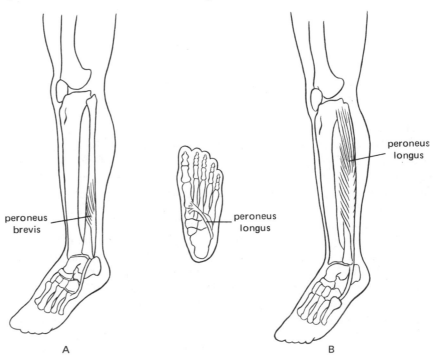

behind the lateral malleolus and through a groove on the lateral aspect of the calcaneus to its distal attachment on the tuberosity of the fifth metatarsal.

In that both of these muscles pass behind the lateral malleolus, they both serve to plantar flex the ankle and to pronate (abduct and evert) the foot.

## The Posterior Leg Muscles

The posterior group of leg muscles is divided into (1) a superficial layer that consists of the gastrocnemius, (2) a middle layer that consists of the soleus and the plantaris, and (3) a deep layer that includes the tibialis posterior, the flexor digitorum longus, and the flexor hallucis longus.

All six muscles of the posterior group remain posterior to the medial malleolus as they attach to the foot and are, therefore, plantar flexors and mostly (excluding the first two layers) supinators (adductors and invertors) of the foot.

The *gastrocnemius* (Fig. 12–8) is the most superficial muscle of the posterior leg muscles. It has two heads that attach to the condyles of the femur and unite at an angle below the posterior aspect of the knee. The tendons of the gastrocnemius and soleus fuse to form the prominent tendon of Achilles, which attaches distally to the tuberosity of the calcaneus.

The *soleus* (Fig. 12–9) is a broad, flat muscle that lies under the gastrocnemius. Its proximal attachment is on the upper part of the posterior surfaces of the tibia, fibula, and interosseous membrane.

The *plantaris* (Fig. 12–9) arises from the distal portion of the lateral supracondylar line of the femur and is situated between the lateral head of the gastrocnemius and the soleus. Its long, slender tendon crosses obliquely and medially between the gastrocnemius and soleus and descends along the medial border of the tendon of Achilles with which it is attached to the calcaneus bone.

The primary action of these muscles is to plantar flex the foot at the ankle joint. In addition to this, however, the gastrocnemius flexes the leg at the knee joint, since its proximal attachment is above this joint. The gastrocnemius and soleus together form a muscular mass commonly called the "calf of the leg," or the *triceps surae*. The importance of these muscles is evident in all cases where the weight of the body is raised by lifting the heel as, for example, in walking, running, or jumping. When their fixed point is at the heel, as in standing, they serve to steady the leg at the ankle joint, that is, to prevent it from falling forward due to the body weight.

The *deep posterior muscles* (Fig. 12–10) are sometimes referred to as the Tom, Dick, and Harry muscles: Tom for tibialis, Dick for digitorum, and Harry for hallucis. The muscles of the deep posterior group are, therefore, the tibialis posterior, the flexor digitorum longus, and the flexor hallucis longus.

The *tibialis posterior* is the most deeply placed muscle of the posterior group and is situated between the flexor digitorum longus and the flexor hallucis longus under cover of the triceps surae. It has its proximal attachment on the upper half of the posterior surface of the

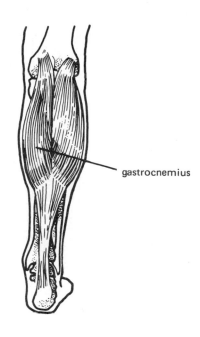

Fig. 12–8. The gastrocnemius—the superficial muscle in the posterior group of leg muscles.

gastrocnemius

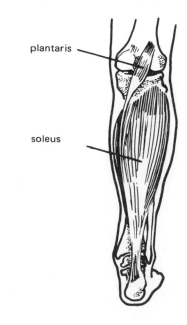

Fig. 12–9. The middle layer of posterior leg muscles.

plantaris

soleus

**Fig. 12–10. The deep layer of posterior leg muscles.**

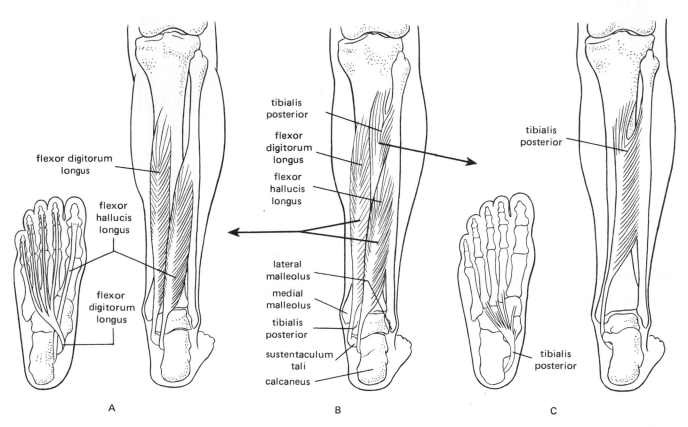

interosseous membrane and the adjacent parts of the tibia and fibula. Its distal attachment is on the tuberosity of the navicular and on the plantar surfaces of the cuneiforms and the cuboid. It passes behind the medial malleolus.

The *flexor digitorum longus* is the long flexor of the toes and lies on the medial side of the posterior aspect of the leg under cover of the soleus in its proximal portion. Its proximal attachment is on the posterior surface of the shaft of the tibia inferior to the popliteal line. Its tendon passes behind the medial malleolus between the tendons of the tibialis posterior and the flexor hallucis longus and continues obliquely forward and laterally into the sole of the foot. Here it divides into four tendons attached to the terminal phalanges of the lateral four toes. In the sole of the foot, it crosses superficially the tendon of the flexor hallucis longus.

The *flexor hallucis longus* is the long flexor of the big toe. It is located on the lateral side of the posterior aspect of the leg in close proximity to the lateral peroneal muscles. Its proximal attachment is on the distal two thirds of the posterior surface of the fibula. Its tendon passes behind the medial malleolus posterior to the tendon of the flexor digitorum longus and enters the sole of the foot by following two grooves, one on the posterior surface of the talus and one on the inferior surface of the sustentaculum tali of the calcaneus. Its distal attachment is on the base of the distal phalanx of the big toe.

All three of these muscles are plantar flexors of the ankle and supinators (adductors and invertors) of the foot.

12.21   Bones of the Leg

A.   Specific Student Objectives

1.   *The Tibia*

a.   The tibia is located on what side of the leg?
b.   What is the common name of the tibia?
c.   With what other bones does the tibia articulate? Describe these articulations.
d.   Locate the tibia on a mounted skeleton and identify the following

medial and lateral condyles       posterior intercondy-
intercondyloid eminence              loid fossa
intercondyloid tubercles          tuberosity of the
anterior intercondyloid              tibia
   fossa                          fibular facet

anterior border                   medial surface
lateral border or inter-          posterior surface
   osseous crest                  popliteal line
medial border                     lateral surface
medial malleolus

fibular notch
articular surface

e.   Locate the tibia in your own body and identify the following:

tuberosity of the tibia           medial surface
anterior border                   medial malleolus
lateral surface

2.   *The Fibula*

a.   Why does the fibula not sustain any of the weight of the body?
b.   What is the primary importance of the fibula?
c.   With what other bones does the fibula articulate? Describe these articulations.
d.   Locate the fibula on a mounted skeleton and identify the following:

head                              shaft
tibia facet                       lateral malleolus

e.   Locate the fibula in your body and identify the following:

head
shaft
lateral malleolus

B. Study Hints

1. The use of actual bones is recommended in the study of specific bone markings.
2. Locating bony landmarks in the student's body is also a valuable aid to learning.

## 12.22 The Ankle and Tibiofibular Joints

A. Specific Student Objectives

1. *The Ankle Joint*

    a. What type of joint is this?
    b. Describe the bony articulations involved in this joint.
    c. What movements are allowed at this joint? Describe these movements.
    d. Describe the ligamentous reinforcements of this joint.
    e. Of what significance is the deltoid ligament?
    f. Of what significance are the three lateral ligaments of the ankle?

2. *The Tibiofibular Joints*

    a. What type of joints are these?
    b. Describe the bony articulations involved in these joints.
    c. What movements are allowed at these joints?
    d. Describe the ligamentous reinforcements of these joints.

B. Study Hints

1. The student should study each of these joints on a mounted skeleton, where he can visualize the bony articulations and ligamentous reinforcements involved in the joint.
2. The student should also identify each joint in his ankle and leg and perform the movements of that joint according to the descriptions presented in the text. It is important that he learn to identify the movements of the ankle by their proper names whenever he sees them performed.

## 12.23 Muscles of the Leg

A. Specific Student Objectives

1. *General Information*

    a. The musculature of the leg can be divided into how many groups? Identify the muscles included in each of these groups.
    b. What is the mechanical function of the malleolus?

      c. What action will be performed by a muscle that has a tendon passing posterior to a malleolus? What will be the action when a tendon passes anterior to a malleolus?

      d. Define inversion and eversion. What are the inter-relationship of inversion, eversion, adduction, abduction, supination, and pronation of the foot.

      e. What action will be performed by a muscle that has a tendon passing posterior to the lateral malleolus?

2. *The Anterior Leg Muscles*

      a. Identify the four muscles located in this group.

      b. Describe the relationship of each of these muscles to the malleoli.

      c. Give the joint actions produced by the contraction of each of these muscles.

      d. What is the importance of these muscles during the act of walking?

      e. Give the proximal and distal attachments of each of these muscles.

      f. Locate each of these muscles in your leg.

3. *The Lateral Leg Muscles*

      a. Identify the two muscles located in this group.

      b. Describe the relationship of each of these muscles to the lateral malleolus.

      c. Give the joint actions produced by the contraction of each of these muscles.

      d. Give the proximal and distal attachments of each of these muscles.

      e. Locate each of these muscles in your leg.

4. *The Posterior Leg Muscles*

      a. Identify the muscles located in each of the three layers of posterior leg muscles.

      b. Describe the relationship of each of these muscles to the malleoli.

      c. Give the joint actions produced by the contraction of each of these muscles.

      d. Give the proximal and distal attachments of each of these muscles.

      e. Locate each of these muscles in your leg.

      f. What muscles form the triceps surae?

B. Study Hints

1. Table 12–1 is presented to aid in the mastery of specific muscle actions and attachments.

2. Instructions as to where the muscles of the leg can be palpated are presented in Table 12–2. The student should perform the movements of dorsal flexion, plantar flexion, supination, and pronation with his foot and attempt to locate through palpation each of the muscles listed in Table 12–2.

**Table 12-1. The Attachments and Actions of the Muscles of the Leg**

| Location | Name | Proximal Attachment | Illustration | Distal Attachment | Action |
|---|---|---|---|---|---|
| Anterior group | Tibialis anterior | Lateral surface of the head and upper two thirds of tibia | Fig. 12–6 | Medial surface of the first cuneiform and base of the first metatarsal | Dorsal flexion of the ankle and supination of the foot (adduction and inversion) |
| | Extensor digitorum longus | Head of tibia and the upper two thirds of the fibula | Fig. 12–6 | Dorsal surface of second and third phalanges of the lateral four toes | Dorsal flexion of the ankle, pronation (abduction and eversion) of the foot, and extension of the four lateral toes |
| | Peroneus tertius | Anterior surface of lower third of fibula | Fig. 12–6 | Dorsal surface of base of fifth metatarsal | Dorsal flexion of the ankle and pronation (eversion and adduction) of the foot |
| | Extensor hallucis longus | Middle half of anterior surface of fibula | Fig. 12–6 | Dorsal surface of base of distal phalanx of the big toe | Dorsal flexion of the ankle, supination (adduction and inversion) of the foot, and extension of the big toe |
| Lateral group | Peroneus longus | Head of tibia; lateral surface of upper two thirds of fibula | Fig. 12–7 | Lateral side of plantar surface of first cuneiform and base of first metatarsal | Plantar flexion of the ankle and pronation (abduction and eversion) of the foot |
| | Peroneus brevis | Lateral surface of lower two thirds of fibula | Fig. 12–7 | Tuberosity on lateral side of base of fifth metatarsal | Plantar flexion of the ankle and pronation (abduction and eversion) of the foot |
| Posterior group | Gastrocnemius | By two tendons to the posterior aspects of the condyles of the femur | Fig. 12–8 | Tuberosity of the calcaneus | Flexion of the knee and plantar flexion of the ankle |
| | Soleus | Upper part of the posterior surfaces of the tibia, fibula, and interosseous membrane | Fig. 12–9 | Tuberosity of the calcaneus | Plantar flexion of the ankle |
| | Plantaris | Distal portion of the lateral supracondylar line of the femur | Fig. 12–9 | Tuberosity of the calcaneus | Very weak assistant in flexion of the knee and plantar flexion of the ankle |

Table 12-1. The Attachments and Actions of the Muscles of the Leg (continued)

| Location | Name | Proximal Attachment | Illustration | Distal Attachment | Action |
|----------|------|---------------------|--------------|-------------------|--------|
| | Tibialis posterior | Upper half of the posterior surface of the interosseous membrane and adjacent parts of the tibia and fibula | Fig. 12-10 | Tuberosity of the navicular and on the plantar surfaces of cuneiforms and cuboid | Plantar flexion of ankle and supination (adduction and inversion) of foot |
| | Flexor digitorum longus | Posterior surface of the shaft of tibia inferior to the popliteal line | Fig. 12-10 | The bases of the distal phalanges of the four lateral toes | Plantar flexion of ankle, supination (adduction and inversion) of foot, and flexion of four lateral toes |
| | Flexor hallucis longus | Distal two thirds of posterior surface of fibula | Fig. 12-10 | Base of the distal phalanx of the big toe | Plantar flexion of ankle, supination (adduction and inversion) of the foot, and flexion of big toe |

Table 12-2. Instructions for Palpating the Muscles of the Leg

| Name of Muscle | Where the Muscle Can Be Palpated |
|----------------|----------------------------------|
| **A. Anterior group (Fig. 12-6)** | |
| 1. Tibialis anterior | Because the muscle is superficial throughout its course, it may be observed and palpated all the way from its proximal to its distal attachment. It is located on the anterior surface of the leg, just lateral to the anterior crest of the tibia. |
| 2. Extensor digitorum longus | The tendons can be seen as they pass the ankle and proceed toward the four medial toes. |
| 3. Peroneus tertius | The tendon crosses the dorsal surface of the foot close to base of fifth metatarsal. |
| 4. Extensor hallucis longus | The tendon crosses the dorsal surface of the foot and the big toe. |
| **B. Lateral group (Fig. 12-7)** | |
| 1. Peroneus longus | The muscular portion of the peroneus longus can be palpated just below the head of the fibula and may be followed down the lateral side of the leg. Above the malleolus, the tendon of the longus lies slightly posterior to that of the brevis. Below the malleolus the tendon of the longus is held close to the bone and is difficult to identify. |
| 2. Peroneus brevis | The tendon of the peroneus brevis stands out more than that of the longus and it can be followed to its attachment on the fifth metatarsal bone. |

**Table 12-2. Instructions for Palpating the Muscles of the Leg (continued)**

| Name of Muscle | Where the Muscle Can Be Palpated |
|---|---|
| C. *Posterior group* | |
| 1. Superficial layer (Fig. 12-8) | |
|    a. Gastrocnemius | Calf of leg and back of ankle. |
| 2. Middle layer (Fig. 12-9) | |
|    a. Soleus | Below and slightly lateral to the lateral bulge of the gastrocnemius during plantar flexion of the ankle. |
|    b. Plantaris | Cannot be palpated in most people. |
| 3. Deep layer (Fig. 12-10) | |
|    a. Tibialis posterior | The tendon can be palpated below the medial malleolus as it heads toward the tuberosity of the navicular bone. This tendon lies closer to the malleolus than do the tendons of the other two deep posterior muscles. |
|    b. Flexor digitorum longus | The tendon of the flexor digitorum longus is the middle of the three tendons which pass around the medial malleolus. |
|    c. Flexor hallucis longus | Difficult to palpate. |

**12.30 Recommended Supplementary Readings**

The student should consult any recent basic anatomy text for supplementary readings on the structure of the leg. A list of selected anatomy texts is given in Appendix B.

# 13

# Movements and Problems of the Toes, Foot, and Ankle

The movements of the toes occur at both the interphalangeal and the metatarsophalangeal joints. Since the interphalangeal joints are hinge and the metatarsophalangeal joints are condyloid, flexion and extension can occur at both locations. Abduction and adduction, however, can occur only at the metatarsophalangeal articulations.

The basic movement of the toes is flexion—the movement responsible for imparting the final impetus to the body in walking, running, and jumping, and the movement that opposes the force of gravity in weight bearing. The muscles responsible for flexion of the toes include all the intrinsic plantar muscles of the foot plus the flexor digitorum longus and the flexor hallucis longus. The specific toes that these muscles act upon are

A. *Flexion of the Big Toe*
   Included here are all the hallucis muscles.

   1. Flexor hallucis longus
   2. Flexor hallucis brevis

**13.11 Movements of the Toes**

    3. Adductor hallucis
    4. Abductor hallucis

B. *Flexion of the Four Lateral Toes*

    1. Muscles that flex all four lateral toes

        a. Flexor digitorum longus
        b. Flexor digitorum brevis
        c. Quadratus plantae
        d. Lumbricales (flexion of proximal phalanges only)

    2. Muscles that flex some of the four lateral toes

        a. Plantar interossei (flexion of the lateral three toes only)
        b. Dorsal interossei (flexion of the middle three toes only)
        c. Flexor digiti minimi (flexion of the little toe only)
        d. Abductor digiti minimi (flexion of the little toe only)

The movements of toe extension, abduction, and adduction in human feet seem to have the sole purpose of positioning the toes so that they can best perform flexion. The muscles responsible for producing these movements are

A. *Extension*

    1. *Big toe*

        a. Extensor hallucis longus
        b. Extensor hallucis brevis (medial tendon of the extensor digitorum brevis)

    2. *Four lateral toes*

        a. Extensor digitorum longus
        b. Extensor digitorum brevis (does not act on little toe)
        c. Lumbricales (extends middle and distal phalanges only)

B. *Abduction*

    1. *Big toe*

        a. Abductor hallucis

    2. *Four lateral toes*

        a. First lumbricales (abducts second toe)
        b. First, third, and fourth dorsal interossei (abduct the second, third, and fourth toes, respectively)
        c. Abductor digiti minimi (abducts only the little toe)
        d. Flexor digiti minimi (abducts only the little toe)

C. *Adduction*

    1. *Big toe*

        a. Adductor hallucis

    2. *Four lateral toes*

        a. Second dorsal interosseus (adducts the second toe)

b. Plantar interossei (adducts the third, fourth, and fifth toes)

c. Second, third, and fourth lumbricales (adduct the third, fourth, and fifth toes, respectively)

The toes are probably the least important part of the foot, and their movements are generally of little importance in either the support of body weight or locomotion. They do serve, however, to widen the anterior area of the foot, which enables the foot to better adapt to inequalities of the supporting surface, and they do assist in propelling the body in the final stages of walking, running, and jumping, as they are the last to leave the ground. The propelling effect is produced especially by the big toe.

The fundamental movements of the foot occurring at the intertarsal joints can be divided into two groups, which we might identify as (1) the medial movements and (2) the lateral movements. The medial movements, which are all produced by the same muscles, are inversion (turning the sole of the foot medially), adduction (medial movement of the forepart of the foot), and supination (a combination of inversion and adduction). The lateral movements, which are all produced by the same muscles, are eversion (turning the sole of the foot laterally), abduction (lateral movement of the forepart of the foot), and pronation (a combination of eversion and abduction).

The muscles that produce the medial and lateral movements of the foot are

## 13.12 Movements of the Foot Occurring at the Intertarsal Joints

A. *Inversion, Adduction,* and *Supination* (Fig. 13–1)

These movements are produced by all the muscles passing to or around the medial border of the foot.

1. Muscles passing behind the medial malleolus

a. Tibialis posterior
b. Flexor digitorum longus
c. Flexor hallucis longus

2. Muscles passing in front of the medial malleolus

a. Tibialis anterior
b. Extensor hallucis longus

B. *Eversion, Abduction,* and *Pronation* (Fig. 13–2)

These movements are produced by all the muscles passing to or around the lateral border of the foot.

1. Muscles passing behind the lateral malleolus

a. Peroneus longus
b. Peroneus brevis

2. Muscles passing in front of the lateral malleolus

a. Peroneus tertius
b. Extensor digitorum longus

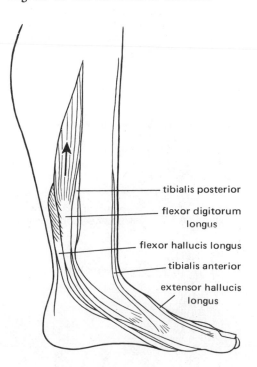

Fig. 13–1. The invertors of the foot.

tibialis posterior

flexor digitorum longus

flexor hallucis longus

tibialis anterior

extensor hallucis longus

**Fig. 13–2. The evertors of the foot.**

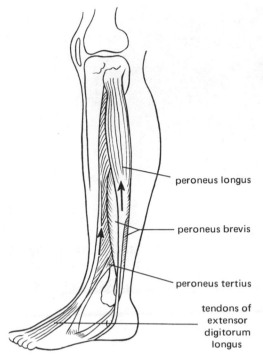

peroneus longus

peroneus brevis

peroneus tertius

tendons of extensor digitorum longus

The medial movements are, of course, produced by all the muscles with tendons passing to or around the medial border of the foot. Thus, posteriorly, the flexor hallucis longus and especially the tibialis posterior serve as invertors and adductors. Because of its attachment on the tibia, the flexor digitorum longus is less advantageously situated for these actions than are the other two deep muscles of the calf. Anteriorly, the tibialis anterior obviously acts as an invertor and adductor, and the extensor hallucis longus aids in these actions.

The lateral movements of eversion and abduction are produced by the three peronei (longus, brevis, and tertius), aided perhaps by the more lateral portion of the extensor digitorum longus.

During inversion, the tibialis anterior and posterior mutually neutralize one another's tendency to dorsiflex and plantar flex the foot and ankle. During eversion, the peroneus longus and brevis are mutually neutralizing with the peroneus tertius and extensor digitorum longus with respect to plantar and dorsal flexion.

Flexion and extension may occur to a slight extent in the foot at the talonavicular and calcaneonavicular joints. Here these movements occur in conjunction with those of the ankle except that they are reversed, i.e., flexion and extension at these joints are simultaneous with extension and flexion of the ankle, respectively. It should be remembered that in reference to the ankle and foot the term dorsal flexion is the same as flexion and that plantar flexion is the same as extension.

## 13.13 Movements of the Foot Occurring at the Ankle Joint

**Fig. 13–3. The dorsal flexors of the ankle.**

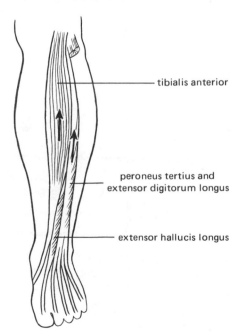

tibialis anterior

peroneus tertius and extensor digitorum longus

extensor hallucis longus

Since the ankle or talocrural joint is of the hinge type, it allows only flexion and extension. The muscles that produce these movements are

A. *Dorsal flexion or flexion* (Fig. 13–3)

This movement is produced by all the anterior muscles of the leg.

1. Tibialis anterior
2. Peroneus tertius
3. Extensor digitorum longus
4. Extensor hallucis longus

B. *Plantar flexion or extension* (Fig. 13–4)

This movement is produced by all the lateral and posterior muscles of the leg.

1. Peroneus longus
2. Peroneus brevis
3. Gastrocnemius
4. Soleus
5. Plantaris
6. Tibialis posterior
7. Flexor digitorum longus
8. Flexor hallucis longus

Dorsal flexion at the ankle is due to the actions of all the muscles crossing the front of the ankle. The tibialis anterior and the peroneus tertius are the chief muscles involved in this action, but they are assisted by the two long extensors of the toes.

Plantar flexion at the ankle is due primarily to the actions of the powerful gastrocnemius and soleus muscles on the calcaneus. The plantaris is a weak assistor in this action.

The three deep posterior muscles that pass behind the medial malleolus and the two lateral peronei muscles that pass behind the lateral malleolus are weak assistors in plantar flexion because of their poor leverage. The leverage of these five muscles is extremely poor compared with that of the gastrocnemius and soleus (the triceps surae). The triceps surae uses the posterior part of the calcaneus as its lever arm, whereas the other muscles pass close to the malleoli. As a result, the greatest torques for plantar flexion are produced by the gastrocnemius and soleus.

During dorsal flexion of the ankle, the peroneus tertius and tibialis anterior mutually neutralize one another's tendency to evert and invert the foot. During plantar flexion, the tibialis posterior, on the one hand, and the peroneus longus and brevis, on the other, mutually neutralize one another's tendency to invert and evert the foot.

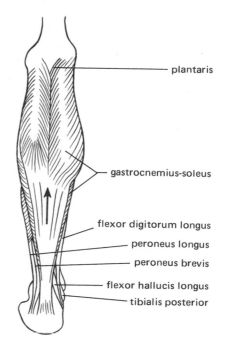

**Fig. 13–4. The plantar flexors of the ankle.**

- plantaris
- gastrocnemius-soleus
- flexor digitorum longus
- peroneus longus
- peroneus brevis
- flexor hallucis longus
- tibialis posterior

## 13.14 Conditioning Problems of the Foot, Ankle, and Leg

The problems of the foot, ankle, and leg are those concerned with the functioning of these structures in either locomotion or in weight bearing. In this section, the discussion will be centered on the function of the foot in locomotion and the conditioning of the foot and leg muscles to better perform this function.

### The Locomotor Function of the Foot

The chief use of the foot in locomotion is as a lever to raise and to propel the body. When the foot strikes the ground in walking or jumping, the weight of the body is borne momentarily on the heel, then on the lateral border of the foot. When the plantar flexors contract, the heel leaves the ground, the lateral border of the foot is raised, and the weight of the body is shifted to the head of the first metatarsal. The phalanges of the big toe are then flexed and thus give the final impetus to the movement. It is evident, therefore, that in locomotor activities the foot functions as a lever. In this lever system, the plantar flexors supply the force, the longitudinal arch is the force arm, and the heads of the metatarsals serve as the fulcrum on which the weight of the body is lifted.

The major problems of the foot, ankle, and leg in performing locomotor activities are those concerned with the flexibility of the foot and ankle joints and with the strength, power, and endurance of the foot and leg muscles.

### Flexibility of the Foot and Ankle Joints

The normal range of motion at the ankle joint is about 60° of voluntary movement (Fig. 13–5), which includes about 20° of dorsal

**Fig. 13–5. Flexibility of the ankle joint.**

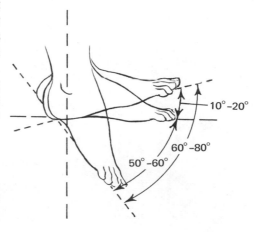

10°–20°

60°–80°

50°–60°

flexion, and 40° of plantar flexion. The amplitude of dorsal flexion can be increased by using the weight of the body. Starting from the standing position, the knees can be flexed until the tibia inclines forward 25 to 30° with the foot flat on the floor; with further movement, the heel is lifted by the posterior ligaments of the ankle joint. The front of the foot can be depressed about 45°. The axis of the ankle joint is parallel to that of the knee joint.

The range of motion from inversion to eversion is about 50°. Some flexibility exercises for the foot and ankle joints are illustrated in Figure 13-6.

Fig. 13-6. Some flexibility exercises for the movements of the foot and ankle joints. In *A* the girls are stretching their plantar flexors, and in *B* they are stretching their evertors.

 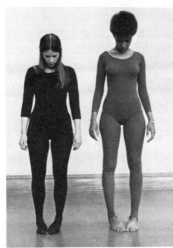

### Isometric Measurements of Strength

The Clark Cable-Tension Strength Tests for the plantar flexors and dorsal flexors of the foot at the ankle joint are illustrated in Figure 13-7. The Martin Breaking Strength Tests for the plantar flexors, dorsal flexors, invertors, and evertors of the foot are described in Table 13-1.

### Isotonic Exercises and Measurements

Some isotonic exercises for the muscles of the legs, which also can be used as isotonic measurements of the strength, power, and endurance of these muscles are illustrated in Figure 13-8. The application of the Logan-Dunkelberg device as an exerciser of the dorsal and plantar flexors and of the invertors and evertors of the foot and ankle is illustrated in Figure 13-9.

Nearly all the exercises designed to strengthen the movements of the toes are for the flexor group of muscles. Running in sand, for instance, produces a great amount of toe-curling action and is often recommended as a good exercise for these flexors. Other examples of toe flexor exercises are shown in Figure 13-10.

**Table 13-1.** **Martin Breaking Strength Tests\* for the Muscles Producing the Movements of the Foot**

1. *Muscles that plantarflex the foot*

   The subject lies on his back on a smooth table. To serve as a foot brace, a stout transverse cleat about 3 in. high is firmly fixed to the foot of the table. The subject steadies himself by holding to the edges of the table with both hands and by firmly pressing against the foot brace the heel of the foot not being tested. The foot to be tested is pressed with the ball resting against a pad, which is exactly one third of the distance up an upright lever about 2 ft long; the fulcrum of the lever is at the level of the table. A stout stick about 1.5 in. square makes an excellent lever. The adjustment of the lever must be such that with the foot in maximum plantar flexion, the ball of the foot rests squarely upon the pad, the lever itself making an angle of about 25° beyond the perpendicular. This is the only test in the Martin series in which a lever is required. The dynamometer is attached to the tip of the lever. The pull is made by the operator from the head of the table. The balance is horizontal and in line with the leg being tested. The pull is increased in intensity until the muscular resistance has been overcome. To prevent slipping on the table, the shoulders of the subject are held by braces. The muscle gives at about 15° of plantar flexion, with a rather sharp break in the resistance offered to the pull.

2. *Muscles that dorsiflex the foot*

   The general position of the subject is the same as that for the preceding test. The foot should be flush with the end of the table (to give freedom of action to the operator in making the pull), and should be slightly lifted and braced by the hands of the adjuster, which encircle the ankle. The leather loop of the dynamometer is placed across the toes at the metatarsophalangeal joints. With the foot of the subject in maximum dorsiflexion, the operator makes the pull at right angles to the plantar surface of the subject's foot, lowering the scale to maintain this angle as the foot gives.

3. *Muscles that invert the foot*

   The position of the subject is the same as for the two preceding tests. The loop is across the inner surface of the metatarsophalangeal joint of the great toe. The ankle is braced by the hands of the adjuster. With the foot at right angles to the leg, the foot is inverted and adducted as far as possible without inward rotation of the leg. The pull is opposite in direction to the muscular contraction, horizontal, and in the same vertical plane as the foot. The operator swings the dynamometer in order to maintain this relationship as the foot gives.

4. *Muscles that evert the foot*

   The position of the subject is the same as for the preceding tests. The loop is at the outer surface of the distal end of the fifth metatarsal. The foot is at right angles to the leg and is everted and abducted as far as possible without outward rotation of the leg. The pull is horizontal and in the same vertical plane as the foot, with a swing of the dynamometer to maintain this position.

\*E. G. Martin: "Tests of Muscular Efficiency," *Physiol. Rev.,* **1**: 454–75, 1921.

Fig. 13-7. The Clark Cable-Tension Strength Tests for the plantar flexors (*A*) and dorsal flexors (*B*) of the foot and ankle joint. In testing the plantar flexors (*A*), the ankle to be tested is placed in 90° of plantar flexion, and the shoulders are braced by one of the testers. In testing the dorsal flexors (*B*), the ankle to be tested is placed in 125° of dorsal flexion, and one tester is used to prevent other movements of foot.

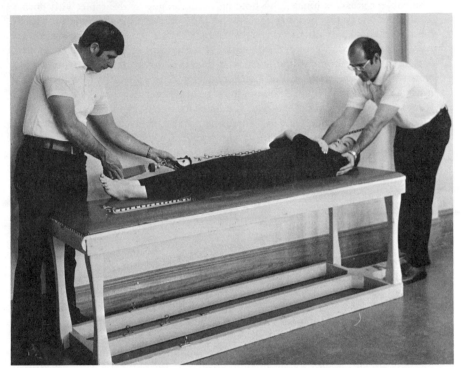

A

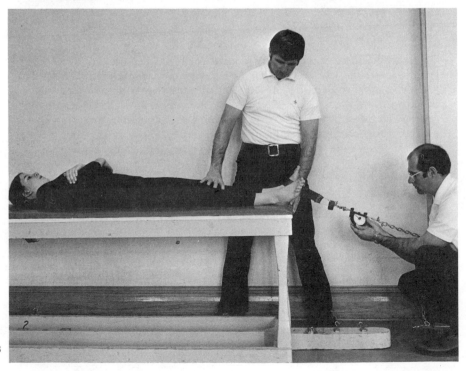

B

Fig. 13-8. Some isotonic exercises that can also be used to measure the strength, power, and endurance of the leg muscles. In *A* a resistive exercise for the plantar flexors is shown, and in *B* an exercise for the dorsal flexors is shown. In the dorsal-flexor exercise, the individual is allowed to move the towel through a full range of motion.

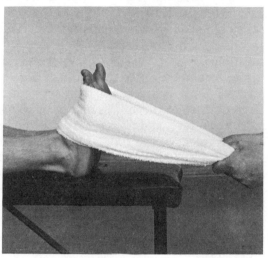

Fig. 13-9. Logan-Dunkelberg exercises for the dorsal and plantar flexors and invertors and evertors of the foot and ankle.

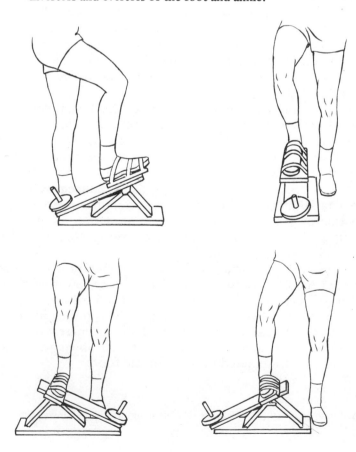

## 13.15 Postural and Pathological Problems of the Foot, Ankle, and Leg

### Postural Problems

In the normal standing posture, the line of gravity passes in front of the normally dorsiflexed ankle joint, so that the weight of the body tends to dorsiflex it even farther. Thus, even quiet standing requires contraction of the plantar flexors of the foot, a duty that normally falls upon the soleus. Here the foot serves as a first-class lever with the fulcrum or axis located at the ankle joint. The point of attachment of the soleus behind the ankle represents the force, and the gravitational line passing in front of the ankle represents the resistance.

The feet function as the support base for the body in the standing position and they receive, therefore, the entire weight of the body. Correct mechanics requires that the body weight be distributed evenly to the two feet, and evenly between the heel and the forward weight-bearing aspect of the foot. Logan and McKinney[1] state, for example, that the weight of a 120-lb person should be distributed evenly with each foot bearing 60 lb. Of this 30 lb would be borne on the calcaneus of each foot, and 30 lb would be borne on the metatarsal heads of each foot. The weight borne on the metatarsal heads is further subdivided as follows: the lateral four heads have 5 lb each, and the remaining 10 lb are distributed under the head of the first metatarsal.

The correct foot-leg alignment requires that certain bony landmarks be aligned in a vertical line. The check points for such alignment when viewed from the front are the center of the knee cap (patella), midpoint of the ankle, and the second toe. When viewed from the rear, a straight line should run through the midline of the Achilles tendon, the midpoint of the ankle, which gives equal prominence to the malleoli, and the midline of the calcaneus. This alignment may be checked by use of a plumb line or by the use of a posture grid screen.

Any foot position that shifts the weight to the medial border of the longitudinal arch will also abduct the forefoot. This movement is caused by the upper portion of the calcaneus rolling downward and inward. This rolling of the calcaneus causes the tibia malleolus to appear further from the heel and, consequently, more prominent. The turning outward of the forefoot is also produced by changes in the normal tarsal-metatarsal and the metatarsal-phalangeal alignments. This position of the foot is referred to as *pronation*. *Supination* is a foot position that shifts the weight to the outer border of the foot and causes adduction of the forefoot.

Continuous weight bearing with the foot in a pronated position (Fig. 13–11) tends to cause the arch to become lower or flattened. The rolling of the calcaneus downward and inward causes a noticeable bowing inward of the Achilles tendon. This rolling increases the distance the tendon must span and results in an increased tenseness of the tendon. The appearance of an outward bowing is an indication of an assumed supinated position of the foot.

Fig. 13–10. Some exercises for the toe flexors. In *A*, the exerciser is picking up a marble with his toes, and in *B* he is rolling up a towel.

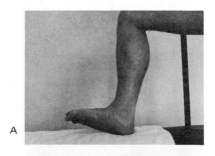

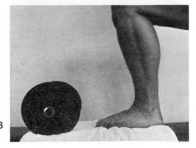

[1] Gene A. Logan and Wayne C. McKinney: *Kinesiology* (Dubuque, Iowa, Wm. C. Brown Publishers, 1970), p. 75.

A flat foot is sometimes called *pes planus*. In this condition the ankles deviate inward and throw an abnormally high percentage of the body weight on the plantar ligaments. The anterior and posterior tibialis and the intrinsic plantar muscles are stretched and allow the foot to sag, an action which may continue until its medial portion contacts the ground. Pes planus may be recorded as first, second, or third degree, depending upon the extent of the sagging. Weak feet, pronated feet, and flat feet may be successive stages of the same defect.

The primary structures that help to maintain the medial longitudinal arch are illustrated in Figure 13–12. Included here are the calcaneonavicular or "spring" ligament and the sustentaculum tali, which, in turn, is supported by the tendon of the flexor hallucis longus. The "spring" ligament is one of the few body ligaments that contains elastic fibers. It serves as a kind of elastic spring upon which rests the head of the talus bone. This ligament is often involved in the "falling" of the long arch, especially when the supporting muscles become weakened due to disuse. Pain is often noted at the site of this ligament. Also illustrated in Figure 13–12 is the direction of the pull of the tendon of the flexor hallucis longus muscle. This muscle helps maintain the calcaneus in an upright position and aids in correct positioning of the bones that compose the arch of the foot.

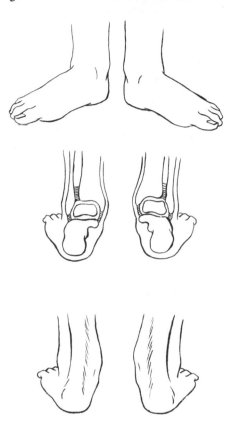

Fig. 13–11. Pronation of the ankles.

**Fig. 13–12. Primary structures that help to maintain the medial longitudinal arch of the foot.**

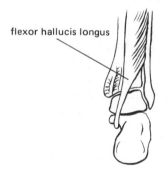

flexor hallucis longus

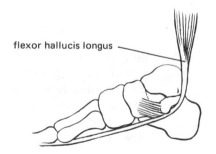

flexor hallucis longus

When assessing anteroposterior deviations from proper foot-leg alignments, it is necessary to observe the body from the side. From this viewpoint, the normal position of the foot is at a right angle to the leg. The gravitational line falls at the front edge of the tibia and in front of the malleolus in the area of the navicular-cuboid articulation. Thus, a plumb line would fall just behind the patella for the knee, and about 1 of 1–1/2 in. in front of the fibular malleolus. Any deviation from this line will indicate either an increase or a decrease of the foot-leg angle.

## Pathological Problems

A talipes (tal'i-pez) condition (Fig. 13–13) is a congenital malformation in which the foot is fixed in any of the normal positions,

**Fig. 13–13. The basic talipes conditions of the foot.**

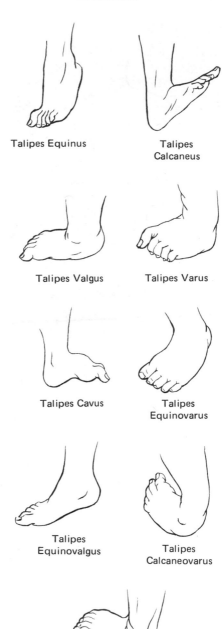

Talipes Equinus

Talipes Calcaneus

Talipes Valgus

Talipes Varus

Talipes Cavus

Talipes Equinovarus

Talipes Equinovalgus

Talipes Calcaneovarus

Talipes Calcaneovulgus

such as dorsiflexion, plantar flexion, inversion, eversion, abduction, and adduction. These fixed positions are classified as follows:

A. *Talipes equinus* (e-kwi′nus), a position of plantar flexion. In the standing position, the body weight is born on the toes. This condition is usually produced by a paralysis of the tibialis anterior, the extensor digitorum longus, or of one of the other dorsiflexors, which permits the triceps surae to go into contracture, so that the heel is raised and the weight is carried on the toes.

B. *Talipes calcaneus*, a position of dorsiflexion. In the standing position, the weight is borne on the heel. This condition is usually produced by a paralysis of the triceps surae, or of the peroneus longus, or of both, which permits the anterior leg muscles to elevate the forefoot so that the weight is carried on the heel.

C. *Talipes valgus* (val′gus), a position of eversion and abduction of the forefoot. In the standing position, the weight is borne on the medial or inner border of the foot (pronation). Loss of the posterior tibialis and/or the intrinsic plantar muscles or contracture of the peroneus longus may cause the foot to be pulled into the pronated position.

D. *Talipes varus* (va′rus), a position of inversion and adduction of the forefoot. In the standing position, the weight is borne on the lateral or outer border of the foot (supination). Paralysis of the peroneus longus and/or peroneus brevis may allow the anterior and posterior tibialis to pull the foot into a supinated position.

E. *Talipes cavus* (kav′us), a position of upward caving of the longitudinal arch of the foot, as though it had been squeezed forcefully together at the toes and heel, and the arch buckled upwards. This condition occurs when loss of the triceps surae permits the flexors to draw the calcaneus forward, the talus to dorsiflex, and the plantar fascia to contract. A high arch is formed, tightening the long extensors of the toes. The toes are cocked up and the condition known as "clawfoot" occurs.

A talipes condition rarely involves any single one of the above fixed positions, but rather a combination of these positions. The most common combination is called *talipes equinovarus*, also referred to as "clubfoot," which is a position of fixed plantar flexion and supination of the foot. This condition constitutes about 75 per cent of all talipes conditions. Other combined talipes conditions are (1) *talipes equinovalgus*, (2) *talipes calcaneovarus*, and (3) *talipes calcaneovalgus*.

**13.16 Traumatic Problems of the Foot, Ankle, and Leg**

The chief traumatic problems of (1) the foot, (2) the ankle, and (3) the leg will be discussed separately in this section.

## The Foot

The major traumatic problems of the foot are (1) the heel bruise, also called calcaneal periostitis, and (2) fractures of the talus, calcaneus, metatarsals, and the phalanges.

The heel bruise is one of the most painful and handicapping kind of bruise that one may receive in athletics. It is most likely to occur in activities that demand stop-and-go responses, such as basketball and jumping, or the landing action in long jumping.

The major sites of fractures in the foot are illustrated in Figure 13–14. Illustrated in diagram *A* is the fracture of the talus that usually results from a severe ankle twist, or from being hit behind the leg while the foot is firmly planted on the ground. The calcaneal fracture, diagram *B*, is the most frequent fracture of the tarsus and is usually caused by a jump or fall from a height. Fractures of the metatarsals (*C*) are usually caused by direct force, such as being stepped on by another player. Fractures of the phalanges (*D*) usually result from the kicking of external objects.

## The Ankle

The chief traumatic problems of the ankle are (1) the ankle sprain, (2) fractures of the malleoli, and (3) Achilles tendon strain.

Sprains of the ankle usually involve either extreme inversion or extreme eversion. Eighty-five per cent of all injuries of the ankle are *inversion* injuries, in which the foot is forced inward in relation to the leg (Fig. 13–15). The three ligaments most often involved in such injuries are the anterior tibiofibular, anterior talofibular, and the calcaneofibular. Although authorities disagree about which is injured most frequently, it can be safely stated that one or more of them will be involved in all inversion sprains.

In *eversion* injuries, the foot is forced outward in relation to the leg. The deltoid ligament, which is involved in this type of injury, has such great tensile strength that it may resist the injuring force and pull off part of the end of the medial malleolus, causing a chip fracture in that area.

Fracture of the lateral malleolus is a rather common injury resulting from either a blow from the medial side or a sudden torsion. Both lateral and medial malleoli fractures usually result from severe twisting actions, such as those incurred in ski injuries, that cause a rotational shear of the joint.

Strains of the Achilles tendon are not uncommon in athletics and occur most often as a result of excessive dorsiflexion of the foot, or from a lack of coordination between the agonistic and the antagonistic muscles during running performances.

## The Leg

The major traumatic problems of the leg are (1) shin splints, (2) fractures, and (3) leg contusions and muscle spasms.

Shin splints are quite common among athletes, especially at the start and at the end of the season. This injury is usually the result of strenuous work on a hard surface, involving starting, stopping, and

**Fig. 13–14.** The major sites of fracture in the foot.

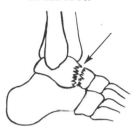

Fracture of the Talus

A

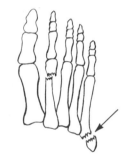

Fracture of the Calcaneus

B

Fractures of the Metatarsals

C

Fracture of a Phalanx

D

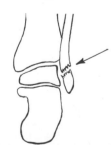

Fracture of the Lateral Malleolus

E

**Fig. 13-15. Inversion injuries of the ankle.**

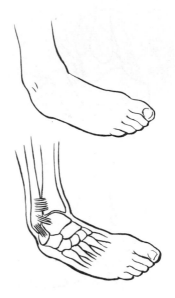

sudden changes of direction. Jumping is also a causal factor, and high jumpers, long jumpers, and pole vaulters, along with gymnasts, frequently experience this handicapping injury. The specific parts of the leg involved in this injury are obscure, but most often mentioned are the anterior tibialis and the interossei between the fibula and tibia.

Fractures of the tibia and fibula result from either direct or indirect trauma during active participation in sports. The fibular fracture has the highest incidence in the leg and occurs principally in the middle third of the bone, whereas fractures of the tibia confine themselves predominantly to the lower one third of the tibial shaft.

Contusions of the leg occur on both the anterior and posterior surfaces of the leg. Blows to the anterior border of the tibia (the shin) are, as everyone knows, quite painful, but blows to the area of the gastrocnemius muscle are also quite common in athletics. A bruise of the gastrocnemius can produce an extremely handicapping injury for the athlete. The gastrocnemius muscle is also particularly prone to muscle spasms.

## 13.20  Study Guidelines

## 13.21  Movements of the Toes

A. Specific Student Objectives

1. Name the joints at which the movements of the toes occur.
2. What is the basic movement of the toes? What is the kinesiological function of this movement?
3. Name the four muscles responsible for flexion of the big toe.
4. Name the eight muscles that flex the four lateral toes.
5. Name the four muscles that flex all four lateral toes.
6. Name the four muscles that flex only some of the four lateral toes.
7. Identify the specific toes that each of the following muscles flex:

   a. Plantar interossei
   b. Dorsal interossei
   c. Flexor digiti minimi
   d. Abductor digiti minimi

8. Name the two muscles that extend the big toe and the three muscles that collectively extend the lateral four toes.
9. Name the one muscle that abducts the big toe and the four muscles that collectively abduct the lateral four toes.
10. Name the one muscle that adducts the big toe and the three muscles that collectively abduct the lateral four toes.
11. Discuss the kinesiological function of the toes in locomotion.

## 13.22 Movements of the Foot Occurring at the Intertarsal Joints

A. Specific Student Objectives

1. Identify and define the fundamental movements of the foot occurring at the intertarsal joints.
2. Name the five muscles that produce inversion, adduction, and supination of the foot. Identify the three muscles of this group which pass behind the medial malleolus. Identify the two muscles of this group that pass in front of the medial malleolus.
3. Name the four muscles that produce eversion, abduction, and pronation of the foot. Identify the two muscles of this group that pass behind the lateral malleolus. Identify the two muscles of this group that pass in front of the lateral malleolus.

## 13.23 Movements of the Foot Occurring at the Ankle Joint

A. Specific Student Objectives

1. Identify and define the fundamental movements of the foot occurring at the ankle joint.
2. Name the four muscles that produce dorsal flexion of the ankle joint.
3. Name the eight muscles that produce plantar flexion of the ankle joint.
4. Name the most important plantar flexors of the ankle joint.

B. Study Hints

1. In his study of the muscles that produce the movements of the toes, foot, and ankle, the student is advised to do a minimal amount of pure memorizing.

   It is much better for the student to study muscle-produced joint actions along with the actual exercises which employ these actions. Exercises of this type are presented in Section 13.14.

## 13.24 Conditioning Problems of the Foot, Ankle, and Leg

A. Specific Student Objectives

1. Discuss the locomotor function of the foot.
2. Identify the specific structures of the foot and ankle joints being stretched in the flexibility exercises presented in Figure 13-6.
3. Identify the specific muscles being tested by the Clark Cable-Tension Strength Tests in Figure 13-7 and by the Martin Breaking Strength Tests in Table 13-1.
4. Identify the specific muscles being exercised in Figures 13-8 and 13-9.
5. Identify the specific muscles being exercised in Figure 13-10.

B. Study Hints

1. The strength tests and the exercises presented in this section are excellent for studying muscles in a way in which they can best be palpated. The palpation instructions presented in Table 12–2 should be used then to locate the muscles producing the joint actions demonstrated in the measurements and exercises presented in this section.

### 13.25  Postural and Pathological Problems of the Foot, Ankle, and Leg

A. Specific Student Objectives

1. *Postural Problems*

    a. Describe the function of the foot in weight bearing.
    b. Describe the proper distribution of weight on the foot during standing.
    c. Describe correct foot-leg alignment.
    d. Describe the pronated foot.
    e. Describe the supinated foot.
    f. Describe the condition of pes planus.
    g. Identify the structures responsible for maintaining medial longitudinal arch of the foot.
    h. Describe proper foot-leg alignment when viewed in the sagittal plane.

2. *Pathological Problems*

    a. Define a talipes condition.
    b. Define the following terms:

        (1)  Talipes equinus
        (2)  Talipes calcaneus
        (3)  Talipes valgus
        (4)  Talipes varus
        (5)  Talipes cavus
        (6)  Talipes equinovarus
        (7)  Talipes equinovalgus
        (8)  Talipes calcaneovarus
        (9)  Talipes calcaneovalgus

### 13.26  Traumatic Problems of the Foot, Ankle, and Leg

A. Specific Student Objectives

1. *The Foot*

    a. Identify and define the major traumatic problems of the foot.

2. *The Ankle*

    a. Identify and define the major traumatic problems of the ankle.
    b. State the type of ankle sprains most often found in athletics.

3. *The Leg*

   a. Identify and define the major traumatic problems of the leg.
   b. Define shin splints.

The student should consult any recent kinesiology text for supplementary readings on the movements and problems of the toes, foot, and ankle. A list of selected kinesiology texts is given in Appendix B. The following readings are especially recommended.

**13.30 Recommended Supplementary Readings**

Basmajian, John V., and Stecko, George: "The Role of Muscles in Arch Support of the Foot," *J. Bone Joint Surg.,* **45A**:1184–90, 1963.

Dempster, W. T.: "The Range of Motion of Cadaver Joints: The Lower Limb," *Univ. Mich. Med. Bull.,* **22**:364–79, 1956.

Elftman, H.: "Forces and Energy Changes in the Leg During Walking," *Am. J. Physiol.,* **125**:339–56, 1959.

Gollnick, Philip D.: "Electrogoniometric Study of Walking on High Heels," *Res. Q. Am. Assoc. Health, Phys, Ed.,* **35**:370–78, 1964.

Gottlieb, A.: "Flatfoot and Its Relation to the Triceps Surae Muscle," *Am. J. Phys. Ther.,* **8**:321–34, 1932.

Haxton, H. A.: "Absolute Muscle Force in the Ankle Flexors of Man," *J. Physiol.,* **103**:267–73, 1944.

Herman, R., and Bragin, S. J.: "Function of the Gastrocnemius and Soleus Muscles," *J. Am. Phys. Ther. Assoc.,* **47**:105–13, 1967.

Houtz, S. J., and Walsh, Frank P.: "Electromyographic Analysis of the Function of the Muscles Acting on the Ankle During Weight Bearing with Special Reference to the Triceps Surae," *J. Bone Joint Surg.,* **41A**:1469–81, 1959.

Jones, Frederic Wood: *Structure and Function as Seen in the Foot.* London, Bailliere, Tindall and Dox, 1944.

Jones, Russell J.: "The Human Foot. An Experimental Study of Its Mechanics and the Role of Its Muscles and Ligaments in the Support of the Arch," *Am. J. Anat.,* **68**:1–41, 1941.

Karpovich, Peter V., and Wilklow, Leighton B.: "Goniometric Study of the Human Foot in Standing and Walking," *Indust. Med. Surg.,* **29**:338–47, 1960.

Kelly, E. D.: "A Comparative Study of Structure and Function of Normal, Pronated and Painful Feet Among Children," *Res. Q. Am. Assoc. Health, Phys. Ed.,* **18**:291–312, 1947.

Lowman, C. L.: "Feet and Body Mechanics," *J. Health Phys. Ed.,* **11**:137, 1940.

Lewin, Philip: *The Foot and Ankle,* 4th ed. Philadelphia, Lea & Febiger, 1959.

Mann, R., and Inman, V. L.: "Phasic Activity of Intrinsic Muscles of the Foot," *J. Bone Joint Surg.,* **46A**:469–81, 1964.

Morton, Dudley J.: *The Human Foot.* New York, Columbia University Press, 1935.

O'Connell, A. L.: "Electromyographic Study of Certain Leg Muscles During Movements of the Free Foot and During Standing," *Am. J. Phys. Med.,* **37**:289–301, December, 1958.

Rarick, L., and Thompson, J.: "Roentgenographic Measures of Leg Muscle Size and Ankle Extensor Strength," *Res. Q.,* **27**:321, October, 1956.

Sheffield, F. J., and others: "Electromyographic Study of the Muscles of the Foot in Normal Walking," *Am. J. Phys. Med.,* **35**:223–36, 1956.

Shephard, Edmund: "Tarsal Movements," *J. Bone Joint Surg.,* **33B**:258–63, 1951.

Smith, J. W.: "Muscular Control of the Arches of the Foot in Standing: An Electromyographic Assessment," *J. Anat.,* **88**:152–62, 1954.

Sutherland, David H.: "An Electromyographic Study of the Plantar Flexors of the Ankle in Normal Walking on the Level," *J. Bone Joint Surg.,* **48A**:66–71, January, 1966.

# Part VI

# Structural
# Kinesiology
# of the
# Thigh and Hip

# 14

# Structure of the Thigh and Hip

**The Patella**

14.11  **The Kneecap, Thigh, and Hip Bones**

The patella (Fig. 14–1), also called the kneecap, is a sesamoid (ses'ah-moid) bone located anterior to the knee joint, which develops within the tendon of the quadriceps femoris muscle. It is somewhat triangular in shape with its *apex* located inferiorly and its *base* superiorly. Its posterior surface articulates with the patellar facet and the condyles of the femur.

**Fig. 14–1. The left patella.**

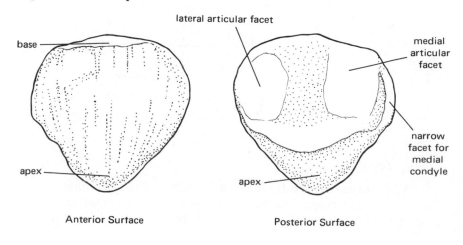

base

lateral articular facet

medial articular facet

apex

narrow facet for medial condyle

apex

Anterior Surface

Posterior Surface

**Fig. 14–2. Anterior view of the left femur.**

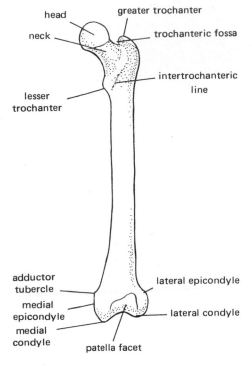

## The Femur

The longest and largest bone in the body is the femur (Figs. 14–2 and 14–3) located in the thigh. It consists of a shaft and two extremities. The important markings on the femur are

A. *Superior extremity*

1. *The head:* the rounded prominence located on the superior extremity, which articulates with the acetabulum of the hip.
2. *The fovea:* a depression located on the head.
3. *The neck:* connects the head with the shaft.
4. *Greater trochanter* (tro-kan'ter): a large roughened prominence located at the superior junction of the neck and shaft.
5. *Trochanteric* (tro''kan-ter'ik) *fossa:* a depression located on the medial surface of the greater trochanter.
6. *Lesser trochanter:* a projection located inferior to the greater trochanter on the posterior and medial aspect of the femur.
7. *Intertrochanteric* (in''ter-tro''kan-ter'ik) *crest:* a prominent ridge that connects the two trochanters posteriorly.
8. *Intertrochanteric line:* a less prominent ridge that connects the two trochanters anteriorly.

**Fig. 14–3. Posterior view of the left femur.**

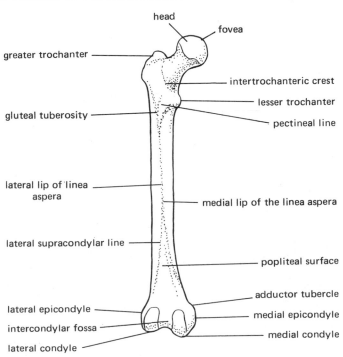

B. *The shaft*

1. *Linea aspera* (lin'e-ah as''per-ah): a longitudinal prominent ridge that marks the posterior aspect of the shaft. It consists of two lips called the outer and inner lips.

2. *Gluteal* (gloo'te-al) *tuberosity*: a roughened area that marks the superior termination of the outer lip of the linea aspera. Superiorly the inner lip is continuous with the lesser trochanter.
3. *Pectineal* (pek-tin'e-al) *line*: a faint line or ridge located between the superior extremities of the lips of the linea aspera.

C. *Inferior extremity*

1. *Lateral and medial condyles* (kon'dils) that articulate with the condyles of the tibia.
2. *Patellar facet*: articulates with the posterior surface of the patella.
3. *Medial and lateral epicondyles* (ep"i-kon'dils): large prominences located on the external aspect of the condyles.
4. *Adductor tubercle*: an additional projection on the medial epicondyle.
5. *Intercondyloid fossa*: a depression that separates the two condyles posteroinferiorly.
6. *Popliteal* (pop-lit'e-al) *surface*: a triangular area located superior to the condyles and to the intercondyloid fossa on the posterior surface of the femur.
7. *Supracondylar* (su"prah-con'di-lar) *lines*: form the boundaries of the popliteal surface and are continuous superiorly with the lips of the linea aspera.

## The Os Coxa

The os coxa or hip bone (Figs. 14–4 and 14–5) is a large, irregularly shaped bone that, with that of the opposite side, forms the side and front walls of the pelvic cavity. In youth it consists of three separate parts separated by a Y-shaped cartilage. In the adult these parts have been united by ossification of the cartilage, but it is usual to describe the bone as divisible into three portions: (1) the ilium, or upper, expanded portion forming the prominence of the hip, (2) the ischium, or lower strong portion, and (3) the pubis, or portion helping to form the front of the pelvis. These three portions of the bone meet and finally fuse in a deep socket, called the acetabulum (as"e-tab'u-lum), into which the head of the femur fits. The ilium contributes about two fifths to the acetabulum (Fig. 14–6). The ischium also contributes about two fifths to the acetabulum, and the remaining one fifth is contributed by the pubis. The *bodies* of the ilium, ischium, and pubis are the parts located inside the acetabulum. An examination of the acetabulum will show that only part of its surface is smooth and obviously adapted for articulation; a deeper, rougher portion located on the bottom called the *acetabular fossa* is occupied by fat and a ligament. The interruption of the inferior rim of the acetabulum so that it resembles a cup with a portion of the lip broken out is called the *acetabular notch*. Located inferior to the acetabulum is a large hole called the *obturator foramen*. This foramen is named obturator (closed) because in life it is almost completely closed by a membrane that gives attachments to muscles on

**Fig. 14–4.  Lateral view of the left hip bone.**

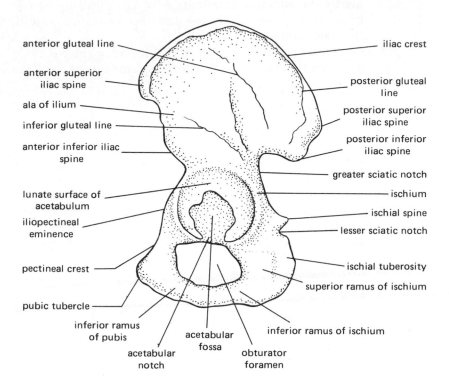

**Fig. 14–5.  Medial view of the left hip bone.**

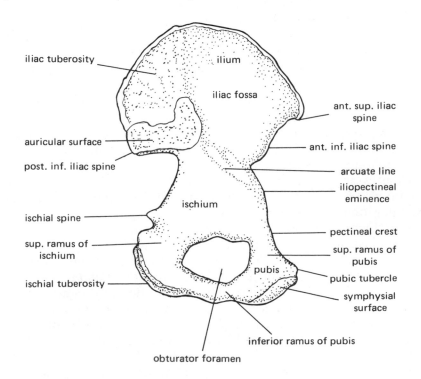

both of its surfaces.  Some of the important markings on the coxal bone are

A. *Ilium*

1. *Borders*

   a. *Iliac* (il′e-ak) *crest*:  the superior border of the ilium. It possesses three lips:  internal, external, and middle.
   b. *Four spines*

      (1) *Anterosuperior iliac spine*: the anterior termination of the iliac crest.
      (2) *Anteroinferior iliac spine*: located inferior to the anterosuperior iliac spine.
      (3) *Posterosuperior iliac spine*:  marks the posterior termination of the iliac crest.
      (4) *Posteroinferior iliac spine*:  located inferior to the posterosuperior iliac spine.

   c. *Greater sciatic* (si-at′ik) *notch*:  a deep notch located inferior to the posteroinferior iliac spine.

2. *The lateral or external surface*

   a. *The gluteal lines*

      (1) *Posterior gluteal line*:  the shortest of the three lines, begins about 5 cm in front of the posterosuperior iliac spine on the iliac crest and passes downward to the upper part of the greater sciatic notch.
      (2) *Anterior gluteal line*:  the longest of the three lines, begins about 4 cm behind the anterosuperior iliac spine on the iliac crest, and taking a curved direction downward and backward, ends at the upper part of the greater sciatic notch.
      (3) *Inferior gluteal line*:  the least distinct of the three lines, begins in front of the notch on the anterior border, located between the anterosuperior and anteroinferior iliac spines, and, curving backward and downward ends near the middle of the greater sciatic notch.

3. *The medial or internal surface*

   a. *Iliac fossa*:  a rather expansive depression on the internal surface of the ilium.
   b. *Tuberosity of the ilium*:  a roughened area posterior to the iliac fossa.
   c. *Auricular* (aw-rik′u-lah) *surface*:  a roughened articular surface inferior to the tuberosity of the ilium.
   d. *Arcuate* (ar′ku-at) or *iliopectineal line*:  a curved line that marks the inferior boundary of the iliac fossa. It also marks the inferior boundary of the major or false pelvis.

Fig. 14–6. The hip bone, showing the union of ilium, ischium, and pubis in the acetabulum.

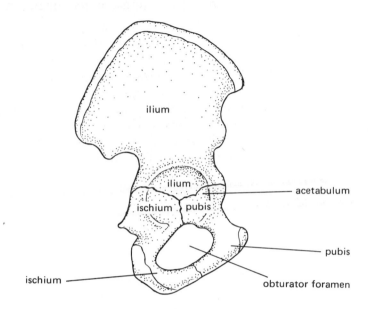

B. *Ischium*

1. *Spine of the ischium*: a projection that forms the inferior boundary of the greater sciatic notch.
2. *Lesser sciatic notch*: located inferior to the spine.
3. *Tuberosity of the ischium*: forms the inferior boundary of the lesser sciatic notch. It is upon the ischial tuberosities that we sit when seated in a chair.

C. *The rami of the ischium and pubis*

Both the ischium and pubis consist of a body and two rami, superior and inferior.

1. *The superior ramus* (ra'mus) *of the ischium* extends vertically downward from the body, located in the acetabulum, to the tuberosity where it meets the inferior ramus.
2. *The superior ramus of the pubis* extends anteromedially from the body, located in the acetabulum, to meet the inferior ramus at the junction of which is the symphysial surface for articulation with its fellow of the opposite side.

3. *The inferior rami of the ischium and pubis* unite and form the inferior boundary of the obturator foramen.

D. *The pubis*

1. *Pubic tubercle*: a slight projection located on the superior ramus of the pubis near the symphysis.
2. *Pectineal crest*: a sharp ridge extending posterolaterally from the pubic tubercle.
3. *Iliopectineal eminence*: a roughened prominence that marks the posterolateral termination of the pectineal crest.

**The Knee Joint**

The knee joint is a hinge joint formed by the condyles of the tibia, the condyles and the patellar facet of the femur, and the patella. The joint may be regarded, therefore, as a double one: a patellofemoral articulation and a tibiofemoral articulation.

*Movements.* Being a hinge joint, the knee permits *flexion* and *extension*. In addition, a certain amount of free rotation is possible during flexion, the range of rotation being greatest at 90° of flexion at which position it amounts to about 50°. No free rotation is possible in the fully extended knee. Rotation of the flexed knee is identified as being either *inward* or *outward.*

*Ligaments.* The external and internal ligaments of the knee are

A. *External ligaments* (Fig. 14–7)

1. *Articular capsule*
2. *The collateral ligaments*: these ligaments reinforce the knee on its medial and lateral sides.

   a. *The fibular collateral ligament*: this ligament reinforces the knee on its lateral side. It is attached superiorly to the lateral epicondyle of the femur and inferiorly to the head of the fibula.
   b. *The tibia collateral ligament*: this ligament reinforces the knee on its medial side. It is attached superiorly to the medial epicondyle of the femur and inferiorly to the medial side of the head of the tibia.

3. *The oblique popliteal ligament*: this ligament reinforces the knee on its posterior side. It is attached superiorly to the lateral portion of the popliteal surface of the femur and inferiorly to the posteromedial surface of the head of the tibia.
4. *The patellar ligament*: reinforces the knee on its anterior side. It attaches the patella and indirectly the tendon of the quadriceps femoris muscle to the tuberosity of the tibia.

**Fig. 14–7. The external ligaments of the knee.**

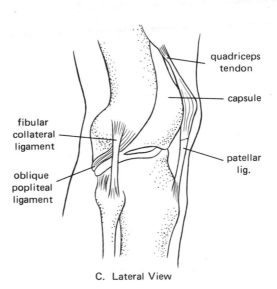

oblique popliteal ligament

tibial collateral ligament

fibular collateral ligament

A. Superficial Posterior View

lateral condyle

anterior cruciate ligament

lateral meniscus

fibular collateral ligament

medial condyle

tibial collateral ligament

medial meniscus

posterior cruciate ligament

interosseous membrane

B. Deep Posterior View

quadriceps tendon

capsule

patellar lig.

fibular collateral ligament

oblique popliteal ligament

C. Lateral View

B. *Internal ligaments* (Fig. 14–8)

1. *Anterior and posterior cruciate ligaments*: these ligaments are located in the middle of the joint and are called cruciate because they cross each other in an X-like manner. The anterior cruciate ligament passes from the anterior intercondyloid fossa of the tibia to the medial back part of the lateral condyle of the femur. The posterior cruciate is attached to the posterior intercondyloid fossa of the tibia posteriorly and to the lateral and front part of the medial condyle of the femur anteriorly.

2. *Medial and lateral menisci or semilunar cartilages*: these are two crescent-shaped fibrocartilaginous plates interposed between the condyles of the femur and tibia.

### The Hip Joint

The hip joint is a ball-and-socket joint formed by the reception of the head of the femur into the acetabulum of the coxal bone.

*Movements.* Since a ball-and-socket joint is a triaxial joint, the hip joint is capable of movements in all three primary directions. Thus, it permits *flexion* (swinging forward), *extension* (return to anatomical position), and *hyperextension* (swinging backward from anatomical position). Hyperextension is extremely limited by the iliofemoral ligament at the front of the joint.

The hip joint also permits *abduction* (swinging sideward away from the midline of the body), *adduction* (return to anatomical position), and *hyperadduction* (swinging across the body) possible only when the other leg is moved out of the way.

Outward or lateral rotation, inward or medial rotation, and circumduction are also permitted. *Outward rotation* is a movement of the femur around its vertical axis so that the knee is turned outward. *Inward rotation* is a movement of the femur around its vertical axis so that the knee is turned inward. *Circumduction* is a combination of flexion, abduction, extension, and adduction, performed sequentially in either direction.

*Ligaments.* The external and internal ligaments of the hip joint are

A. *External ligaments* (Fig. 14–9).

    1. *Articular capsule:* attached superiorly to the rim of the acetabulum and inferiorly to the neck of the femur.

    2. *Iliofemoral ligament:* attached superiorly to the antero-inferior iliac spine and inferiorly to the whole of the intertrochanteric line.

    3. *Pubofemoral ligament:* attached medially to the ilio-pectineal eminence of the pubis and laterally to the point of junction of the lesser trochanter and the intertrochanteric line.

    4. *Ischiofemoral ligament:* attached medially to the posteroinferior margin of the acetabulum and laterally to the trochanteric fossa.

B. *Internal ligaments* (Fig. 14–10).

    1. *The glenoid lip:* attached to the margin of the acetabulum. It serves to increase the depth of the cavity, protect the bony margin, constrict the mouth of the cavity, and, by embracing the head of the femur, assist in holding the articular surfaces in apposition.

    2. *The transverse acetabular ligament:* passes transversely across the acetabular notch external to the glenoid lip and serves to complete the rim of the acetabulum to support the glenoid lip at this point and to convert the notch into a foramen for the entrance of nutrient vessels into the joint.

    3. *The ligamentum teres or the ligament of the head:* attached medially to the acetabular fossa and laterally to the head of the femur at the fovea.

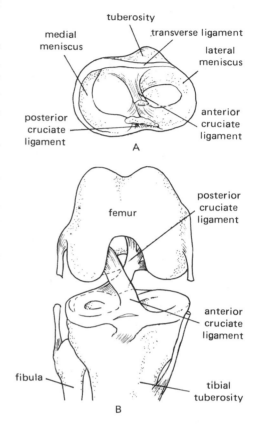

**Fig. 14–8. The internal ligaments of the knee.**

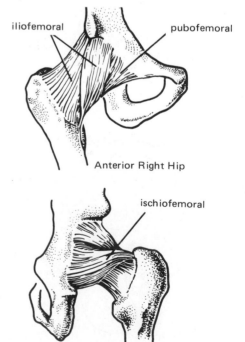

**Fig. 14–9. The external ligaments of the hip.**

## 14.13   The Pelvis

The hips are called the pelvis because they resemble a basin. The pelvis (Fig. 14-11) is composed of four bones, the two hipbones forming the sides and front, and the sacrum and coccyx completing it behind. It is divided by a narrow bony ring, called the *brim of the pelvis*, into an upper part called the *greater*, or *false* pelvis, and a lower part called the *lesser*, or *true pelvis*. The greater pelvis is the expanded portion situated above the brim and is bounded on either side by the ilium. The lesser pelvis is below and behind the brim and is bounded on the front sides by the pubis and ischia and behind by the sacrum and coccyx.

The pelvis also consists of an outlet, an inlet, and a cavity. The space included within the brim of the pelvis is called the *superior aperture*, or *inlet*. The space included below the brim, between the tip of the coccyx behind and the tuberosities of the ischia on either side, is called the *inferior aperture*, or *outlet*. The *cavity* of the lesser pelvis is a short, curved canal, which is deeper on the posterior wall than it is on the anterior wall.

The two joints of the pelvis are the symphysis pubis and the sacroiliac joint.

### The Symphysis Pubis

The symphysis pubis is a symphysis joint formed by the symphysial surfaces of the pubic bones, where these come together and complete the pelvic girdle anteriorly.

*Movements.* Very little movement occurs at this joint and the movement that does take place consists merely of a slight yielding of the interpubic fibrocartilage. In pregnant women this yielding is more pronounced, and the bones may spread apart so as to allow enlargement of the pelvic cavity.

*Ligaments* (Fig. 14-12). The three primary ligaments of the symphysis pubis are

A. *Interpubic fibrocartilage*: this fibrocartilaginous disk connects the opposed surfaces of the pubic bones.
B. *Superior pubic ligament*: this ligament connects the two pubic bones superiorly.
C. *Inferior pubic ligament*: this ligament connects the two pubic bones inferiorly.

### The Sacroiliac Joint

The sacroiliac is a sliding joint formed by the articulation of the auricular surfaces of the sacrum and ilium.

Unlike the shoulder girdle of the upper extremity, the pelvic girdle is firmly attached to the axial skeleton at the sacroiliac joint, i.e., the union between sacrum of the vertebral column and the ilium of the hip. This strong attachment is necessary in order for the joint to transmit the weight of the body from the vertebral column to the lower limb. In addition to the weight they receive from the vertebral column, the flared hipbones directly support some of the weight of

Fig. 14-10. The internal ligaments of the hip: (*A*) the acetabulum and glenoid lip and (*B*) the ligamentum teres as viewed from within the hip joint.

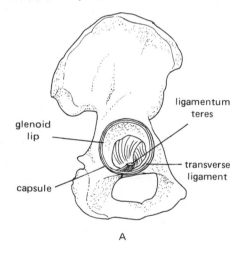

glenoid lip

ligamentum teres

capsule

transverse ligament

A

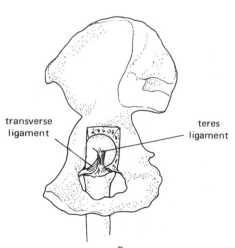

transverse ligament

teres ligament

B

the viscera, along with the muscles and ligaments that bridge the pelvic outlet.

*Movements.* This joint is essentially a steady one, and the slight movement permitted is gliding both upward and downward, as well as forward and backward, and a rotation around a transverse axis so that the pelvis can be tilted slightly. Rotation forward is called *flexion*; rotation backward is called *extension*.

*Ligaments* (Fig. 14-13). The primary ligaments of the sacroiliac joint are

A. Anterior sacroiliac ligament
B. Posterior sacroiliac ligament
C. Interosseous ligament
D. Accessory ligaments

    1. Sacrotuberous ligament
    2. Sacrospinous ligament

The muscles of the thigh are divided into three groups: anterior or extensor, posterior or flexor and medial or adductor. The muscles in each of these groups are

A. Anterior group

    1. Sartorius (sar-to′re-us) (Fig. 14-14)
    2. Quadriceps femoris (fem′oris) (Fig. 14-15)

        a. Rectus femoris
        b. Vastus medialis (vas′tus media′lis)
        c. Vastus lateralis (latera′lis)
        d. Vastus intermedius (interme′dius)

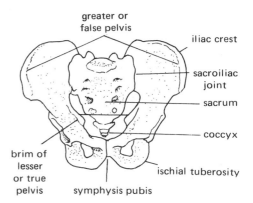

Fig. 14-11. **Anterior view of the male pelvis.**

## 14.14 The Muscles of the Thigh

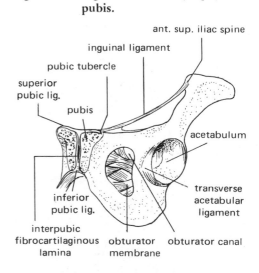

Fig. 14-12. **Ligaments of the symphysis pubis.**

Fig. 14-13. **Ligaments of the sacroiliac articulation.**

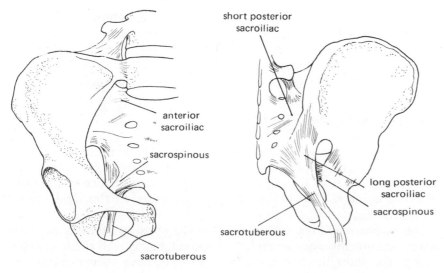

A. Anterior View      B. Posterior View

B. Posterior group (Fig. 14–16)

1. Popliteus (pop″li-te′us)
2. Hamstrings (Fig. 14–17)

   a. Semitendinosus (sem″e-ten″di-no′sus)
   b. Semimembranosus (sem″e-mem′brah-no′sus)
   c. Biceps femoris

C. Medial group (Fig. 14–18)

1. Gracilis (grac′i-lis)
2. Pectineus (pek-tin′e-us)
3. Adductor longus
4. Adductor brevis
5. Adductor magnus

### The Anterior Muscles of the Thigh

The *anterior group* includes the sartorius and the quadriceps femoris. *The sartorius* (Fig. 14–14) is a narrow, bandlike muscle that is superficial throughout its whole extent. It arises from the antero-superior iliac spine and passes obliquely downward and medially across the anterior aspect of the thigh. It crosses the knee joint and attaches to the anteromedial aspect of the tibia head. It flexes the thigh at the hip joint and, since it passes behind the knee joint, it also flexes this joint. It also serves to abduct and outward rotate the thigh at the hip joint and to inward rotate the flexed knee. When the legs are fixed, both muscles act to flex the pelvis upon the thighs, as in doing a sit-up and if one muscle contracts, it tends to rotate the pelvis.

The *quadriceps femoris* (Fig. 14–15) consists of the rectus femoris and the three vasti muscles. From these four muscles a common tendon is formed, which attaches distally into the superior border of the patella and indirectly through the patella ligament into the tuberosity of the tibia. The *rectus femoris* (Fig. 14–15) has its proximal attachment on the anteroinferior iliac spine and groove above the brim of the acetabulum. It acts to extend the knee and flex the hip. The *vastus lateralis* has its proximal attachment on the greater trochanter and outer lip of the linea aspera of the femur. The *vastus medialis* arises from the medial lip of the linea aspera. The *vastus intermedius* has its proximal attachment on the anterolateral surface of the shaft of the femur and lateral lip of the linea aspera. All four quadriceps femoris muscles extend the leg at the knee joint.

### The Posterior Muscles of the Thigh

The posterior muscles of the thigh consist of the popliteus and the hamstrings. The *popliteus* (Fig. 14–16) arises from the lateral epicondyle of the femur and passes to the posterior surface of the tibial shaft superior to the popliteal line. It serves to flex and inward rotate the leg.

The *hamstring* (Figs. 14–16 and 14–17) consists of the semitendinosus, semimembranosus, and the biceps femoris. All these muscles, except the short head of the biceps femoris, have their proximal attachments on the tuberosity of the ischium. The short head of the

**Fig. 14–14. The sartorius.**

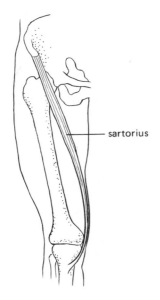

sartorius

**Fig. 14–15. The quadriceps femoris.**

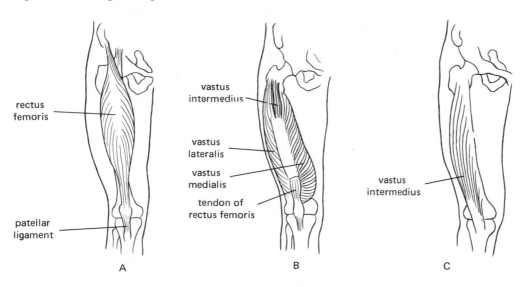

**Fig. 14–16. The posterior muscles of the thigh.**

**Fig. 14–17. The hamstrings.**

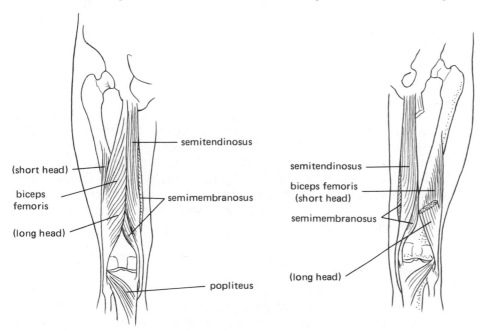

biceps femoris arises from the outer lip of the distal portion of the linea aspera. The *semitendinosus* has its distal attachment on the medial surface of the head of the tibia. The *semimembranosus* has its distal attachment on the medial surface of the head of the tibia also, but more posteriorly than that of the semitendinosus. The *biceps femoris* has its distal attachment on the lateral surface of the head of the tibia and on the head of the fibula. Therefore, the hamstring has two muscles that attach to medial side of the knee and one, biceps femoris, that attaches to the lateral side of the knee.

The hamstring serves to extend the thigh at the hip joint and to flex the leg at the knee joint. Obviously only the long head of the

**Fig. 14–18. The medial muscles of the thigh.**

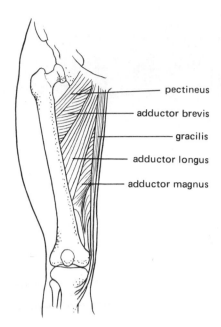

- pectineus
- adductor brevis
- gracilis
- adductor longus
- adductor magnus

biceps femoris acts at the hip joint. The semitendinosus and semi-membranosus act as prime movers for inward rotation of the semiflexed knee, whereas the biceps femoris serves as an outward rotator of the knee. These muscles perform the same rotation actions at the hip joint, but not as strongly.

### The Medial Muscles of the Thigh (Fig. 14–18)

The medial muscles of the thigh include the gracilis, the pectineus, and the three adductor muscles. The gracilis arises from the anterior aspect of the lower half of the symphysis pubis and attaches distally on the medial surface of the tibial head. It is a prime mover for adduction at the hip joint, where it also assists with flexion and inward rotation. At the knee, it assists with flexion and inward rotation.

The *pectineus* arises from the pectineal crest of the pubis, which is a space an inch wide on the front of the pubis, just below the rim of the pelvic basin between the iliopectineal eminence and the tubercle of the pubis. It attaches distally on the pectineal line of the femur, which is a rough line leading from the lesser trochanter to the linea aspera. It adducts, flexes, and outward rotates the thigh.

The *adductor longus* has its proximal attachment on the superior ramus of the pubis and it attaches distally on the linea aspera in the middle third of the thigh. It adducts and assists in flexion and outward rotation of the thigh. The *adductor brevis* has its proximal attachment on the inferior ramus of the pubis and attaches distally to the upper half of the linea aspera of the femur. It has the same actions as the adductor longus, i.e., it adducts and assists in flexion and outward rotation of the thigh. The *adductor magnus* has its proximal attachment on the external surface of the inferior rami of the ischium and pubis and attaches distally on the linea aspera throughout its whole extent and on the medial supracondylar line and adductor tubercle on the medial condyle of the femur. The whole muscle adducts the hip joint. The proximal fibers assist with outward rotation and flexion; the distal fibers assist with inward rotation and extension.

### 14.15 Muscles of the Hip

The muscles of the hip are divided into an anterior group and a posterior group. The muscles in each of these groups are

    A. Anterior group (Fig. 14–19)

        1. Iliacus (il-i′ah-kus)
        2. Psoas (so′as)

    B. Posterior group

        1. Tensor fasciae latae (Figs. 14–20 and 14–21)
        2. Gluteus maximus (Figs. 14–20 and 14–21)
        3. Gluteus medius (Fig. 14–22)
        4. Gluteus minimus (Fig. 14–22)
        5. The six deep outward rotators (Fig. 14–23)

            a. Piriformis (pir″i-for′mis)

b. Superior gemellus (je-mel′us)
c. Inferior gemellus
d. Obturator internus
e. Obturator externus
f. Quadratus femoris

**Fig. 14-19. The anterior muscles of the hip.**

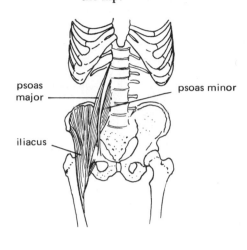

## The Anterior Muscles of the Hip (Fig. 14-19)

The anterior group of hip muscles consist of the iliacus and psoas. The *iliacus* is a triangular muscle that occupies the iliac fossa, within the abdominal cavity. Its tendon emerges from the abdominal cavity along with that of the psoas major muscle with which it fuses, thus forming a common tendon and giving these two muscles the name *iliopsoas*. Its proximal attachment is on the iliac fossa and a part of the inner surface of the sacrum near the ilium. Its distal attachment is the lesser trochanter of the femur. The *psoas*, sometimes called the psoas major to distinguish it from psoas minor present in most vertebrate animals but often absent in man, has its proximal attachment on the bodies and transverse processes of the lumbar vertebrae and the intervertebral disks. Its distal attachment is on the lesser trochanter.

The iliopsoas muscle flexes the thigh at the hip joint, tends to outward rotate the thigh when the limb is free, and serves to adduct it slightly. When the thighs are fixed, the muscles on both sides act together in flexing the trunk (psoas major) and pelvis (iliacus) upon the femur, as in doing a sit-up.

## The Posterior Muscles of the Hip

The posterior muscles of the hip include the tensor fasciae latae, the three gluteal muscles, and the six deep outward rotators. The *tensor fasciae latae* (Fig. 14-20) arises from the anterior part of the outer lip of the iliac crest and terminates in the iliotibial band of the fascia lata. It inward rotates the thigh and assists in flexion and abduction at the hip joint. With the thigh fixed, it serves to steady the pelvis upon the head of the femur and, thus, tends to prevent the trunk from falling backward. It also assists in steadying the femur on the condyles of the tibia in the standing position.

The *gluteus maximus* (Figs. 14-20 and 14-21) has its proximal attachment on the posterior gluteal line of ilium and adjacent portion of crest and on the posterior surface of the lower part of the sacrum and the side of the coccyx. Its distal attachment is on the gluteal tuberosity of the femur and into the iliotibial tract of the fascia lata. It acts to extend and outward rotate the thigh. Its lower fibers assist in adduction, and its upper fibers assist in abduction. It also serves to steady and support the knee joint in the standing position by its action on the iliotibial band.

The *gluteus medius* (Fig. 14-22) has its proximal attachment on the external surface of the ilium, between the anterior and posterior gluteal lines. It terminates on the greater trochanter of the femur. The *gluteus minimus* (Fig. 14-22) has its proximal attachment on the external surface of the ilium between the anterior and inferior gluteal lines. It terminates on the greater trochanter. Both the

**Fig. 14-20. Lateral view of the gluteus maximus and the tensor fasciae latae.**

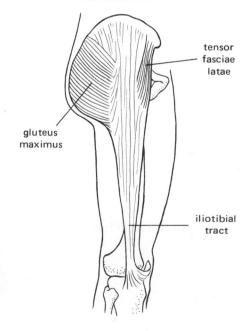

**Fig. 14–21. Posterior view of the gluteus maximus and the tensor fasciae latae.**

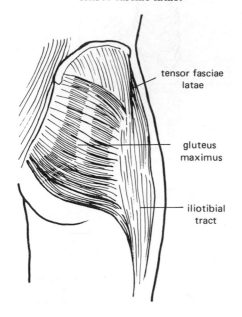

tensor fasciae latae

gluteus maximus

iliotibial tract

gluteus medius and the gluteus minimus abduct the thigh, which is the main function of the muscles. The anterior fibers of both glutei inward rotate the femur and assist in flexing it, whereas the posterior fibers outward rotate and extend it. With the femur fixed, these two muscles serve to tilt the pelvis laterally, as when the pelvis is supported on one leg.

**Fig. 14–22. The gluteus medius and the gluteus minimus.**

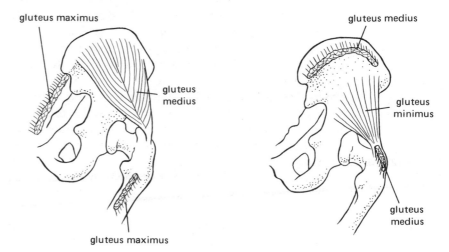

gluteus maximus

gluteus medius

gluteus maximus

gluteus medius

gluteus minimus

gluteus medius

The *six deep outward rotators* (Fig. 14–23) are situated behind the hip joint, and their most important function is outward rotation of the thigh. They also help in holding the head of the femur in the acetabulum.

**Fig. 14–23. The six deep, outward rotators of the thigh.**

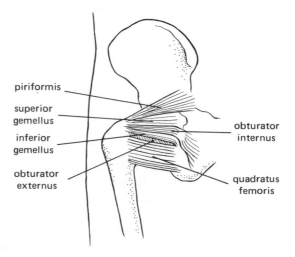

piriformis

superior gemellus

inferior gemellus

obturator externus

obturator internus

quadratus femoris

## 14.20  Study Guidelines

## 14.21  The Kneecap, Thigh, and Hip Bones

A. Specific Student Objective

1. *The Patella*

   a. What is the common name of the patella?
   b. This bone develops in the tendon of what muscle?

c. Locate the patella on a mounted skeleton and identify its apex and its base.

d. With what parts of the femur does the patella articulate?

2. *The Femur*

a. What is the common name of the femur?

b. Locate the femur on a mounted skeleton and identify the following:

| | |
|---|---|
| head | pectineal line |
| fovea | lateral and medial |
| neck |    condyles |
| greater trochanter | patellar facet |
| trochanteric fossa | lateral and medial |
| lesser trochanter |    epicondyles |
| intertrochanteric crest | adductor tubercle |
| intertrochanteric line | intercondyloid fossa |
| linea aspera | popliteal surface |
| gluteal tuberosity | supracondylar lines |

c. With what other bones does the femur articulate? Describe these articulations.

d. Locate the femur in your own body and identify the following:

    greater trochanter
    lateral and medial epicondyles

3. *Os Coxa*

a. What is the common name of the os coxa?

b. With what other bones does the femur articulate? Describe these articulations.

c. Locate the os coxa on a mounted skeleton and identify the following:

| | |
|---|---|
| iliac crest | arcuate or iliopectineal |
| anterosuperior iliac spine |    line |
| anteroinferior iliac spine | spine of ischium |
| posterosuperior iliac spine | lesser sciatic notch |
| posteroinferior iliac spine | tuberosity of the ischium |
| greater sciatic notch | superior ramus of ischium |
| posterior gluteal line | superior ramus of pubis |
| anterior gluteal line | inferior ramus of ischium |
| inferior gluteal line | inferior ramus of pubis |
| iliac fossa | pubic tubercle |
| tuberosity of the ilium | pectineal crest |
| auricular surface | iliopectineal eminence |

d. Locate the os coxa in your own body and identify the following:

    iliac crest
    anterosuperior iliac spine
    tuberosity of ischium
    crest of pubis

B. Study Hints

1. The use of actual bones is recommended in the study of specific bone markings.
2. Locating bony landmarks in the student's body is also a valuable aid to learning.

### 14.22   The Knee and Hip Joints

A. Specific Student Objectives

1. *The Knee Joint*

   a. What type of joint is this?
   b. Describe the bony articulations involved in this joint.
   c. What movements are allowed at this joint? Describe these movements.
   d. Describe the ligamentous reinforcements of this joint.

2. *The Hip Joint*

   a. What type of joint is this?
   b. Describe the bony articulations involved in this joint.
   c. What movements are allowed at this joint? Describe these movements.
   d. Describe the ligamentous reinforcements of this joint.

B. Study Hints

1. The student should study each of these joints on a mounted skeleton, where he can visualize the bony articulations and ligamentous reinforcements involved in the joint.
2. The student should also identify each joint in his body and perform the movements of that joint according to the descriptions presented in the text.
3. It is important that the student learn to identify the movements of knee and hip joints whenever he sees them performed.

### 14.23   The Pelvis

A. Specific Student Objectives

1. *General Information*

   a. Why are the hips called the pelvis?
   b. What bones form the pelvis?
   c. Locate the pelvis on a mounted skeleton and identify the following:

      brim of the pelvis
      false pelvis
      lesser or true pelvis
      superior aperture or inlet
      inferior aperture or outlet
      pelvic cavity

2. *The Symphysis Pubis*

    a. What type of joint is this?
    b. Describe the bony articulations involved in this joint.
    c. What movements are allowed at this joint?
    d. Describe the ligamentous reinforcements of this joint.

3. *The Sacroiliac Joint*

    a. What type of joint is this?
    b. Describe the bony articulations involved in this joint.
    c. What movements are allowed at this joint? Describe these movements.
    d. Describe the ligamentous reinforcements of this joint.

B. Study Hints

1. The student should study the pelvis and each of the pelvic articulations on a mounted skeleton, where he can visualize the various landmarks, bony articulations, and ligamentous reinforcements involved.

## 14.24 The Muscles of the Thigh

A. Specific Student Objectives

1. *The Anterior Thigh Muscles*

    a. Identify the five muscles located in this group.
    b. Give the proximal and distal attachments of each of these muscles.
    c. Give the joint actions produced by the contraction of each of these muscles.
    d. Locate each of these muscles in your own thigh.

2. *The Posterior Thigh Muscles*

    a. Identify the five muscles located in this group.
    b. Give the proximal and distal attachments of each of these muscles.
    c. Give the joint actions produced by the contraction of each of these muscles.
    d. Locate each of these muscles in your own thigh.

3. *The Medial Thigh Muscles*

    a. Identify the five muscles located in this group.
    b. Give the proximal and distal attachments of each of these muscles.
    c. Give the joint actions produced by the contraction of each of these muscles.
    d. Locate each of these muscles in your own thigh.

B. Study Hints

1. Table 14–1 is presented to aid in the mastery of specific muscle actions and attachments.

**Table 14-1. The Attachments and Actions of the Thigh Muscles**

| Location | Name | Proximal Attachment | Illustration | Distal Attachment | Action |
|---|---|---|---|---|---|
| Anterior group | Sartorius | Anterior superior iliac spine | Fig. 14-14 | Anteromedial aspect of the head of the tibia | Flexion, abduction, and outward rotation of the thigh at the hip joint and flexion and inward rotation of the knee |
| | Rectus femoris | Anterior inferior iliac spine, and groove above the brim of the acetabulum | Fig. 14-15 | Proximal border of patella | Flexion of the hip and extension of the knee |
| | Vastus lateralis | Greater trochanter and outer lip of the linea aspera | Fig. 14-15 | Proximal border of patella | Extension of the knee |
| | Vastus medialis | Medial lip of the linea aspera | Fig. 14-15 | Proximal border of patella | Extension of the knee |
| | Vastus intermedius | Anterolateral surface of the shaft of the femur and lateral lip of the linea aspera | Fig. 14-15 | Proximal border of patella | Extension of the knee |
| Posterior group | Semitendinosus | Tuberosity of the ischium | Figs. 14-16 and 14-17 | Medial surface of the head of the tibia | Extension and inward rotation of hip and flexion and inward rotation of knee |
| | Semimembranosus | Tuberosity of the ischium | Figs. 14-16 and 14-17 | Posterior medial surface of the head of the tibia | Extension and inward rotation of hip and flexion and inward rotation of knee |
| | Biceps femoris | Long head: tuberosity of the ischium Short head: lateral lip of linea aspera | Figs. 14-16 and 14-17 | Lateral surface of the head of the tibia and on the head of the fibula | Long head: extension and outward rotation of hip. Both heads: flexion and outward rotation of knee |
| | Popliteus | Lateral epicondyle of femur | Fig. 14-16 | Posterior surface of the tibial shaft superior to the popliteal line | Flexion and inward rotation of the knee |
| Medial group | Gracilis | Anterior aspect of the lower half of the symphysis pubis | Fig. 14-18 | Medial surface of the head of the tibia | Adduction, flexion, and inward rotation at hip and flexion and inward rotation at knee |
| | Pectineus | Pectineal crest of the pubis | Fig. 14-18 | Pectineal line of the femur | Adduction, flexion, and outward rotation at hip |
| | Adductor longus | Superior ramus of the pubis | Fig. 14-18 | Middle third of linea aspera | Adduction, flexion, and outward rotation at hip |
| | Adductor brevis | Inferior ramus of the pubis | Fig. 14-18 | Upper half of linea aspera | Adduction, flexion, and outward rotation at hip |
| | Adductor magnus | Inferior rami of the ischium and pubis | Fig. 14-18 | Whole length of linea aspera, medial supracondylar line and adductor tubercle on medial condyle of femur | Adduction of hip. Upper fibers: outward rotation and flexion. Lower fibers: inward rotation and extension |

2. Instructions as to where the muscles of the thigh can be palpated are presented in Table 14–2. The student should perform each of the movements of the knee and hip and attempt to locate through palpation each of the muscles listed.

**Table 14–2. Instructions for Palpating the Muscles of the Thigh**

| Name of Muscle | Where the Muscle Can Be Palpated |
| --- | --- |
| A. *Anterior group* | |
| 1. Sartorius (Fig. 14–14) | When the hip is flexed and externally rotated, the muscle can be palpated from its attachment on the anterosuperior iliac spine, across the front of the thigh and down almost to its distal attachment on the tibia. |
| 2. Quadriceps femoris (Fig. 14–15) | |
| a. Rectus femoris | The muscular portion is superficial and may be followed down the anterior surface of the thigh to its distal attachment on the patella. When the hip is flexed, the proximal tendon may be palpated in the V-shaped area between the sartorius and the tensor fasciae latae. |
| b. Vastus medialis | Anteromedial aspect of the lower third of the thigh, medial to the rectus femoris. |
| c. Vastus lateralis | Anterolateral aspect of the thigh from just below the greater trochanter down to the patella, lateral to the rectus femoris. |
| d. Vastus intermedius | Cannot be palpated. |
| B. *Posterior group* (Fig. 14–16) | |
| 1. Popliteus | Cannot be palpated. |
| 2. Hamstring (Fig. 14–17) | |
| a. Semitendinosus | Medial aspect of posterior surface of knee. Its tendon is the most prominent in the back of the knee. The other tendon in this region is that of the gracilis which is more anterior. |
| b. Semimembranosus | The tendon lies beneath the tendons of the gracilis and semitendinosus at the knee, and it is difficult to identify. |
| c. Biceps femoris | The tendon can be palpated on the lateral aspect of the posterior surface of the knee. |
| C. *Medial group* (Fig. 14–18) | |
| 1. Gracilis | The tendon can be palpated on the medial aspect of the posterior surface of the knee, anterior to the tendon of the semitendinosus. |
| 2. Pectineus | At the front of the pubis, just lateral to the adductor longus from which it is difficult to distinguish. |
| 3. Adductor longus | This muscle can be palpated just below its proximal attachment at the medial aspect of the groin. |
| 4. Adductor brevis | Cannot be palpated. |
| 5. Adductor magnus | This muscle can be palpated on the medial surface of middle half of the thigh. |

### 14.25   The Muscles of the Hip

A.   Specific Student Objectives

1. *The Anterior Hip Muscles*

   a.   Identify the two muscles located in this group.
   b.   Give the proximal and distal attachments of each of these muscles.
   c.   Give the joint actions produced by the contraction of each of these muscles.
   d.   Locate each of these muscles in your own body.

2. *The Posterior Hip Muscles*

   a.   Identify the six muscles that comprise the six deep outward rotators group.
   b.   Identify the four other posterior muscles of the hip.
   c.   Give the proximal and distal attachments and joint actions produced by the contraction of the following muscles:

   > tensor fasciae latae
   > gluteus maximus
   > gluteus medius
   > gluteus minimus

   d.   Locate each of these muscles in your own hip.

B.   Study Hints

1.   Table 14–3 is presented to aid in the mastery of specific muscle actions and attachments.
2.   Instructions as to where the muscles of the hip can be palpated are presented in Table 14–4. The student should perform each of the movements of the hip and attempt to locate through palpation each of the muscles listed.

**Table 14–3.  The Attachments and Actions of the Hip Muscles**

| Location | Name | Proximal Attachment | Illustration | Distal Attachment | Action |
|---|---|---|---|---|---|
| Anterior group | Iliacus | Iliac fossa and a part of the inner surface of the sacrum near the ilium | Fig. 14–19 | Lesser trochanter of femur | Flexion of the hip and assistant in outward rotation and adduction of hip |
| | Psoas | Bodies and transverse processes of the lumbar vertebrae and the intervertebral disks between the vertebrae | Fig. 14–19 | Lesser trochanter of femur | Flexion of the hip and assistant in outward rotation and adduction of hip |
| Posterior group | Tensor fasciae latae | Anterior part of the outer lip of the iliac crest | Figs. 14–20 and 14–21 | Iliotibial band of the fascia lata | Inward rotation and assistant in flexion and abduction of hip |

Table 14-3. The Attachments and Actions of the Hip Muscles (continued)

| Location | Name | Proximal Attachment | Illustration | Distal Attachment | Action |
|---|---|---|---|---|---|
| | Gluteus maximus | Posterior gluteal line of ilium and adjacent portion of crest, and on the posterior surface of lower part of sacrum and side of coccyx | Figs. 14-20 and 14-21 | Gluteal tuberosity of the femur and into the iliotibial tract of the fascia lata | Extension and outward rotation at hip. Upper fibers assist in abduction; lower fibers assist in adduction |
| | Gluteus medius | Between anterior and posterior gluteal lines of ilium | Fig. 14-22 | Greater trochanter of femur | Abduction at hip. Anterior fibers: inward rotation and flexion. Posterior fibers: outward rotation and extension |
| | Gluteus minimus | Between anterior and inferior gluteal lines of ilium | Fig. 14-22 | Greater trochanter of femur | Abduction at hip. Anterior fibers: inward rotation and flexion. Posterior fibers: outward rotation and extension |
| | Six deep outward rotators | Around acetabulum | Fig. 14-23 | Around head of femur | Outward rotation at hip |

Table 14-4. Instructions for Palpating the Muscles of the Hip

| Name of Muscle | Where the Muscle Can Be Palpated |
|---|---|

A. *Anterior group* (Fig. 14-19)

   1. Iliopsoas — This muscle is almost impossible to palpate.

B. *Posterior group*

   1. Tensor fasciae latae (Fig. 14-20) — This muscle is best palpated when the movement of flexion of the inwardly rotated thigh is performed. It can be palpated about 2 in. anterior to the greater trochanter.

   2. Gluteus maximus (Figs. 14-20 and 14-21) — Posterior surface of buttock.

   3. Gluteus medius (Fig. 14-22) — The middle portion of the gluteus medius is palpated laterally below the crest of the ilium, about 2 or 3 in. above the greater trochanter, when the thigh is abducted.

   4. Gluteus minimus (Fig. 14-22) — Cannot be palpated.

   5. The six deep outward rotators (Fig. 14-23) — Cannot be palpated.

14.30 Recommended
Supplementary
Readings

The student should consult any recent basic anatomy text for supplementary readings on the structure of the thigh and hip. A list of selected anatomy texts is given in Appendix B.

# 15

# Movements and Problems of the Knee, Thigh, and Hip

**General Student Objective**

*In his study of the basic concepts of this chapter the student should become familiar with:*

The primary movements of the knee joint are flexion and extension. A slight amount of rotation can take place, however, when the knee is in the flexed position.

**15.11  Movements of the Knee Joint**

### Flexion and Extension

The muscles that produce flexion and extension of the knee are

A. *Extension* (Fig. 15-1)

   1. Quadriceps femoris

      a. Rectus femoris
      b. Vastus medialis
      c. Vastus lateralis
      d. Vastus intermedius

**Fig. 15-1. The extensors of the knee.**

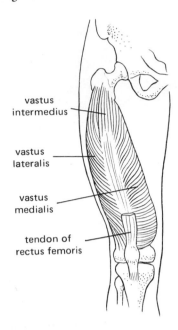

vastus
intermedius

vastus
lateralis

vastus
medialis

tendon of
rectus femoris

**Fig. 15-2. The flexors of the knee.**

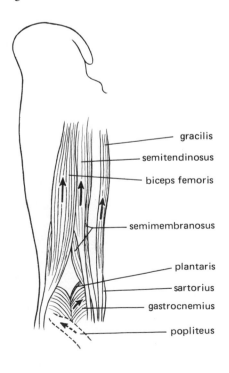

gracilis

semitendinosus

biceps femoris

semimembranosus

plantaris

sartorius

gastrocnemius

popliteus

B. *Flexion* (Fig. 15-2)

1. Hamstrings

    a. Biceps femoris
    b. Semitendinosus
    c. Semimembranosus

2. Sartorius
3. Gracilis
4. Popliteus
5. Gastrocnemius
6. Plantaris

The quadriceps femoris acting as a whole *extends* the leg at the knee joint by elevating the patella, which, in turn, transfers the force of the contraction through the patellar ligament to the tibia. The lines of pull of the rectus femoris and vastus intermedius are directly upward on the patella. The lines of pull of the vastus medialis and vastus lateralis, however, are diagonal. The vastus medialis pulls diagonally inward, whereas the vastus lateralis pulls diagonally outward. These two lines of pull counterbalance each other to give a straight line of pull on the patella. The three vasti, with their three lines of pull, serve to steady the knee joint in all weight-bearing positions.

The principal *flexors* of the knee are the three hamstrings located on the posterior thigh, the sartorius located on the anterior thigh, and the gracilis located on the medial thigh. The tendons of all these muscles pass posterior to the knee joint. In addition to these muscles are three muscles of the posterior leg that extend across the knee joint and have a flexor action. These muscles are the gastrocnemius, the plantaris (so small that it can be disregarded), and the popliteus. The gastrocnemius is primarily a plantar flexor of the ankle; however, when the leg is free, it also acts to flex the knee. The popliteus is a weak flexor, although it is believed to be particularly important in the starting of flexion. This may also be true of the long head of the biceps femoris, because the contraction of this muscle is strongest at the beginning of flexion and becomes progressively relaxed as flexion is continued.

### Inward and Outward Rotation

A certain amount of rotation of the knee is possible during flexion, the range of rotation being greatest at 90° of flexion at which position it amounts to about 50°. Since the rotation of the knee is associated so closely with knee flexion, the same muscles act as rotators at the knee as have just been listed as flexors, with the exception of the gastrocnemius. These muscles are

A. *Outward rotation* (Fig. 15-3)

1. Biceps femoris

B. *Inward rotation* (Fig. 15-4)

1. Semitendinosus
2. Semimembranosus

3. Popliteus
4. Gracilis
5. Sartorius

The only outward rotator of the flexed knee is the biceps femoris attached on the lateral side of the tibia and fibula. All the other rotators are attached on the medial side of the knee and are, therefore, inward rotators. The popliteus, passing distally and medially across the posterior aspect of the knee joint, is an especially good inward rotator. The thigh muscles that act to inward rotate the flexed knee are the two remaining hamstrings, the semitendinosus and the semimembranosus, plus the sartorius and the gracilis.

No rotation is possible in the extended knee, because of the mechanical disadvantage of the muscles, the tautness of the ligaments, and the interlocking of the articular surfaces.

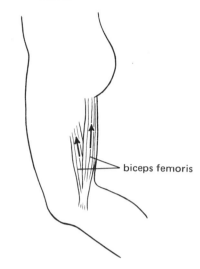

Fig. 15–3. The outward rotator of the knee.

## 15.12 Movements of the Hip Joint

Since the hip joint is a ball-and-socket joint that allows movement in all three planes, the specific joint actions allowed are flexion and extension, abduction and adduction, and inward and outward rotation.

### Flexion and Extension

The muscles that produce flexion and extension of the hip joint are

A. *Extension* (Fig. 15–5)

1. Gluteus maximus
2. Adductor magnus (distal or sciatic part)
3. Hamstrings

   a. Biceps femoris
   b. Semitendinosus
   c. Semimembranosus

4. Gluteus medius (posterior part)
5. Gluteus minimus (posterior part)
6. Periformis

B. *Flexion* (Fig. 15–6)

1. All anterior muscles that cross the hip joint

   a. Iliopsoas
   b. Sartorius
   c. Rectus femoris

2. All medial muscles of the thigh

   a. Pectineus
   b. Adductor longus
   c. Adductor brevis
   d. Adductor magnus (upper fibers)
   e. Gracilis

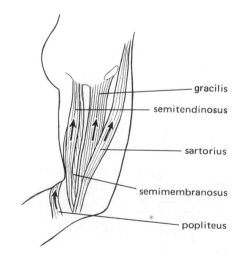

Fig. 15–4. The inward rotators of the knee.

gracilis
semitendinosus
sartorius
semimembranosus
popliteus

**Fig. 15-5. The extensors of the hip.**

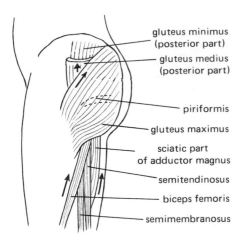

**Fig. 15-6. The flexors of the hip.**

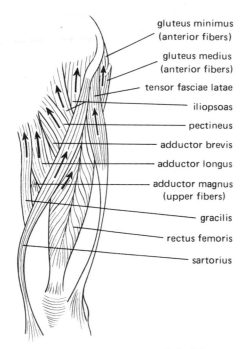

3. All lateral muscles of the hip and thigh

   a. Tensor fasciae latae
   b. Gluteus medius (anterior fibers)
   c. Gluteus minimus (anterior fibers)

The gluteus maximus is an especially strong *extensor* of the hip, particularly when the movement is performed against resistance and when the thigh is flexed beyond a 45° angle. In this action, it is assisted by the adductor magnus, especially that part arising from the ischial tuberosity and innervated by the sciatic nerve. The action of the adductor magnus is strongest when the thigh is flexed beyond a 45° angle. The hamstrings are involved and so may be the more posterior fibers of the gluteus medius, gluteus minimus, and the periformis.

The *flexor* muscles are mostly the anterior and medial muscles of the thigh and hip. The anterior muscles that cross the hip joint are the iliopsoas, sartorius, and rectus femoris. The iliopsoas is the strongest of this group. All the medial thigh muscles are involved in hip flexion. These muscles include the pectineus, adductor longus, adductor brevis, gracilis, and the upper fibers of the adductor magnus. The pectineus is the strongest flexor in this group. The tensor fasciae latae is a strong flexor in the lateral group, which also includes the anterior fibers of the gluteus medius and gluteus minimus.

**Abduction and Adduction**

The muscles that produce abduction and adduction of the hip joint are

  A. Abduction (Fig. 15-7)

    1. Gluteus medius
    2. Gluteus minimus
    3. Tensor fasciae latae
    4. Gluteus maximus, uppermost fibers
    5. Sartorius
    6. Piriformis

  B. Adduction (Fig. 15-8)

    1. Adductor longus
    2. Adductor brevis
    3. Adductor magnus
    4. Pectineus
    5. Gracilis
    6. Gluteus maximus, lower fibers
    7. Iliopsoas
    8. Hamstrings

      a. Biceps femoris, long head
      b. Semitendinosus
      c. Semimembranosus

    9. Obturator externus
   10. Quadratus femoris

**Fig. 15-7. The abductors of the hip.**

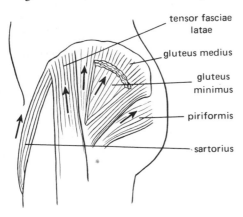

**Fig. 15–8. The adductors of the hip: (*A*) anterior view and (*B*) posterior view.**

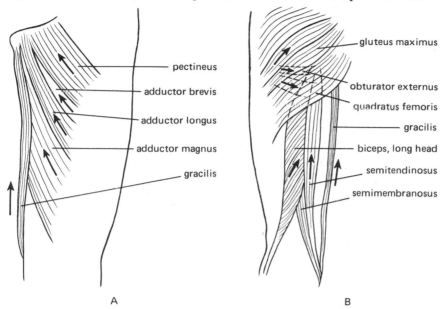

The chief *abductors* of the hip are the gluteus medius and minimus and the tensor fasciae latae. These muscles are assisted by the uppermost fibers of the gluteus maximus and by the sartorius and periformis.

The *adductors* of the hip are the adductor longus, adductor brevis, adductor magnus, pectineus, and gracilis, which are located on the medial side of the thigh. These muscles are assisted by the lower fibers of the gluteus maximus by the hamstrings, obturator externus, and quadratus femoris, and, with the thigh fixed, by the iliopsoas.

**Inward and Outward Rotation**

The muscles that produce inward and outward rotation of the hip joint are

A. *Inward rotation* (Fig. 15–9)

1. Gluteus medius (anterior fibers)
2. Gluteus minimus (anterior fibers)
3. Tensor fasciae latae
4. Semitendinosus
5. Semimembranosus
6. Adductor magnus (distal part)

B. *Outward rotation* (Fig. 15–10)

1. Six deep outward rotators
2. Gluteus maximus
3. Posterior fibers of the gluteus medius and gluteus minimus
4. The adductor group

    a. Pectineus
    b. Adductor longus
    c. Adductor brevis
    d. Adductor magnus (anterior part)

**Fig. 15–9. The inward rotators of the hip.**

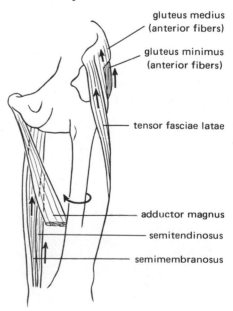

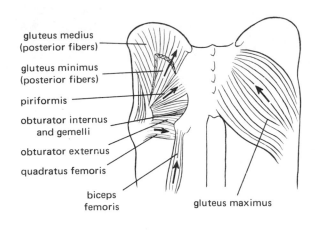

Fig. 15–10. The outward rotators of the hip: (A) anterior view and (B) posterior view.

5. Sartorius
6. Biceps femoris (long head)
7. Iliopsoas

The chief *inward rotators* are the gluteus medius, minimus, and tensor fasciae latae, which are also the chief abductors. These muscles are perhaps assisted slightly by the semitendinosus, semimembranosus, and the distal or sciatic portion of the adductor magnus.

*Outward rotation* at the hip is stronger than inward rotation, because of the large number of muscles involved. Practically all the muscles of the buttock can act as outward rotators. The gluteus maximus and the six deep outward rotators, however, participate in the movement to the greatest extent. The adductor group as a whole and the posterior fibers of the gluteus medius and minimus assist in the movement. The sartorius, long head of the biceps femoris, and the iliopsoas have weak actions as outward rotators of the hip.

## 15.13 Actions of Two-Joint Muscles

The preceding analysis has shown that certain muscles act simultaneously on both the hip joint and the knee joint. The hamstrings, for instance, extend the hip and flex the knee, the rectus femoris flexes the hip and extends the knee, and the sartorius flexes both the hip and the knee. The joint actions produced by the contraction of two-joint muscles are quite complex, and special consideration of these actions is required. The primary concern here is with the explanation of (1) Lombard's paradox and (2) the pulley action of these muscles.

### Lombard's Paradox

Some students find it surprising that the hamstrings and the rectus femoris, which have antagonistic actions at both the hip and knee joints, are brought into play simultaneously, for example, in rising from a chair. The resulting action is obviously extension at both the hip and knee joints. Why does the flexor action of the rectus femoris not neutralize the extensor action of the hamstrings at the hip joint, and why does the flexor action of the hamstrings not neutralize the extensor action of the rectus femoris at the knee joint? This question is known as Lombard's paradox, after W. P. Lombard[1] who first suggested that the answer is found by comparing the opposing torques involved.

Elftman[2] has found that the length of the lever arm of the rectus femoris in a typical individual at the hip joint is about 3.9 cm, whereas that of the hamstrings is about 6.7 cm. Therefore, should the forces developed in the hamstrings and rectus femoris be equal, the torque ($T = F \times f$) of the hamstrings for hip extension is greater than the torque of the rectus femoris for hip flexion. Thus, the actual joint action produced will be hip extension.

Elftman found the opposite situation to exist at the knee joint, where the rectus femoris has a lever arm of about 4.4 cm and the hamstrings have a lever arm of about 3.4 cm. Therefore, the torque per unit of force of the rectus femoris for knee extension is greater than the torque of the hamstrings for knee flexion. Thus, the actual joint action produced is knee extension.

### The Pulley Action of Two Joint Muscles

A characteristic of all two-joint muscles is that they are not long enough to allow complete movement in both of the joints that they cross at the same time. Therefore, flexion of the hip, for instance, stretches the hamstrings and thereby increases their tension even though they may be completely relaxed. This increased tension in the hamstrings causes them to flex the knee. This effect works in much the same manner that a downward pull on a rope that passes through an overhead pulley is transmitted in the form of a pull in the reverse direction to the rope on the other side of the pulley. Thus, if the hamstrings contract to help extend the hip, tension is transmitted to the rectus femoris, causing it to extend the knee.

The pulley action of two-joint muscles will occur even if the lever arms of the antagonistic muscles are of the same length. Therefore, these pulley actions should not be confused with the principle of differential leverage used to explain Lombard's paradox, as these two effects differ and are independent of each other.

The conditioning problems of the knee, thigh, and hips are those concerned with the flexibility of the knee and hip joints and with the strength, power, and endurance of the thigh and hip muscles.

**15.14 Conditioning Problems of the Knee, Thigh, and Hips**

[1] W. P. Lombard and F. M. Abbott: "The Mechanical Effects Produced by the Contraction of Individual Muscles of the Thigh of the Frog," *Am. J. Phys.*, **20**, 1–60, 1907.
[2] Herbert Elftman: "The Function of Muscles in Locomotion," *Am. J. Phys.*, **125**, 357–66, 1939.

## Flexibility of the Knee and Hip Joints

Flexion of the knee is possible through about 135°. After about 90° of flexion, as much as 60 to 90° of rotation may be possible.

The chief flexibility problem of the hip joint is the restriction of hip flexion by the hamstrings. Some flexibility exercises for the hip joint, which are mostly stretching exercises for the hamstrings, are illustrated in Figure 15-11.

**Fig. 15-11. Some flexibility exercises for the movements of the hip joint.**

## Isometric Measurements of Strength

The Clark Cable-Tension Strength Tests for the knee extensors and for the knee flexors are illustrated in Figures 15-12, and 15-13. The Clark strength tests for the hip movements of flexion, extension, abduction, and adduction are illustrated in Figures 15-14 through 15-17. The Martin Breaking Strength Tests for the movements of the knee are described in Table 15-1, and the Martin tests for the movements of the hip are described in Table 15-2.

## Isotonic Exercises and Measurements

Some isotonic exercises, which also can be used to measure the strength, power, and endurance of the thigh and hip muscles, are illustrated in Figure 15-18.

Fig. 15–12. The Clark Cable-Tension Strength Test for the knee extensors. In this test, the knee to be tested is in 115° extension, and one tester is used to steady the subject on the table.

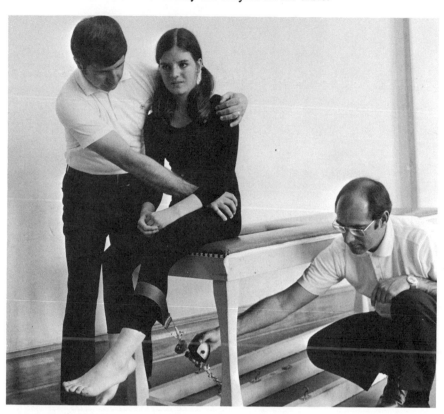

Fig. 15–13. The Clark Cable-Tension Strength Test for the knee flexors. In this test, the knee to be tested is placed at 165° of flexion.

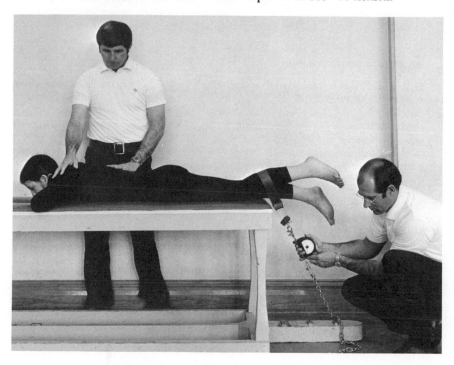

**Fig. 15–14. The Clark Cable-Tension Strength Test for the hip flexors.**

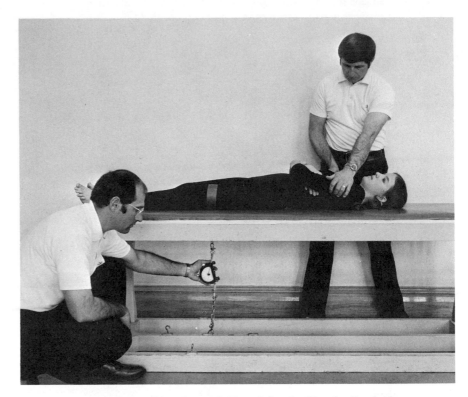

**Table 15–1. Martin Breaking Strength Tests\* for the Muscles Producing the Movements of the Knee**

---

1. *Muscles that flex the leg*

   The subject lies prone on the table. The operator stands at the foot of the table. The loop passes behind the ankle. The subject places the lower leg in maximum flexion. The pull is horizontal, and the rotation of the thigh should be minimized. The adjuster calls "Stop" as the lower leg crosses the perpendicular position.

2. *Muscles that extend the leg*

   The subject lies prone on the table. The lower leg is flexed 90° at the knee. The loop passes in front of the ankle. The operator, standing at the head of the subject, braces the subject's shoulder with one hand. The pull is horizontal and parallel to the median plane. The adjuster braces the subject's knee on the table with one hand, and, with the other hand at the subject's ankle, limits the extension of the lower leg. The movement begins from the perpendicular position. The effort of the subject to extend the lower leg and the pull of the operator must start simultaneously at the command of the adjuster. Both pulls should begin slowly: it is essential in this test that the muscle pull and the pull of the dynamometer should develop together. The lower leg is not permitted to extend more than 25° from the perpendicular position. Greater extension than this changes the leverage so much that inaccuracy results. The pull of the operator continues until the lower leg has been drawn back to the original position. This test is one of the most accurate of all the Martin Tests; it is, however, the most liable to error if overextension of the lower leg is permitted before the balance pull begins to draw the leg back to the vertical position.

---

\*E. G. Martin: "Tests of Muscular Efficiency," *Phys. Rev.,* **1**: 454–75, 1921.

Fig. 15–15. The Clark Cable-Tension Strength Test for the hip extensors.

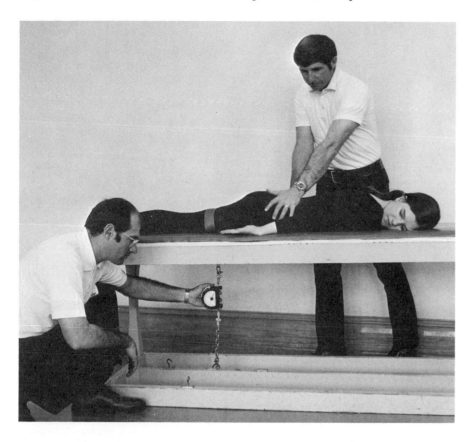

Fig. 15–16. The Clark Cable-Tension Strength Test for the hip abductors.

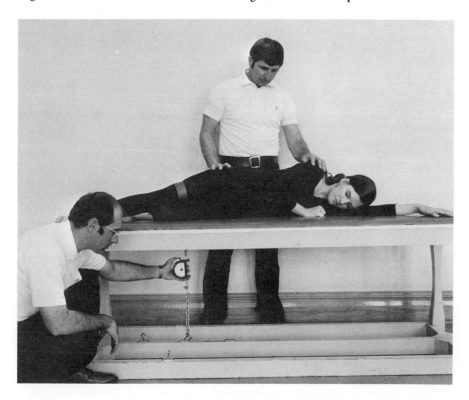

Fig. 15–17. The Clark Cable-Tension Strength Test for the hip adductors.

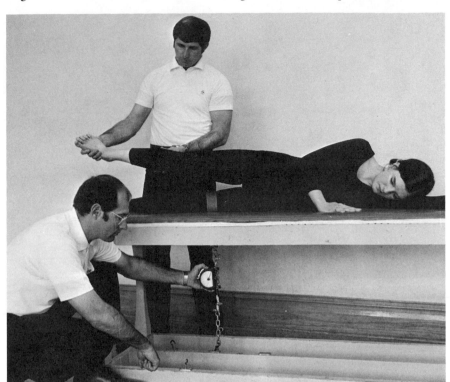

Table 15–2. Martin Breaking Strength Tests* for the Muscles Producing the Movements of the Hip

1. *Muscles that adduct the thigh*

   The position of the subject is the same as for the preceding tests. The adjuster stands at the foot of the table. With one hand he places the loop in the hollow just above the malleolus (an equally correct method is to have the strap just clear the top of a man's shoe), seizes the subject's heel with the other hand, lifts the leg until the heel is just high enough to clear the toes of the other foot, and then draws the leg into extreme adduction. The foot of the leg to be tested must be kept vertical. The operator stands at the side of the table and develops tension at the word of command. The command "Stop" should be given as soon as the leg has been drawn into line with the longitudinal axis of the body.

2. *Muscles that abduct the thigh*

   The position of the subject and that of the adjuster are the same as for the preceding test. The loop is adjusted as in the preceding test, but the direction of the pull is opposite to that used in the preceding test. The leg to be tested is drawn 15° beyond the midline of the body, and at the command "Hold back" the subject attempts to prevent the operator from drawing the leg into line with the body. The command "Stop" is given just as the leg reaches the midline.

3. *Muscles that extend the thigh*

   The subject lies on the side opposite to that to be tested, with one hip directly above the other. The abdomen is braced firm in position, and, to secure steadiness, the subject pushes against the foot brace with the foot of the leg not being tested. The trunk is braced forward by the subject's holding to the edge of the table with the hands. The adjuster assists in maintaining, with one hand, the position of the abdomen, and in supporting, with the other hand, the weight of the leg to be tested, and keeps the subject's leg parallel to the table. The loop is placed across the popliteal space (behind

**Table 15-2. Martin Breaking Strength Tests\* for the Muscles Producing the Movements of the Hip (continued)**

the knee). The thigh is placed in maximum extension, and the lower leg is kept extended. The direction of pull of the balance is slightly less than 90° to the thigh, being deflected toward the trunk; and it is exerted horizontally. The angle of pull must be constant throughout the movement. The adjuster signals as the thigh crosses the line of the trunk, or if the muscle gives before this, the reading is taken when the muscle yields.

4. *Muscles that flex the thigh*

The subject lies on the side opposite that to be tested, with one hip directly above the other. To secure steadiness he pushes against the foot brace with the foot of the leg not being tested. The small of the back is braced. The subject maintains the rigidity of the trunk by pushing with the hands against a support in front of him. The adjuster supports the thigh parallel to the table, with one hand at the subject's knee and the other at the subject's ankle. The loop is placed just above the patella. The lower leg is well flexed, and the thigh is flexed more than 90°. The pull is horizontal and as nearly as possible at a right angle to the thigh.

\*E. G. Martin: "Tests of Muscular Efficiency," *Phys. Rev.,* **1**: 454–75, 1921.

Fig. 15-18. Some isotonic exercises that can also be used to measure the strength, power, and endurance of the thigh and hip muscles. Exercises for the knee flexors and knee extensors are shown in *A* and *B*, respectively, and *C* shows an exercise for the hip flexors. Two exercises for the knee and hip extensors are shown in *D* and *E*.

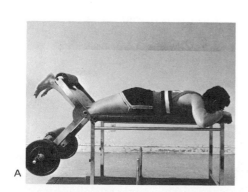

15.15 Postural and Pathological
Problems of the Knee,
Thigh, and Hip

**Postural Problems**

The normal position of both the knee and hip joints is extension, but not complete extension. The femur and tibia should form a straight line when viewed from the side. By use of a plumb line to represent the line of gravity, the vertical alignment for the leg and thigh should fall behind the patella and through the midpoint of the hip. This line also passes through the greater trochanter.

When viewed from the front, the normal standing position should be with the feet parallel, no rotation of the thighs, and with the medial malleoli and the medial aspect of the knees in contact. A plumb line, representing the line of gravity, should intersect the anterior iliac spine, the midline of the knee, and the midpoint of the ankle.

The patellae can be used to check femoral rotation. If the patellae are turned inward, giving the appearance of looking at each other "cross-eyed," they indicate inward rotation of the thighs; if the patellae are turned outward, they indicate outward rotation of the thighs.

If the knees do not touch when standing with the feet together, the individual has "bow legs," or *genu varum* (Fig. 15–19). If the knees are in contact and the subject is unable to place the feet together and parallel so that the medial malleoli are in contact, the individual has "knock-knees" or *genu valgum*.

An increase in the foot-leg angle (plantar flexion) causes the thigh to be hyperextended. The result is an assumed position of hyperextension of the knees. This position is referred to as "back knee" or *genu recurvatum*.

Fig. 15–19. Some abnormal conditions of the knees.

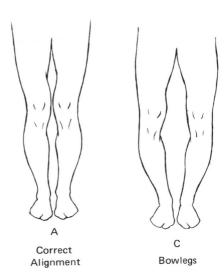

A
Correct
Alignment

C
Bowlegs

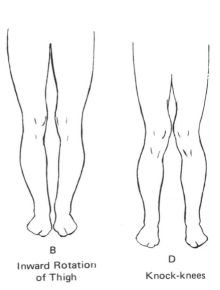

B
Inward Rotation
of Thigh

D
Knock-knees

**Pathological Problems**

Some of the major pathological problems of the knee, thigh, and hip (Fig. 15–20) are (1) coxa vara and coxa valga, (2) coxa plana, (3) Osgood-Schlatter disease, and (4) slipped femoral epiphysis.

Normally, the angle between the neck of the femur and the shaft is approximately 135°. A decrease in this angle is called *coxa vara* and in this condition the affected leg is usually shorter and its external rotation is limited. An increase in the angle of the femur is called *coxa valga*, which usually results in the affected leg being longer and rotation being limited.

*Coxa plana* is characterized by atrophy and loss of density of the head of the femur. As a result, the femoral neck becomes shorter and thicker, the femoral head becomes broad and flat, and the femoral epiphysis becomes flattened.

*Osgood-Schlatter disease* is an inflammation or partial separation of the tibial tuberosity. Therefore, all extension exercises of the knee are performed with great amount of pain. A slipped femoral epiphysis results in a nontraumatic separation of the femoral head at the epiphysis. This condition causes an external rotation of the thigh, which causes the individual to walk in a toed-out position.

Fig. 15-20. Some major pathological problems of the knee and hip.

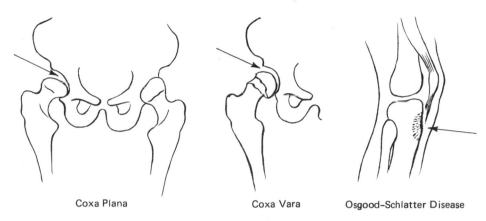

Coxa Plana          Coxa Vara          Osgood-Schlatter Disease

## 15.16 Traumatic Problems of the Knee, Thigh, and Hip

The chief traumatic problems of (1) the knee, which includes the patella, (2) the thigh, and (3) the hip will be discussed separately in this section.

### The Knee

Traumatic knee problems fall mainly into three categories: contusions, sprains, and abnormal conditions of the patella.

The knee is particularly vulnerable to bruising (contusions) because of its lack of padding. Frequently bruised are the vastus medialis, the capsular tissue that surrounds the joint, and the periosteum of the bony articulations. Also prone to bruising are the bursae located on the anterior aspect of the knee.

Since the knee's only lateral and medial stability is achieved by collateral ligaments, sprains of these ligaments are quite frequent in athletics. The greatest incidence of knee sprains affects the medial collateral ligament as a result either of a direct blow from the lateral side or of a severe inward twist.

Closely associated with medial collateral ligament injuries are tears or dislocations of the medial meniscus. This association is due to the direct attachment of the medial collateral ligament to the medial meniscus as illustrated in Figure 15-21. A blow to the lateral side of the knee, therefore, stretches the medial collateral ligament, which, in turn, may dislodge the medial meniscus from the head of the tibia.

The most common type of medial meniscus injury is an elongated tear occurring within the cartilage itself, with an interior part being cut and lifted from the periphery while it is still held fast at both ends. These tears are commonly called *bucket-handle tears* (Fig. 15-22).

Even though lateral collateral ligament and lateral meniscus injuries do occur in athletics when the knee is hit from the medial side, they occur much less frequently than do injuries to the medial structures. One reason for fewer lateral meniscus injuries is that the lateral meniscus does not attach to the lateral collateral ligament.

Fig. 15-21. Attachment of the medial collateral ligament to the medial meniscus.

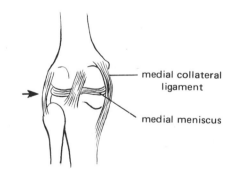

medial collateral ligament

medial meniscus

Fig. 15-22. Bucket-handle tears of the medial meniscus.

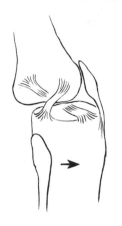

Fig. 15-23. The posterior cruciate ligament prevents the backward displacement of the tibia on a fixed femur.

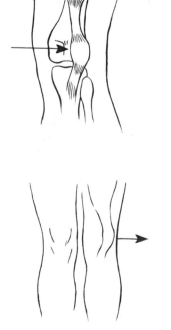

Fig. 15-24. Dislocation of the patella.

The second most frequently injured ligaments of the knee are the cruciates. These ligaments are designed to stabilize the tibia on the femur, and they are named as anterior or posterior in terms of their relationship to the tibia. The anterior cruciate ligament prevents the forward displacement of the tibia on the femur. The posterior cruciate ligament, on the other hand, prevents the backward displacement of the tibia on a fixed femur (Fig. 15-23). Forced hyperextensions of the knee, therefore, may injure the posterior cruciate.

Anterior cruciate injuries in sports occur most often when the knee is partially flexed and a force is applied across the back of the leg below the knee, as often occurs in the football "clip." The football "clip" can result in driving the tibia toward the ground and thereby tearing the anterior cruciate.

The most common traumatic problem of the patella is its dislocation, which usually occurs as a result of a direct blow (Fig. 15-24). Dislocations of this type occur most often in females or individuals who have poor quadriceps tone. Individuals who are knock-kneed or who have a flattened lateral or medial condyle may also be prone to patellar dislocations. As a rule, displacement takes place outwardly with the patella resting on the lateral condyle.

## The Thigh

The major traumatic problems of the thigh (Fig. 15-25) are (1) the charley horse (thigh contusion), (2) myositis ossificans traumatica, (3) hamstring pulls (strains), and (4) fractures of the femur.

Because of the relative accessibility and bulkiness of the quadriceps femoris muscle, it is particularly prone to bruising, which is commonly called a charley horse. A charley horse usually develops as the result of a severe impact to the relaxed thigh in which the tissue is compressed against the hard surface of the femur. The best treatment for a mild charley horse is to stretch the quadriceps muscle by performing its antagonistic joint actions, i.e., hip extension and knee flexion.

Severe charley horses can actually result in muscle herniation. This condition should be treated by complete rest of the muscle. In some severe cases, the original trauma is so deep that several osteoblastic periosteal cells are loosened from the femur by the force and float in the tissue fluids. These cells proliferate and actually begin to cause calcifications to form in the quadriceps muscle. This is one reason that massage is contraindicated in the treatment of charley horses.

Hamstring pulls (strains) rank second only to the charley horse in athletic injuries to the thigh. A pulled hamstring occurs most frequently in persons with some deficiency in the reciprocal or complementary action of opposing muscle groups. The cause of muscle incoordination could be fatigue, poor posture, uneven muscle strength, inflexibility, and/or poor performance techniques.

Fractures of the femur occur most often to the middle third of the shaft as a result of a direct blow. Usually accompanying this injury are lacerations of the vastus intermedius.

Fig. 15–25. Major injuries of the thigh.

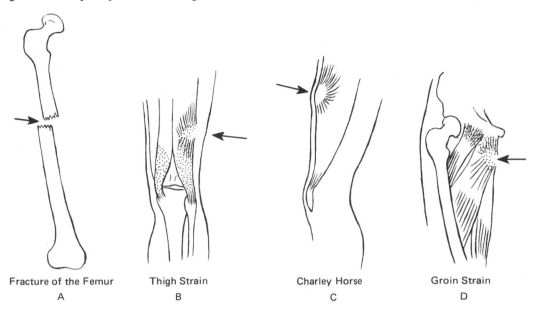

| Fracture of the Femur | Thigh Strain | Charley Horse | Groin Strain |
| A | B | C | D |

## The Hip

The major traumatic problems of the hip are (1) sprains and dislocations of the hip joint and (2) strains of the groin.

Since the hip joint is substantially supported by ligaments and muscles, any movements that exceed the normal range of motion may result in tearing tissue. Such an injury may occur as the result of a twist or through impact with external objects. Dislocations of the hip are rare, but when they do occur the displacement is usually posterior to the acetabulum and with the femoral shaft adducted and flexed.

The groin is considered the depression that lies between the thigh and the abdominal region. The musculature encompassed includes all the medial muscles of the thigh and the anterior muscles of the hip. Any one of these muscles can be torn in athletic activity and elicit what is commonly called a groin strain.

## 15.21 Movements of the Knee Joint

A. Specific Student Objectives

1. Name the four muscles that form the quadriceps femoris.
2. Name the extensors of the knee joint.
3. Name the three muscles that form the hamstrings.
4. Name the eight muscles that flex the knee joint.
5. Name the one muscle responsible for producing outward rotation of the hip joint.

## 15.20 Study Guidelines

6. Name the five muscles responsible for producing inward rotation of the flexed knee.
7. State the reason that no rotation is possible in the extended knee.

### 15.22 Movements of the Hip Joint

A. Specific Student Objectives

1. Name the eight muscles responsible for producing hip extension.
2. Name the eleven muscles responsible for producing hip flexion.
3. Name the six muscles responsible for producing hip abduction.
4. Name the twelve muscles responsible for producing hip adduction.
5. Name the six muscles responsible for producing inward rotation of the hip joint.
6. Name the ten muscles, counting the six deep outward rotators as one muscle, responsible for producing outward rotation of the hip joint.

B. Study Hints

1. In his study of the muscles that produce the movements of the knee and hip joints, the student is advised to do a minimal amount of pure memorizing.

   It is much better for the student to study muscle-produced joint actions along with the actual exercises which employ these actions. Exercises of this type are presented in Section 15.14.

### 15.23 Actions of Two-Joint Muscles

A. Specific Student Objectives

1. What is the explanation for Lombard's paradox?
2. Describe the pulley action of two-joint muscles.

### 15.24 Conditioning Problems of the Knee, Thigh, and Hips

A. Specific Student Objectives

1. Identify the specific structures of the knee, thigh, and hip being stretched in the flexibility exercises presented in Figure 15–11.
2. Identify the specific muscles being tested by the Clark Cable-Tension Strength Tests in Figures 15–12 through 15–17 and by the Martin Breaking Strength Tests in Table 15–1.
3. Identify the specific muscles being exercised in Figure 15–18.

B. Study Hints

1. The strength tests and the exercises presented in this section are excellent for studying muscles in a way in which they can best be palpated.

   The palpation instructions presented in Tables 14-2 and 14-4 should be used to locate the muscles producing the joint actions demonstrated in the measurements and exercises presented in this section.

## 15.25 Postural and Pathological Problems of the Knee, Thigh, and Hip

A. Specific Student Objectives

1. *Postural Problems*

   a. Identify the normal position of both the knee and hip joints.
   b. Describe the correct alignment for the leg and thigh.
   c. Define the following terms:

      (1) genu varum
      (2) genu valgum
      (3) genu recurvatum

2. *Pathological Problems*

   a. Identify the major pathological problems of the knee, thigh, and hip.
   b. Define the following terms:

      (1) coxa vara
      (2) coxa valga
      (3) coxa plana

   c. Define Osgood-Schlatter disease.
   d. Define slipped femoral epiphysis.

## 15.26 Traumatic Problems of the Knee, Thigh, and Hip

A. Specific Student Objectives

1. *The Knee*

   a. Identify and define the major traumatic problems of the knee.
   b. Identify the knee ligament most often sprained in athletics.
   c. State how a force applied to the lateral side of the knee can produce a tear of the medial meniscus.
   d. Define bucket-handle tears of the menisci.
   e. State how a football "clip" can tear the anterior cruciate ligament.

2. *The Thigh*

   a. Identify and define the major traumatic problems of the thigh.

3. *The Hip*

   a. Identify and define the major traumatic problems of the hip.

## 15.30 Recommended Supplementary Readings

The student should consult any recent kinesiology text for supplementary readings on the movements and problems of the knee, thigh, and hip. A list of selected kinesiology texts is given in Appendix B. The following readings are especially recommended.

Allington, R. O., and others: "Strengthening Techniques of the Quadriceps Muscles: An Electromyographic Evaluation," *Phys. Ther.,* **46**:1173-76, November, 1966.

Bierman, W., and Ralston, M. J.: "Electromyographic Study During Passive and Active Flexion and Extension of the Knee of the Normal Human Subject," *Arch. Phys. Med. Rehabil.,* **46**:71-75, January, 1965.

Brewerton, D. A.: "The Function of the Vastus Medialis Muscle," *Ann. Phys. Med.,* **2**:164-68, 1955.

Inman, Verne T.: "Functional Aspects of the Abductor Muscles of the Hip," *J. Bone Joint Surg.,* **29**:607-19, 1947.

Kaplan, E. B.: "The Iliotibial Tract," *J. Bone Joint Surg.,* **40A**:817-32, 1958.

Klein, Karl K.: "The Deep Squat Exercise as Utilized in Weight Training for Athletics and Its Effect on the Ligaments of the Knee," *J. Assoc. Phys. Ment. Rehabil.,* **15**:6-11, 1961.

———: "The Knee and the Ligaments," *J. Bone Joint Surg.,* **44A**:1191-93, 1962.

LaBan, M. M., and others: "Electromyographic Study of Function of Iliopsoas Muscle," *Arch. Phys. Med. Rehabil.,* **46**:676-79, 1965.

Lawrence, Mary S., and others: "Comparative Increase in Muscle Strength in the Quadriceps Femoris by Isometric and Isotonic Exercises and Effects on the Contralateral Muscle," *J. Am. Phys. Ther. Assoc.,* **42**:15-20, 1962.

Mendler, H. M.: "Relationship of Hip Abductor Muscles to Posture," *J. Am. Phys. Ther. Assoc.,* **44**:98-102, 1964.

Merrifield, H. H.: "An Electromyographic Study of the Gluteus Maximus, the Vastus Lateralis and the Tensor Fasciae Latae," *Diss. Abstr.,* **21**:1833, 1961.

Wheatley, M. D., and Jahnke, W. D.: "Electromyographic Study of the Superficial Thigh and Hip Muscles in Normal Individuals," *Arch. Phys. Ther.,* **31**:508-22, 1951.

# Part VII

# Structural Kinesiology of the Trunk

# 16

# Structure
# of the Trunk

**General Student Objective**

*In his study of the basic concepts of this chapter the student should become familiar with:*

16.11   *Bones of the Vertebral Column*
16.12   *Joints of the Vertebral Column*
16.13   *Bones of the Thorax*
16.14   *Joints of the Thorax*
16.15   *Muscles of the Abdomen*
16.16   *Muscles of the Thorax*
16.17   *Muscles of the Back*
16.18   *Muscles of the Neck*

The vertebral column (Fig. 16–1), often called the "spinal column" or "the spine," is formed of a series of bones called vertebrae and in a man of average height is about 28 in. long. It constitutes the longitudinal axis of the skeleton. It is a flexible rather than a rigid column because it is segmented, i.e., made up of 26 (typical in adult) separate bones, so joined to each other as to permit forward, backward, and sideways movement of the column. The head is balanced on top of this column, the ribs and viscera are suspended in front, the lower extremities are attached below, and the spinal cord is enclosed within. It is, indeed, the "backbone" of the body.

The skeletal framework of the neck consists of seven *cervical vertebrae*; the next twelve vertebrae are known as *thoracic* because they lie behind the thoracic cavity and are attached to the ribs; the next five, which support the small of the back, are called *lumbar vertebrae*; below are the *sacrum* and the *coccyx*.

All the vertebrae resemble each other in certain features and differ in others. For example, all except the first cervical vertebra have a flat, rounded mass placed anteriorly and centrally, known as the *body*, plus a sharp and blunt *spinous process* projecting inferiorly in the posterior midline, and two *transverse processes* projecting later-

**16.11   Bones of the Vertebral Column**

**Fig. 16–1. Dorsal view of the vertebral column.**

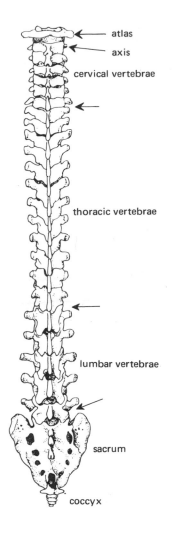

ally. All but the sacrum and coccyx have a central opening, the *vertebral foramen.* Because nearly all vertebrae have certain general characteristics in common, the examination of a typical vertebra followed by a study of the unique characteristics of the vertebrae in each region should be beneficial. The general characteristics of a typical vertebra (Fig. 16–2) are

A. *Body or centrum*: the disklike anterior portion.
B. *Neural arch*: formed by two roots or *pedicles* (ped'i-k'ls) and two *laminae* (lam'i-ne).
C. *Vertebral foramen*: bounded laterally and posteriorly by the neural arch and anteriorly by the body, thus forming, by the apposition of all the vertebrae, the vertebral canal for the spinal cord.
D. *Vertebral notches*: one on the superior border of each pedicle and one on the inferior border, thus forming, by the apposition of adjacent vertebrae, an *intervertebral foramen* for the exit of the spinal nerves.
E. *Processes*

1. *Spinous process*: directed dorsally and formed at the junction of the two laminae.
2. *Two transverse processes*: projected laterally and formed at the junction of the pedicles and laminae.
3. *Two superior articular processes*: project upward, face dorsally, and are situated opposite the attachments of the transverse processes.
4. *Two inferior articular processes*: project downward, face ventrally, and are situated opposite the superior ones.

F. *Articulations*

1. The superior and inferior surfaces of the body articulate with the bodies of the adjacent superior and inferior vertebrae, respectively, through the interposition of *intervertebral fibrocartilaginous disks.*
2. The superior articular processes articulate with the inferior articular processes of the vertebra above.
3. The inferior articular processes articulate with the superior articular process of the vertebra below.
4. The transverse and spinous processes of a typical vertebra serve for the attachment of muscles and ligaments.

The vertebrae in different parts of the spinal column show regional differences so that it is usually possible to recognize the group to which any one of them belongs. The *cervical vertebrae* (Fig. 16–3) as a whole are characterized by a foramen in their transverse processes called the transverse foramen. The *thoracic* and *lumbar vertebrae* (Fig. 16–3) are usually identified by their spinous processes. The spinous processes of the thoracic vertebrae are long, knobbed at the end, and slant downward, so that they overlap each other. The spinous processes of the lumbar vertebrae are broad from above downward and project horizontally backward.

The first and second cervical vertebrae (Fig. 16–4) differ considerably from the rest. The first cervical vertebra, or *atlas*, so named

**Fig. 16–2. Superior view of a typical thoracic vertebra.**

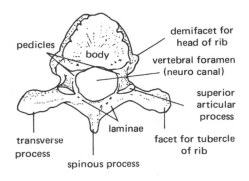

because it supports the globe of the head, is a bony ring consisting of an anterior and posterior arch and two bulky masses. Each mass has a superior and inferior articular surface. Each superior surface forms a cup for the corresponding condyles of the occipital bone and thus makes possible the backward and forward movements of the head. The bony ring is divided into an anterior and posterior section by a transverse ligament. The posterior section of this ring contains the spinal cord, and the anterior, or front, section contains the bony projection that arises from the upper surface of the body of the second cervical vertebrae. The atlas is characterized by the absence of a body and a spinous process.

The *axis* differs primarily from a typical cervical vertebra in that the body is characterized by the presence of the toothlike process called *dens* or *odontoid* (o-don'toid) process. The odontoid process forms a pivot around which the atlas rotates when the head is turned from side to side.

The bodies of the various vertebrae gradually increase in size as the vertebral column is followed downward. The bodies of the thoracic vertebrae are unique because of the presence of four *demifacets*, two superior and two inferior, which form, with those of adjacent vertebrae, *costal pits* for the heads of the ribs. The transverse processes of the thoracic vertebrae are marked on their anterior surfaces by the presence of *costal pits* for the tubercle of the corresponding rib. The spinous processes of the middle cervical vertebrae are usually bifid (cleft).

The spinous processes of the upper cervical vertebrae may be indistinctly felt. Those of the sixth and seventh are, however, quite prominent, especially the latter known as the *vertebra prominens*.

The first and last thoracic vertebrae are transitional, the first resembling somewhat the seventh cervical, and the twelfth the first lumbar. Furthermore the first, tenth, eleventh, and twelfth present complete facets or costal pits rather than demifacets for the corresponding ribs.

The fifth lumbar is more massive than the others, and its body forms the sacrovertebral angle with the base of the sacrum.

The great freedom of movement of the *cervical* region is accounted for by the shape of the articular surfaces and the position of the spinous processes, the articular surfaces being somewhat flattened and the spinous processes being directed horizontally. Movements of the vertebral column are least free in the thoracic region owing to the influence of the articular surfaces and the presence of ribs. Great freedom of movement is permitted in the lumbar region because of (1) the thickness of the intervertebral cartilaginous disks, (2) the shape of the articular surfaces, and (3) the horizontally directed spinous processes, which do not interfere with the movements.

The *sacrum* is formed by the union of the five sacral vertebrae. It is a large, triangular bone situated like a wedge between the coxal bones and curved upon itself so as to give increased capacity to the pelvic cavity.

The coccyx is usually formed of four small segments of bone and is the most rudimentary part of the vertebral column. It represents the atrophied human tail.

**Fig. 16-3. Typical vertebrae from the cervical (*A*), thoracic (*B*), and lumbar (*C*) regions of the vertebral column.**

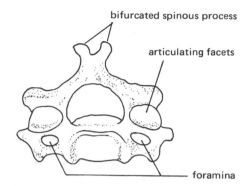

A. A Cervical Vertebra

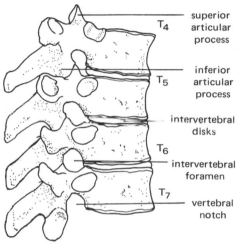

B. Thoracic Vertebrae

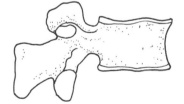

C. A Lumbar Vertebra

**Fig. 16–4. The first and second cervical vertebrae.**

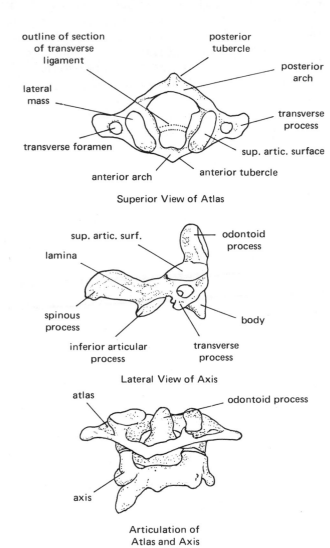

Superior View of Atlas

Lateral View of Axis

Articulation of
Atlas and Axis

16.12 Joints of the
Vertebral
Column

The joints of the vertebral column are

A. *The Atlantooccipital Joint*
B. *The Intervertebral Joints*

1. The atlantoaxial joints
2. The articulations of the bodies of the vertebrae
3. The articulations of the neural arches

**The Atlantooccipital Articulation**

The atlantooccipital articulation (Fig. 16–5) is a condyloid joint formed by the condyles of the occipital bone and the superior articular processes of the atlas.

*Movements.* The movements of the skull permitted at the atlanto-occipital joint are *flexion* (bending forward), *extension* (return to anatomical position), *hyperextension* (bending backward from the anatomical position), *abduction* or *lateral flexion* (bending sideward), *adduction* (return to anatomical position), and *circumduction*.

## The Atlantoaxial Articulations

The atlantoaxial articulations (Fig. 16–4) consist of the two lateral atlantoaxial joints, and the atlantodental joint. The *lateral atlanto-axial joints* are sliding joints formed between the superior articular processes of the axis and the inferior articular processes of the atlas. The *atlantodental joint* is a pivot joint formed by the dens or odontoid process of the axis and the articular (dental) facet on the posterior surface of the anterior arch of the atlas, the two being held in apposition by means of the transverse ligament.

*Movements.* The chief movement between the atlas and axis is rotation around a vertical axis. Owing to the ligamentous attachments and the nature of the articular surfaces, the head and atlas rotate as one around the dens. At the same time, the inferior articular processes of the atlas glide, one forward and the other backward, on the superior articular processes of the axis.

## The Articulations of the Bodies of the Vertebrae

The articulations of the bodies of the vertebrae (Fig. 16–6) are symphysis-type joints formed by the location of intervertebral fibrocartilaginous disks between the bodies of adjacent vertebrae. The important structures in these joints are

A. *The intervertebral fibrocartilaginous disks*: interposed between the bodies of adjacent vertebrae. Each is made up of an external portion composed of elastic fibrocartilage called the annulus fibrosus, and a central portion composed of a soft, pulpy, and elastic substance called *nucleus pulposus*.

**Fig. 16–5. The bones forming the atlantooccipital articulation.**

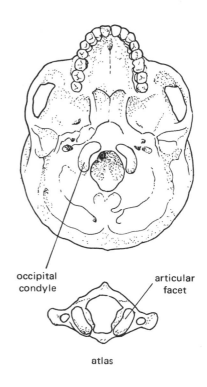

occipital condyle

articular facet

atlas

**Fig. 16–6.** The articulations of the bodies of the vertebrae and the neural arches.

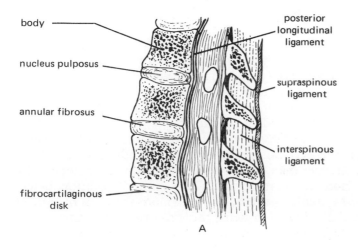

body

nucleus pulposus

annular fibrosus

fibrocartilaginous disk

posterior longitudinal ligament

supraspinous ligament

interspinous ligament

A

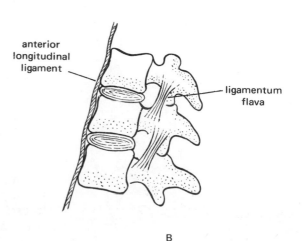

anterior longitudinal ligament

ligamentum flava

B

The size, thickness, and shape of the disks vary in different regions of the vertebral column and are associated with the curvatures. Thus, in the cervical and lumbar regions, where the curvatures are convex anteriorly, the disks are thick and wedge-shaped, whereas in the thoracic region, where the curvature is concave anteriorly, they are relatively thin and uniform in thickness, the concavity here being due primarily to the shape of the bodies.

B. *The anterior longitudinal ligament*: extends throughout the length of the vertebral column on the anterior aspect of the bodies of the vertebrae.

C. *The posterior longitudinal ligament*: extends throughout the length of the vertebral column on the posterior aspect of the bodies of the vertebrae within the vertebral canal.

## The Articulations of the Neural Arches

The articulations of the neural arches (Fig. 16–6) are sliding joints formed between the articular processes of adjacent vertebrae. The ligaments of these articulations are

A. *The ligamenta flava* (Fig. 16–7): connect the laminae of adjacent vertebrae, each being attached to the superior margin of the lamina of one vertebra and to the inferior margin of the lamina of the vertebra above.

B. *The supraspinous ligament*: attached to the tips of the spinous processes of the thoracic and lumbar vertebrae. In the cervical region, it becomes highly developed and receives the name ligamentum nuchae.

C. *The ligamentum nuchae*: attached to the occipital bone and to the spinous processes of the cervical vertebrae. Its posterior free border and lateral surfaces give attachment to the posterior muscles of the neck, including the trapezius.

D. *The interspinous ligaments*: extend between the spinous processes of adjacent vertebrae and are connected with the supraspinous ligaments posteriorly and with the ligamenta flava anteriorly.

E. *The intertransverse ligaments*: extend between the transverse processes of adjacent vertebrae. They are thin and membranous.

*Movements.* The movements of the vertebral column as a whole are *flexion, extension, hyperextension, abduction* or *lateral flexion, adduction,* and *rotation* (twisting) in the cervical and thoracic regions. *Circumduction* is a circular movement of the upper trunk on the lower, being a combination of flexion, lateral flexion, and hyperextension, but not including rotation.

The degree of motion varies in different regions of the vertebral column. In the cervical region, extension, abduction, and rotation are more extensive than in any other region of the column. In the thoracic region, these movements are limited, rotation being the freest. In the lumbar region, there is more freedom of movement than in the thoracic region, with the exception of rotation which is practically negligible, but less than in the cervical region.

**Fig. 16–7. The ligamentum nuchae.**

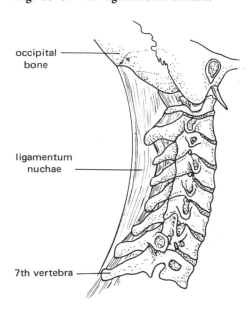

occipital bone

ligamentum nuchae

7th vertebra

The thorax (Fig. 16–8) is a bony cage formed by the sternum and costal cartilages, the ribs, and the bodies of the thoracic vertebrae. The unique bones of the thorax, however, are the sternum and the ribs. The functions of the thorax are (1) to protect the lungs, the heart, and great vessels, (2) to serve for the attachment of muscles, such as certain of the shoulder girdle and spinal muscles, and (3) to serve as a mechanical agent in the breathing process.

## 16.13 Bones of the Thorax

**Fig. 16–8. The thorax.**

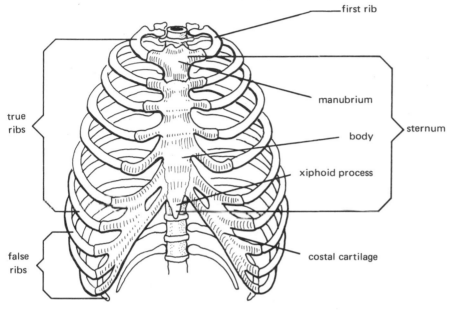

**The Sternum**

The sternum (Fig. 16–9), or breastbone, is a flat, narrow bone about 6 in. long, situated in the median line in the front of the chest. It is a somewhat dagger-shaped bone consisting of three parts: the upper handle part or *manubrium* (mah-nu'bre-um), the middle blade or *body*, and a blunt cartilaginous lower tip, the xiphoid (zif'oid) process. The xiphoid ossifies during adult life.

The superior border of the manubrium presents three notches, a middle *jugular* (jug'u-lar) *notch* and two lateral *clavicular notches*, which receive the sternal ends of the clavicle. The inferior border articulates with the superior border of the body forming an angle, called the *sternal angle*, which may be readily palpated. Each lateral border presents at its junction with the superior border a *costal notch* for articulation with the first costal cartilage and, at its junction with the inferior border, a facet that forms, with the adjacent facet on the body, a *costal notch* for the second costal cartilage. The significance of the sternal angle, therefore, is that it marks the position of the second rib as well as the junction of the manubrium and body.

On the lateral borders of the *body* of the sternum are complete *costal notches* for the third to the sixth costal cartilages and, in addition to the facet for the second costal cartilage at the sternal angle, a facet for the seventh costal cartilage at the junction of the

**Fig. 16–9. The sternum.**

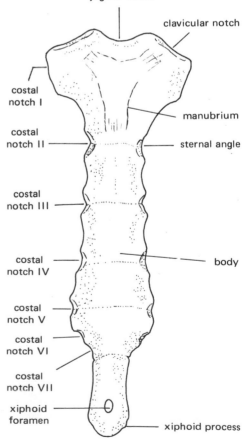

body and the xiphoid process. The latter portion of the sternum varies considerably in form. It may be partly or wholly cartilaginous, perforated by a foramen, or bifid.

### The Ribs

The greater portion of the thoracic wall consists of the twelve *ribs* and the costal cartilages that connect them to the sternum. The ribs articulate posteriorly with the thoracic vertebrae, the first, eleventh, and twelfth with the corresponding vertebra, and the others with the corresponding vertebra as well as with the vertebra above. The first seven pairs are called *true* or *sternal ribs*, in that their anterior extremities articulate by means of costal cartilages with the sternum. The remaining five pairs of ribs are called *false*, or *asternal ribs* because they do not articulate with the sternum. The costal cartilages of the eighth, ninth, and tenth ribs are joined together, that of the eighth joining with the seventh. The anterior ends of the eleventh and twelfth ribs are free and are, therefore called *floating ribs.*

Fig. 16–10.  A typical rib.

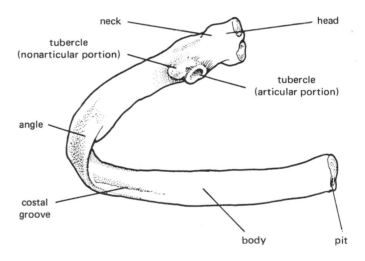

A typical rib (Fig. 16–10) presents the following characteristic features:

A. *A posterior (vertebral) extremity* or *head* that articulates with the superior demifacet of the corresponding thoracic vertebra and with the inferior demifacet of the vertebra above.
B. *A neck* that is the constricted part between the head and tubercle.
C. *A tubercle* that consists of a lateral portion for the attachment of ligaments and a *medial* or articular portion for articulation with the costal pit on the transverse process of the corresponding thoracic vertebra.
D. *A shaft* or *body* marked by an *angle* and a *costal groove.*
E. *An anterior* or *sternal extremity* marked by an *oval pit* for the reception of the costal cartilage.

The joints of the thorax (Fig. 16–11) are

**16.14   Joints of the Thorax**

A. *The costovertebral articulations*

1. *The capitular articulation* (sliding joint): formed by the head of the rib and the costal pit on the bodies of the thoracic vertebrae.
2. *The costotransverse articulation* (sliding joint): formed by the tubercle of the rib and the costal pit on the transverse process of the corresponding thoracic vertebra.

B. *The intersternal articulations*

1. *The superior intersternal joint* (synchondrosis): formed by the inferior border of the manubrium and the superior border of the body.
2. *The inferior intersternal joint* (synchondrosis): formed by the inferior border of the body and the superior border of the xiphoid process.

C. *The costochondral joints* (synchondrosis): articulations between the sternal ends of the ribs and the costal cartilages.
D. *The sternocostal joints* (synchondrosis): formed by the costal notches on the lateral borders of the sternum and the sternal ends of the costal cartilages.
E. *The interchondral joints* (sliding joints): formed by facets on the contiguous borders of the sixth to the tenth costal cartilages.

*Movements.* The movements of the thorax are those concerned with the process of breathing, i.e., inhalation and exhalation. Inhalation is brought about by an increase in the anteroposterior, transverse, and longitudinal axes of the thorax. In exhalation, the movements at the various thoracic joints are the reverse of those in inhalation.

The *increase in the anteroposterior axis in inhalation* is due to the elevation of the ribs and to the consequent forward thrust of the sternum. The center of rotation for the elevation of the ribs is at the capitular and costotransverse articulations. At the capitular articulations the heads of the ribs undergo a slight rotatory and gliding movement; at the costotransverse articulations the tubercles glide upward and backward. Owing to the obliquity of the ribs, elevation is accompanied by a lateral displacement of the shafts and a forward, as well as upward, movement of the sternal ribs. As a result of movements of the sternal ends of the ribs, the costal cartilages and sternum are thrust upward and forward, thus increasing the anteroposterior axis of the thorax. During these movements the costal cartilages, at the sternocostal articulations, rotate upward and forward, while at the same time the seventh to the tenth costal cartilages glide upon each other at the interchondral articulations.

The *increase in the transverse diameter of the thorax* is due to the elevation of the ribs, during which their shafts are displaced laterally. The *increase in the longitudinal axis* is brought about by the elevation of the ribs, with the consequent widening of the intercostal spaces and by the contraction of the diaphragm, which descends.

**Fig. 16–11. The joints of the thorax.**

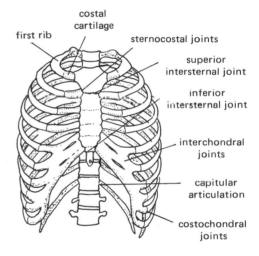

A. Anterior View

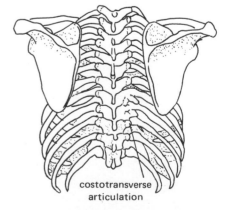

B. Posterior View

## 16.15 The Muscles of the Abdomen

The muscles of the trunk include those located on the abdomen, thorax, back, and neck.

The muscles of the abdomen are as follows:

A. *Anterior*

1. Rectus abdominis (Fig. 16-12)
2. External oblique (Fig. 16-13)
3. Internal oblique (Fig. 16-13)
4. Transversus abdominis (Fig. 16-14), also called transversalis

B. *Posterior*

1. Quadratus lumborum (Fig. 16-15)

### Anterior Muscles of the Abdomen

The muscles of the anterior abdomen include the rectus abdominis, the external oblique, the internal oblique, and the transversus abdominis. The *rectus abdominis* (Fig. 16-12) is situated on the anterior abdomen on either side of the linea alba. At three different levels transverse fibrous bands, known as tendinous inscriptions, cross the muscle fibers. Its lower attachment is on the crest of the pubis, and its upper attachment is on the cartilages of the fifth, sixth, and seventh ribs. Its action when both sides contract is flexion of the thoracic and lumbar spine. When only one side contracts, it produces lateral flexion to the same side of the thoracic and lumbar spine.

The *external oblique* (Fig. 16-13) has its upper and lateral attachments on the external surfaces of the lower eight ribs by tendinous lips that interdigitate with those of the serratus anterior. Its lower and medial attachments are on the anterior half of the iliac crest and

**Fig. 16-12. The rectus abdominis.**

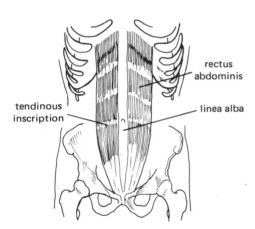

**Fig. 16-13. The external and internal obliques.**

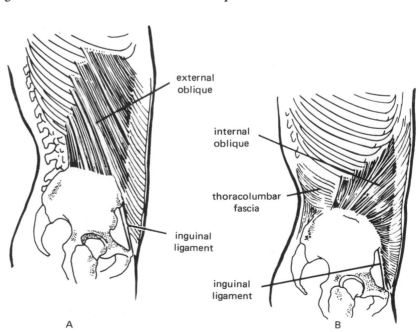

in the linea alba. When acting singly, each muscle lateral flexes and rotates the spine to the opposite side. When both sides contract, they produce flexion of the thoracic and lumbar spine. In respiration, they depress the ribs and increase abdominal pressure.

The *internal oblique* (Fig. 16-13) lies beneath the external oblique and has its lower and lateral attachments on the thoracolumbar fascia, the iliac crest, and the lateral half of the inguinal ligament. Its upper attachments are on the inferior borders of the last three ribs; its medial attachment is on the linea alba and the crest of the pubis. When both sides contract, they produce flexion of the thoracic and lumbar spine. When only one side contracts, it produces lateral flexion and rotation to the same side. The fibers of the internal oblique run in the direction opposite to those of the external oblique.

The *transversus abdominis* (Fig. 16-14) lies beneath the internal oblique, its fibers running transversely, as its name implies. Its lateral attachments are on the inguinal ligament, the crest of the ilium, the thoracolumbar fascia, and the cartilages of the lower six ribs. Its medial attachments are on the linea alba and the crest of the pubis. Its actions are compression of the abdomen and depression of the lower ribs.

### The Posterior Muscle of the Abdomen

The *quadratus lumborum* (Fig. 16-15) is situated behind the abdominal cavity at the side of the lumbar spine. It has its lower attachments on the crest of the ilium and the iliolumbar ligament. Its upper attachments are on the twelfth rib and the tips of the transverse processes of the upper four lumbar vertebrae. The only action of the quadratus lumborum is lateral flexion of the lumbar spine.

**Fig. 16-14. The transversus abdominis.**

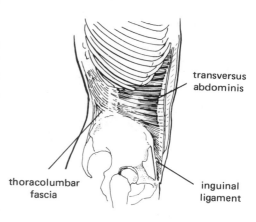

transversus abdominis

thoracolumbar fascia

inguinal ligament

**Fig. 16-15. The quadratus lumborum.**

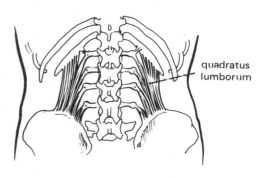

quadratus lumborum

The muscles of the thorax are as follows:

A. *Internal*

   1. Diaphragm (Fig. 16-16)
   2. Transversus thoracis (Fig. 16-17)

B. *External*

   1. *Anterior and lateral* (Fig. 16-18)

      a. External intercostals
      b. Internal intercostals

   2. *Posterior* (Fig. 16-19)

      a. Serratus posterior superior
      b. Serratus posterior inferior

## 16.16 The Muscles of the Thorax

### The Internal Muscles of the Thorax

The internal muscles of the thorax include the diaphragm and the transversus thoracis. The *diaphragm* (Fig. 16-16) is a dome-shaped

**Fig. 16-16. The diaphragm.**

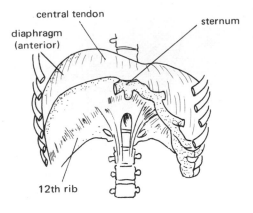

muscular sheet that separates the thoracic and abdominal cavities. Its peripheral attachment is on the circumference of the thoracic cavity, and its central attachment is on the central tendon, which is a cloverleaf-shaped aponeurosis. It is involved in inhalation by depressing the central tendon and, hence, increasing the vertical diameter of the thorax; it also has a tendency to lift the lower ribs to which it is attached.

The *transversus thoracis* (Fig. 16-17) has its medial attachments on the lower half of the inner surface of the sternum and adjoining costal cartilages. Its lateral attachments are on the lower borders and inner surfaces of the costal cartilages of the second, third, fourth, fifth, and sixth ribs. Its only action is to depress the ribs. It is important to notice that this muscle is located on the inner surface of the front wall of the thorax. The bands of fibers radiate upward and outward from the sternum to the ribs, the lowest fibers being continuous with those of the transversus abdominis.

## The External Muscles of the Thorax

The external muscles of the thorax include the external and internal intercostals and the superior and inferior serratus posterior muscles.

The *external intercostals* (Fig. 16-18) lie between the ribs, from the spine in back to the costal cartilages in front. They consist of short, parallel fibers that slant downward and forward in the same direction as the fibers of the external oblique muscle. More specifically, they attach to the lower border of one rib and the upper border of the rib beneath. They lift the ribs, thus increasing the thoracic cavity in both the transverse and anteroposterior diameters.

The *internal intercostals* (Fig. 16-18), like the external intercostals, consist of short, parallel fibers that lie between the ribs, but, unlike them, slant downward and backward. This is the same direction taken by the fibers of the internal oblique abdominal muscle. They extend from the sternum in front to the angles of the ribs in back. Since the external intercostals extend only as far forward as the costal cartilages, the anterior portion of the internal intercostals is not covered by the external intercostals. They attach to the inner surface and costal cartilage of one rib and upper border of the rib immediately below. The action of the anterior portion is elevation of the ribs; the posterior and lateral portions depress the ribs.

The *serratus posterior superior* (Fig. 16-19) has its upper attachments on the spinous processes and ligaments of the lower two or three cervical and the upper two thoracic vertebrae. Its lower attachments are on the upper borders of the second, third, fourth, and fifth ribs, and it acts to elevate these ribs.

The *serratus posterior inferior* (Fig. 16-19) has its lower, medial attachments on the spinous processes and ligaments of the lower thoracic and upper two or three lumbar vertebrae. Its upper, lateral attachments are on the lower borders of the lower four ribs. Its action is depression of the lower four ribs.

**Fig. 16-17. The transversus thoracis.**

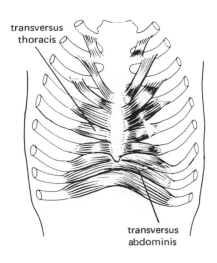

**Fig. 16–18.** The external and internal intercostals.

**Fig. 16–19.** The serratus posterior superior and inferior.

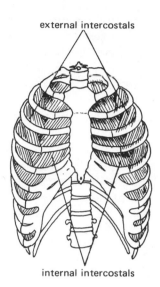

external intercostals

internal intercostals

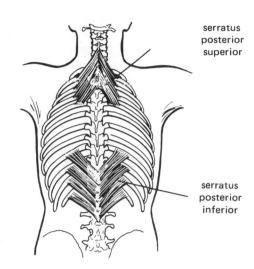

serratus posterior superior

serratus posterior inferior

The muscles of the trunk located on the back are

A. *Erector spinae* (spi′ne), once called the *sacrospinalis* (sa″kro-spi-na′lis), three groups (Fig. 16–20)

    1. Iliocostalis (il″e-o-kos-ta′lis): lateral group

        a. Iliocostalis thoracis
        b. Iliocostalis cervicis
        c. Iliocostalis lumborum

    2. Longissimus (lon-jis′i-mus): middle group

        a. Longissimus thoracis
        b. Longissimus cervicis
        c. Longissimus capitis

    3. Spinalis (spi-na′lis): medial group

        a. Spinalis thoracis
        b. Spinalis cervicis

B. *Semispinalis* (Fig. 16–21)

    1. Semispinalis thoracis
    2. Semispinalis cervicis
    3. Semispinalis capitis

C. *Deep posterior muscles of the spine* (Fig. 16–22)

    1. Multifidus
    2. Rotatores, longus and brevis
    3. Interspinalis
    4. Intertransversus, lateralis and medius
    5. Levator costae, longus and brevis

The *erector spinae* (Fig. 16–20) are the most superficial of the back muscles. They consist of three groups: iliocostalis, the lateral group; longissimus, the middle group, and spinalis, the medial group. This

### 16.17 The Muscles of the Back

**Fig. 16–20.** The erector spinae.

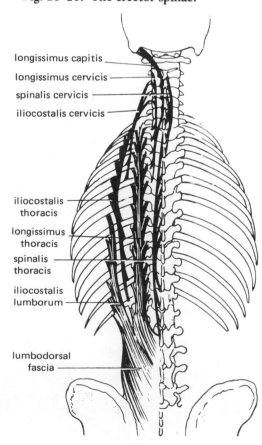

longissimus capitis

longissimus cervicis

spinalis cervicis

iliocostalis cervicis

iliocostalis thoracis

longissimus thoracis

spinalis thoracis

iliocostalis lumborum

lumbodorsal fascia

**Fig. 16-21. The semispinalis.**

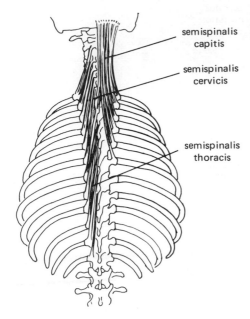

- semispinalis capitis
- semispinalis cervicis
- semispinalis thoracis

extensive muscle mass of the back has its lower attachments on the lumbodorsal fascia, the posterior portions of the lumbar, thoracic, and lower cervical vertebrae, and the angles of the ribs. Its upper attachments span six to eight segments and are on the angles of the ribs, the posterior portions of the cervical and thoracic vertebrae, and the mastoid process of the temporal bone. When both sides contract, they produce extension and hyperextension of the head and entire spine. When only one side contracts, it results in lateral flexion and rotation of the head and spine to same side.

The *semispinalis thoracis, cervicis,* and *capitis* (Fig. 16-21) have their lower attachments on the transverse processes of all thoracic and seventh cervical vertebrae and on the articular processes of the lower four cervical vertebrae. As their name implies, they cover half the spine and have no attachment in the lumbar or sacral area. Their upper attachments span three to four segments and are on the spinous processes of the upper four thoracic and lower five cervical vertebrae, and on the occipital bone. These muscles form a middle mass of muscle between the erector spinae and the deep posterior muscles. When both sides contract, the actions are extension and hyperextension of the head, neck, and thoracic spine. When only one side contracts, it produces lateral flexion of the head, neck, and thoracic spine and rotation of the thoracic spine to the opposite side.

The *deep posterior muscles of the spine* (Fig. 16-22) have their lower attachments on the posterior surface of the sacrum and spinous processes of all the vertebrae. Their upper attachments span one or two segments and are on the spinous and transverse processes and laminae of the vertebrae slightly higher than their lower attachments. When both sides contract, they cause extension and hyperextension of the spine. When only one side contracts, it produces rotation to the opposite side and assists in lateral flexion.

It can be observed from the preceding discussion that as one progresses from the superficial to the deep mass, the number of segments spanned by the muscles is reduced. This is of value in that it reduces the muscle bulk and aids in the smoothness of the movement.

## 16.18 The Muscles of the Neck

The muscles of the trunk located in the neck region are

A. *Anterior*

  1. *Prevertebral* (pre-ver'te-bral) muscles (Fig. 16-23)

     a. Longus capitis
     b. Longus cervicis
     c. Rectus capitis anterior
     d. Rectus capitis lateralis

  2. *Hyoid* (hi'oid) muscles (Fig. 16-24)

     a. Suprahyoids

        (1) Mylohyoid

    (2) Geniohyoid
    (3) Digastric
    (4) Stylohyoid

  b. Infrahyoids

    (1) Thyrohyoid
    (2) Sternothyroid
    (3) Sternohyoid
    (4) Omohyoid

  3. *Sternocleidomastoid* (ster′no-kli″do-mas′toid)
    (Fig. 16–25)

B. *Lateral*

  1. *The three scaleni* (Fig. 16–26)

    a. Scalenus (ska-le′nus) anterior
    b. Scalenus posterior
    c. Scalenus medius

C. *Posterior*

  1. *The two spleni muscles* (Fig. 16–27)

    a. Splenius (sple′ne-us) capitis
    b. Splenius cervicis

  2. *The suboccipitals* (sub″ok-sip′i-tals) (Fig. 16–28)

    a. Obliquus capitis superior
    b. Obliquus capitis inferior
    c. Rectus capitis posterior minor
    d. Rectus capitis posterior major

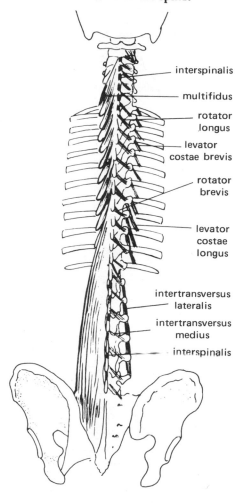

Fig. 16–22. The deep posterior muscles of the spine.

## Anterior Muscles of the Neck

The anterior group of neck muscles includes the prevertebral muscles, the hyoid muscles, and the sternocleidomastoid. The *pre-*

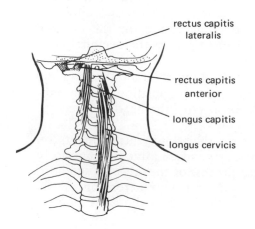

Fig. 16–23. The prevertebral muscles.

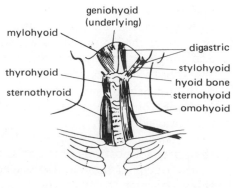

Fig. 16–24. The hyoid muscles.

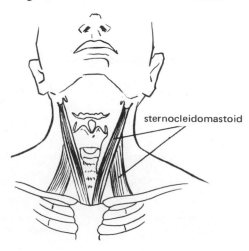

Fig. 16–25. The sternocleidomastoid.

**Fig. 16-26. The three scaleni muscles.**

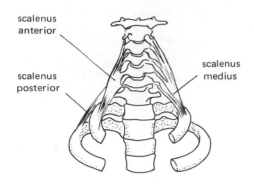

**Fig. 16-27. The two spleni muscles.**

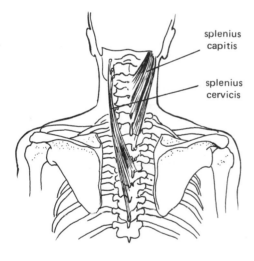

**Fig. 16-28. The suboccipitals.**

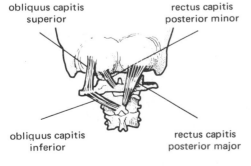

*vertebral muscles* (Fig. 16-23) are attached inferiorly to the anterior surfaces of the upper three thoracic vertebrae and to all seven cervical vertebrae. They are attached superiorly to the anterior portions of the occipital bone and the cervical vertebrae. When both sides contract, they produce flexion of the head and neck. When only one side contracts, it produces lateral flexion of the head and neck.

The *hyoid muscles* (Fig. 16-24) include the suprahyoids and the infrahyoids, i.e., the muscles above and below the hyoid bone. The suprahyoids are attached to the temporal bone and the mandible above, and to the hyoid bone below. The infrahyoids are attached to the hyoid bone above and to the sternum and shoulder girdle below. These muscles are primarily muscles of some phase of the act of swallowing. They produce flexion of the *cervical* spine, however, whenever the movement is performed against resistance.

The *sternocleidomastoid* (Fig. 16-25) has two heads at its lower attachment: one from the top of the sternum and the other from the medial third of the clavicle. It is attached superiorly to the mastoid process of the temporal bone and adjacent portion of the occipital bone. When both sides contract, they flex the head and neck. When only one side contracts, it results in lateral flexion and rotation to the opposite side.

## Lateral Muscles of the Neck

The lateral neck muscles include the three scaleni: the scalenus anterior, scalenus posterior, and the scalenus medius. The *three scaleni* (Fig. 16-26) are attached inferiorly to the first two ribs and are attached superiorly to the transverse processes of the cervical vertebrae. When both sides contract, they help to flex the neck. When only one side contracts, it results in lateral flexion of the neck.

## Posterior Muscles of the Neck

The posterior muscles of the neck consist of the two spleni (capitis and cervicis) and the suboccipitals. The *two spleni* (Fig. 16-27) have their lower attachments on the lower half of the ligamentum nuchae and on the spinous processes of the seventh cervical and upper six thoracic vertebrae. Their upper attachments are on the mastoid process of the temporal bone and adjacent part of the occipital bone and on the transverse processes of the upper three cervical vertebrae. When both sides contract, they extend and hyperextend the head and neck and help to support the head in the erect position. When only one side contracts, it lateral flexes and rotates the head and neck to the same side.

The *suboccipitals* (Fig. 16-28) have their lower attachments on the posterior portions of the atlas and axis and are attached superiorly to the occipital bone and transverse process of the atlas. When both sides contract, they produce extension and hyperextension of the head. Lateral flexion and rotation of the head to the same side are the results of only one side contracting.

16.21   Bones of the Vertebral Column                    16.20   Study Guidelines

A. Specific Student Objectives

1. How long is the vertebral column in a man of average height?
2. How many separate bones make up the vertebral column in a typical adult?
3. How many vertebrae are found in the following areas and what are the names of these vertebrae?

        neck                    small of the back
        thorax                  pelvis

4. Which vertebra does not have a body or a spinous process?
5. Which vertebrae do not have vertebral foramen?
6. Locate a typical vertebra in a mounted skeleton and identify the following:

        body or centrum         spinous process
        neural arch             transverse process
        pedicles                superior articular processes
        laminae                 inferior articular processes
        vertebral foramen       intervertebral fibrocartilagi-
        vertebral notches          nous disks

7. Describe the four articulations found between two typical vertebrae.
8. Give the identifying characteristics of the following vertebrae:

        cervical vertebrae      axis
        thoracic vertebrae      sacrum
        lumbar vertebrae        coccyx
        atlas

9. Locate the vertebral column in a mounted skeleton and identify the following:

        cervical, thoracic, and lumbar vertebrae
        sacrum and coccyx
        atlas and axis
        bony ring of atlas
        dens or odontoid process of axis
        demifacets and costal pits of thoracic vertebrae
        vertebra prominens

10. Why is there greater freedom of movement in the cervical and lumbar regions of the column than there is in the thoracic region?
11. Locate the vertebral column in your own body and identify the following:

        vertebra prominens
        spinous processes
        sacrum

B. Study Hints

1. The use of actual bones is recommended in the study of specific bone markings.
2. Locating bony landmarks in the student's body is also a valuable aid to learning.

### 16.22 Joints of the Vertebral Column

A. Specific Student Objectives

1. *The Atlantooccipital Articulation*

   a. What type of joint is this?
   b. Describe the bony articulations involved in this joint.
   c. What movements are allowed at this joint? Describe these movements.

2. *The Atlantoaxial Articulations*

   a. How many joints are involved in these articulations?
   b. Describe the bony articulations involved in each of these joints.
   c. What type of joints are these?
   d. Identify the names of each of these joints.
   e. What movements are allowed at these joints?

3. *The Articulations of the Bodies of the Vertebrae*

   a. What type of joints are these?
   b. Describe the bony articulations involved in these joints.
   c. Describe the features of the intervertebral fibrocartilaginous disks.
   d. Describe the ligamentous reinforcements of these joints.

4. *The Articulations of the Neural Arches*

   a. What type of joints are these?
   b. Describe the bony articulations involved in these joints.
   c. Describe the ligamentous reinforcements of these joints.
   d. What are the movements of the vertebral column as a whole? Describe these movements.
   e. What degree of motion is allowed in each of the three major regions of the vertebral column?

B. Study Hints

1. The student should study each of these joints on a mounted skeleton, where he can visualize the bony articulations and ligamentous reinforcements involved in the joint.

2. The student should also perform the movements of the vertebral column as a whole and the movements of the head according to the descriptions presented in the text.

It is important that the student learn to identify the movements of the vertebral column and of the head whenever he sees them performed.

## 16.23  Bones of the Thorax

A. Specific Student Objectives

1. *General Information*

   a. What bones form the thorax?
   b. What are the unique bones of the thorax?
   c. What are the functions of the thorax?

2. *The Sternum*

   a. About how long is the sternum?
   b. What are the three major parts of the sternum?
   c. Locate the sternum on a mounted skeleton and identify the following:

   | | |
   |---|---|
   | manubrium | body |
   | jugular notch | costal notches |
   | clavicular notches | xiphoid process |
   | sternal angle | |

   d. Locate the sternum in your body and identify the following:

   | | |
   |---|---|
   | manubrium | body |
   | jugular notch | xiphoid process |
   | sternal angle | |

3. *The Ribs*

   a. How many ribs are located on each side of the thorax?
   b. What is a costal cartilage?
   c. Describe the articulations of the ribs.
   d. Locate a typical rib on a mounted skeleton and identify the following:

   | | |
   |---|---|
   | head | angle |
   | neck | costal groove |
   | tubercle | sternal extremity |
   | shaft or body | oval pit |

   e. Locate the ribs in your body and identify the following:

   | | |
   |---|---|
   | angle | shaft |

B. Study Hints

1. The use of actual bones is recommended in the study of specific bone markings.

### 16.24 Joints of the Thorax

A. Specific Student Objectives

1. Identify the seven classifications of thoracic joints.
2. Identify the type of joints involved in each classification.
3. Describe the bony articulations involved in each classification.
4. Locate each joint on a mounted skeleton.
5. Describe the movements of the thorax. At what joints do these movements occur?

B. Study Hints

1. The student should study each of these joints on a mounted skeleton, where he can visualize the bony articulations involved in the movements allowed at each joint.

### 16.25 The Muscles of the Abdomen

A. Specific Student Objectives

1. Identify the four muscles located on the anterior abdomen, and give their attachments.
2. Identify the one muscle located on the posterior abdomen, and give its attachment.

### 16.26 The Muscles of the Thorax

A. Specific Student Objectives

1. Identify the two internal muscles of the thorax.
2. Identify the two external muscles located on the anterior and lateral aspects of the thorax.
3. Identify the two external muscles located on the posterior aspects of the thorax.
4. Give the attachments of each of these muscles.
5. Give the actions of each of these muscles.

### 16.27 The Muscles of the Back

A. Specific Student Objectives

1. Name the three layers of back muscles.
2. Name the three groups of erector spinae muscles.
3. What muscles are located in each of the three groups of erector spinae muscles?
4. What are the three parts of the semispinalis layer of back muscles?
5. What five muscles are located in the deepest layer of back muscles?
6. What are the joint actions produced by each of the three groups of back muscles?

## 16.28   The Muscles of the Neck

A.  Specific Student Objectives

1.  *The Anterior Neck Muscles*

a.  Name the two groups of muscles located on the anterior neck along with the sternocleidomastoid.
b.  What joint actions are produced by these groups?
c.  What joint actions are produced by the sternocleidomastoid?
d.  What four muscles are located in the prevertebral group?
e.  Give the two major divisions of hyoid muscles.

2.  *The Lateral Neck Muscles*

a.  What three muscles are located on the lateral side of the neck?
b.  What are the attachments of these muscles?
c.  What are the joint actions of these muscles?

3.  *The Posterior Neck Muscles*

a.  What two groups of muscles are located on the posterior side of the neck?
b.  What are the joint actions produced by each of these groups?
c.  What two muscles are located in the spleni group?
d.  What four muscles are located in the suboccipital group?

B.  Study Hints

1.  Table 16–1 is presented to aid in the mastery of specific muscle actions and attachments.
2.  Instructions as to where the muscles of the trunk can be palpated are presented in Table 16–2.  The student should perform each of the movements of the trunk and attempt to locate through palpation each of the muscles listed in Table 16–2.

**Table 16–1.  The Attachments and Actions of the Trunk Muscles**

| Location | Name | Upper Attachment | Illustration | Lower Attachment | Action |
|---|---|---|---|---|---|
| Abdomen anterior group | Rectus abdominis | Cartilages of fifth, sixth, and seventh ribs | Fig. 16–12 | Crest of the pubis | Flexion and lateral flexion of thoracic and lumbar spine |
| | External oblique | Upper and lateral: external surfaces of lower eight ribs | Fig. 16–13 | Lower and medial: anterior half of iliac crest and into linea alba | Flexion, lateral flexion, and rotation opposite of thoracic and lumbar spine; depression of ribs |

**Table 16-1. The Attachments and Actions of the Trunk Muscles (continued)**

| Location | Name | Upper Attachment | Illustration | Lower Attachment | Action |
|---|---|---|---|---|---|
| | Internal oblique | Upper: inferior borders of last three ribs. Medial: linea alba, crest of pubis | Fig. 16-13 | Lower and lateral: thoracolumbar fascia, iliac crest, and lateral half of inguinal ligament | Flexion, lateral flexion, and rotation same side of thoracic and lumbar spine |
| | Transverse abdominis | Lateral: inguinal ligament, crest of ilium, and thoracolumbar fascia, and cartilages of lower six ribs | Fig. 16-14 | Medial: linea alba and crest of the pubis | Compression of abdomen and depression of lower ribs |
| posterior muscle | Quadratus lumborum | Twelfth rib and tips of the transverse processes of upper four lumbar vertebrae | Fig. 16-15 | Crest of ilium and iliolumbar ligament | Lateral flexion of lumbar spine |
| Thorax internal group | Diaphragm | Peripheral: circumference of the thoracic cavity | Fig. 16-16 | Central: central tendon | Increase in vertical diameter of thorax |
| | Transversus thoracis | Upper: inferior borders of last three ribs. Medial: linea alba, crest of pubis | Fig. 16-17 | Lower and lateral: thoracolumbar fascia, iliac crest, and lateral half of inguinal ligament | Depression of ribs |
| external group | External intercostals | Lower border of one rib | Fig. 16-18 | Upper border of the rib beneath | Elevation of ribs |
| | Internal intercostals | Inner surface and costal cartilage of one rib | Fig. 16-18 | Upper border of the rib immediately below | Anterior part: elevation of ribs Posterior and lateral part: depression of ribs |
| | Serratus posterior superior | Spinous processes and ligaments of lower two or three cervical and upper two thoracic vertebrae | Fig. 16-19 | Upper borders of second, third, fourth, and fifth ribs | Elevation of ribs |
| | Serratus posterior inferior | Lower borders of the lower four ribs | Fig. 16-19 | Spinous processes and ligaments of lower thoracic and upper two or three lumbar vertebrae | Depression of lower four ribs |
| Back | Erector spinae | Angles of ribs, posterior portions of cervical and thoracic vertebrae, and mastoid process of temporal bone | Fig. 16-20 | Lumbodorsal fascia, posterior portions of lumbar, thoracic, and lower cervical vertebrae and on angles of ribs | Extension, lateral flexion, and rotation of head and spine to same side |
| | Semispinalis | Spinous processes of upper four thoracic and lower five cervical vertebrae and occipital bone | Fig. 16-21 | Transverse processes of all thoracic and seventh cervical vertebrae and articular processes of lower four cervical vertebrae | Extension, lateral flexion, and rotation of thoracic spine to opposite side |
| | Deep posterior muscles | Spinous and transverse processes and laminae of the vertebrae slightly higher than their lower attachments | Fig. 16-22 | Posterior surface of sacrum, and spinous processes of all vertebrae | Extension, lateral flexion, and rotation of opposite side |

Table 16–1. The Attachments and Actions of the Trunk Muscles

| Location | Name | Upper Attachment | Illustration | Lower Attachment | Action |
|---|---|---|---|---|---|
| Neck: anterior | Prevertebral | Anterior portions of occipital bone and cervical vertebrae | Fig. 16–23 | Anterior surfaces of the upper three thoracic vertebrae, and to all seven cervical vertebrae | Flexion and lateral flexion of head and neck |
| | Hyoids | Temporal bone and mandible | Fig. 16–24 | Hyoid bone, sternum, and clavicle | Flexion of cervical spine |
| | Sternocleidomastoid | Mastoid process of temporal bone | Fig. 16–25 | Top of sternum, and on medial third of clavicle | Flexion, lateral flexion, and rotation of head to opposite side |
| lateral | Three scaleni | Transverse process of cervical vertebrae | Fig. 16–26 | First two ribs | Flexion and lateral flexion of the neck |
| posterior | Two spleni | Mastoid process of temporal bone, occipital bone, transverse processes of upper three cervical vertebrae | Fig. 16–27 | Lower half of ligamentum nuchae, spinous processes of seventh cervical and upper six thoracic vertebrae | Extension, lateral flexion, and rotation of head and neck to same side |
| | Suboccipitals | Occipital bone and transverse process of atlas | Fig. 16–28 | Posterior portions of atlas and axis | Extension, lateral flexion, and rotation of head to same side |

Table 16–2. Instructions for Palpating the Muscles of the Trunk

| Name of Muscle | Where the Muscle Can Be Palpated |
|---|---|

I. The muscles of the abdomen

    A. Anterior

| | |
|---|---|
|   1. Rectus abdominis (Fig. 16–12) | In well-developed subjects the rectus abdominis may be palpated throughout its length on the front of the abdomen, from the pubis to the sternum. |
|   2. External oblique (Fig. 16–13) | This muscle is located at the side of the abdomen. |
|   3. Internal oblique (Fig. 16–13) | This muscle is located at the side of the abdomen, beneath the external oblique. It may be palpated through the external oblique when the latter is relaxed, as in rotation. For example, the left external oblique is relaxed when the trunk is rotated to the left. |
|   4. Transversus abdominis (Fig. 16–14) | Cannot be palpated. |

    B. Posterior

| | |
|---|---|
|   1. Quadratus lumborum (Fig. 16–15) | In thin, muscular subjects this muscle can be palpated in the lumbar region of the back just lateral to the erector spinae. |

**Table 16-2. Instructions for Palpating the Muscles of the Trunk (continued)**

| *Name of Muscle* | *Where the Muscle Can Be Palpated* |
| --- | --- |
| II.  *The muscles of the thorax* | |
| A. Internal | |
| 1. Diaphragm (Fig. 16-16) | Cannot be palpated. |
| 2. Transversus thoracis (Fig. 16-17) | Cannot be palpated. |
| B. External | |
| 1. Anterior and lateral (Fig. 16-18) | |
| a. External intercostals | On thin subjects, this muscle can be palpated between the ribs anterior to the serratus anterior. |
| b. Internal intercostals | Cannot be palpated. |
| 2. Posterior (Fig. 16-19) | |
| a. Serratus posterior superior | Cannot be palpated. |
| b. Serratus posterior inferior | Cannot be palpated. |
| III.  *The muscles of the back* | |
| A. Erector spinae (Fig. 16-20) | This muscle can be palpated in the lumbar and lower thoracic regions of the back where it appears as two broad ridges on either side of the vertebral column. |
| B. Semispinalis (Fig. 16-21) | Cannot be palpated. |
| C. Deep posterior muscles of the spine (Fig. 16-22) | Cannot be palpated. |
| IV.  *The muscles of the neck* | |
| A. Anterior | |
| 1. Prevertebral (Fig. 16-23) | Cannot be palpated. |
| 2. Hyoid muscles (Fig. 16-24) | The suprahyoids may be palpated just below the jawbone. The infrahyoids cannot be palpated. |
| 3. Sternocleidomastoid | This muscle can be palpated on the side of the neck from just below the ear to the front of the neck at the junction of the clavicle and sternum. |
| B. Lateral | |
| 1. The three scaleni (Fig. 16-26) | These muscles can be palpated on the side of the neck between the sternocleidomastoid and upper trapezius, which is often difficult to identify. |
| C. Posterior | |
| 1. The two spleni (Fig. 16-27) | These muscles can be palpated, with difficulty, on the back of the neck just lateral to the trapezius and posterior to the sternocleidomastoid, above the levator scapulae. |
| 2. The suboccipitals (Fig. 16-28) | Cannot be palpated. |

**16.30 Recommended Supplementary Readings**

The student should consult any recent basic anatomy text for supplementary readings on the structure of the trunk. A list of selected anatomy texts is given in Appendix B.

# 17

# Movements and Problems
of the Trunk

**General Student Objective**

*In his study of the basic concepts of this chapter the student should become familiar with:*

    *17.11  Movements of the Cervical Spine and Atlantooccipital Joint*
    *17.12  Movements of the Thoracic and Lumbar Spine*
    *17.13  Movements of the Thorax in Respiration*
    *17.14  Movements of the Pelvis*
    *17.15  Conditioning Problems of the Trunk*
    *17.16  Postural and Pathological Problems of the Trunk*
    *17.17  Traumatic Problems of the Trunk*

The movements of the cervical spine and of the atlantooccipital joint are flexion and extension, lateral flexion, and rotation.

**17.11 Movements of the Cervical Spine and Atlantooccipital Joint**

**Flexion and Extension**

The muscles that produce flexion and extension of the cervical spine and of the atlantooccipital joint are

    A. *Flexion* (Fig. 17–1)

        1.  Sternocleidomastoid
        2.  Prevertebral muscles
        3.  Three scaleni
        4.  Hyoid muscles

    B. *Extension* (Fig. 17–2)

        1.  Splenius cervicis and capitis
        2.  Erector spinae, cervicis and capitis portions

**Fig. 17–1. Flexors of the head and neck.**

**Fig. 17–2. Extensors of the head and neck.**

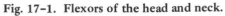

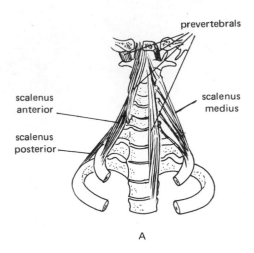

prevertebrals

scalenus anterior

scalenus posterior

scalenus medius

A

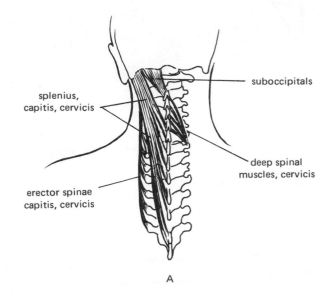

suboccipitals

splenius, capitis, cervicis

deep spinal muscles, cervicis

erector spinae capitis, cervicis

A

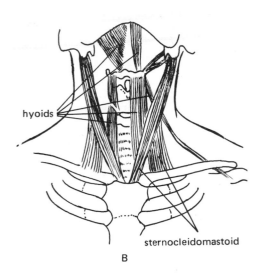

hyoids

sternocleidomastoid

B

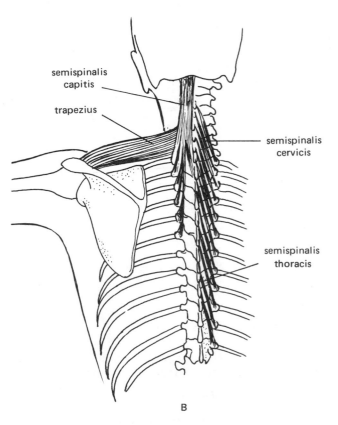

semispinalis capitis

trapezius

semispinalis cervicis

semispinalis thoracis

B

3. Semispinalis, cervicis and capitis portions
4. The suboccipitals
5. The deep posterior spinal muscles, cervicis portions
6. Trapezius I

*Flexion* of the head and neck is brought about by all the anterior and lateral muscles of the neck. These include the prevertebrals, sternocleidomastoid and hyoid muscles anteriorly and the three scaleni laterally.

*Extension* and *hyperextension* of the head and neck are brought about by all the posterior muscles of the neck and back. These include the two spleni muscles and the suboccipitals in the neck, plus the cervicis and capitis portions of the erector spinae, semispinalis, the deep posterior spinal muscles located on the back, and trapezius I.

## Rotation

Rotation of the head and neck is produced by the sternocleidomastoid and the cervicis portion of the deep posterior spinal muscles, which rotate the trunk to the opposite side from their own location. The suboccipitals and the capitis and cervicis portions of the splenius and erector spinae rotate the trunk to the same side as their own location. In list form, these muscles are

A. *Rotation* (Fig. 17–3)

1. Rotators to the opposite side

a. Sternocleidomastoid
b. Deep posterior spinal muscles, cervicis portions

2. Rotators to the same side

a. Splenius, capitis and cervicis
b. Erector spinae, capitis and certivis portions
c. Suboccipitals

## Lateral Flexion

Lateral flexion of the head and neck is brought about by all the muscles of the neck and back with the exception of the hyoids, which are involved only in flexion. In list form, these muscles are

A. *Lateral flexion* (Fig. 17–4)

1. Three scaleni
2. Splenius, capitis and cervicis
3. Prevertebral muscles, lateral portion
4. Sternocleidomastoid
5. Erector spinae, capitis and cervicis portions
6. Semispinalis, capitis and cervicis portions
7. Suboccipitals
8. Deep posterior spinal muscles, certicis portion
9. Lavator scapulae

**Fig. 17–3.** Rotators of the head and neck. The muscles that rotate to the same side and those that rotate to the opposite side are indicated.

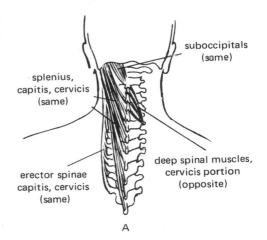

suboccipitals (same)

splenius, capitis, cervicis (same)

deep spinal muscles, cervicis portion (opposite)

erector spinae capitis, cervicis (same)

A

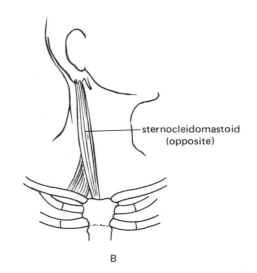

sternocleidomastoid (opposite)

B

**Fig. 17–4. Lateral flexors of the head and neck.**

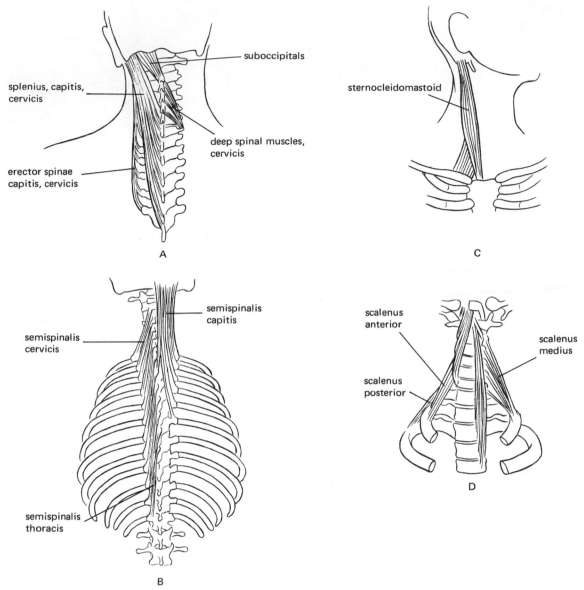

The movements of the thoracic and lumbar spine are flexion and extension, lateral flexion and rotation.

**17.12 Movements of the Thoracic and Lumbar Spine**

### Flexion and Extension

The muscles that produce flexion and extension of the thoracic and lumbar spine are

A. *Flexion* (Fig. 17–5)

1. Rectus abdominis
2. External oblique
3. Internal oblique
4. Psoas

B. *Extension* and *hyperextension* (Fig. 17–6)

1. Erector spinae, thoracic and lumbar portions
2. Semispinalis thoracis
3. Deep posterior spinal muscles

*Flexion* of the thoracic and lumbar spine is brought about by the rectus abdominis, external and internal obliques, and the psoas. This obviously includes all the anterior muscles of the abdomen except the transversalis, which is mostly a muscle of respiration. The quadratus lumborum, which is the posterior member of the abdomen, is only involved in lateral flexion. The three abdominal muscles are the principal movers in flexion with some assistance from the psoas.

*Extension* of the thoracic and lumbar spine is brought about by the erector spinae, thoracic and lumbar portions, and the semispinalis thoracis with some assistance from the deep posterior spinal muscles.

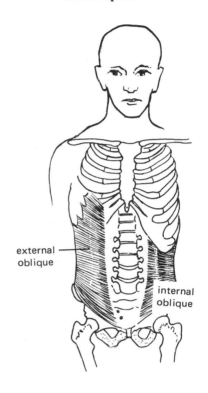

**Fig. 17–5. Flexors of the thoracic and lumbar spine.**

external oblique

internal oblique

**Fig. 17–6. Extensors of the thoracic and lumbar spine.**

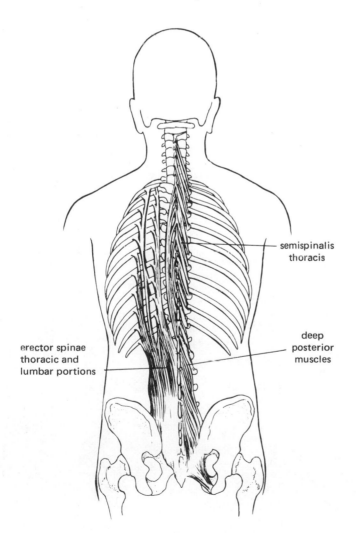

erector spinae thoracic and lumbar portions

semispinalis thoracis

deep posterior muscles

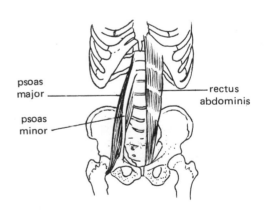

psoas major

psoas minor

rectus abdominis

## Rotation

Rotation of the thoracic and lumbar spine is produced by the external oblique, semispinalis thoracis, and the deep posterior spinal muscles, which rotate the trunk to the opposite side from their own location. The internal oblique and the erector spinae rotate the trunk to the same side as their own location. In list form, these muscles are

A. *Rotation* (Fig. 17-7)

   1. Rotators to the opposite side

      a. External oblique
      b. Semispinalis thoracis
      c. Deep posterior spinal muscles

   2. Rotators to the same side

      a. Internal oblique
      b. Erector spinae, thoracic and lumbar portions

## Lateral Flexion

Lateral flexion of the thoracic and lumbar spine is brought about by all the flexors and extensors listed above, plus the strong action of the quadratus lumborum, and perhaps with some assistance from the latissimus dorsi. In list form, these muscles are

**17-7.** Rotators of the thoracic and lumbar spine. The muscles that rotate to the same side and those that rotate to the opposite side are indicated.

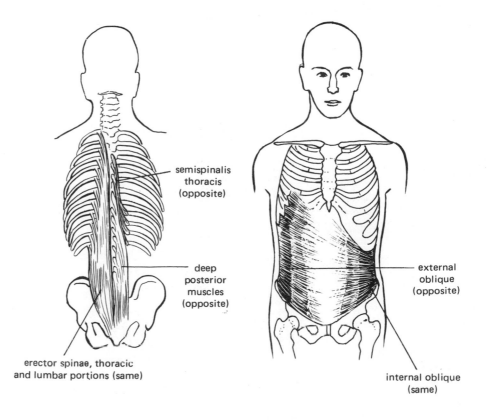

semispinalis thoracis (opposite)

deep posterior muscles (opposite)

erector spinae, thoracic and lumbar portions (same)

external oblique (opposite)

internal oblique (same)

A. *Lateral flexion* (Fig. 17–4)

1. Erector spinae, thoracic and lumbar portions
2. Semispinalis thoracis
3. Deep posterior spinal muscles
4. Rectus abdominis
5. External oblique
6. Internal oblique
7. Psoas
8. Quadratus lumborum
9. Latissimus dorsi

The movements of the thorax in respiration and the muscles that produce them are

**17.13 Movements of the Thorax in Respiration**

A. *Normal inhalation*

Muscular action is required for all inhalation, regardless of how shallow.

1. Diaphragm
2. External intercostals
3. Internal intercostals, anterior part

B. *Additional muscles of vigorous inhalation*

The following muscles are brought into the movement only when inhalation is vigorous or is resisted.

1. Serratus posterior superior
2. The thoracic spine extensors
3. Sternocleidomastoid
4. The three scaleni
5. Pectoralis minor (a shoulder muscle)
6. Trapezius I (a shoulder muscle)
7. Levator scapulae

C. *Vigorous exhalation*

Normal exhalation is brought about by the weight of the chest and the relaxation of the muscles of normal inhalation, plus the normal recoil of the elastic structures of the thorax. The following muscles, therefore, are brought into the movement only when exhalation is vigorous or is resisted.

1. Serratus posterior inferior
2. Transversus thoracis
3. Internal intercostals, lateral and posterior parts
4. The abdominal muscles

    a. Transversus abdominis
    b. Rectus abdominis
    c. External oblique
    d. Internal oblique

*Normal inhalation* involves the weak contraction of the diaphragm and the slight elevation of the ribs produced by the external intercostals and the anterior part of the internal intercostals. *Vigorous inhalation,* on the other hand, involves a strong contraction by the diaphragm, which presses downward against the abdominal organs, which, in turn, push forward against the relaxed abdominal wall. This downward movement of the diaphragm increases the vertical diameter of the thorax. The transverse and anteroposterior diameters of the thorax are increased by certain muscles of the thorax, shoulder, neck, and back that act to elevate the ribs. These muscles are listed above.

*Normal exhalation* is produced by the relaxation of the intercostals and the weight of the chest, plus the elastic recoil of the diaphragm. *Vigorous exhalation,* however, requires the contraction of the abdominal organs, which, in turn, push upward against the relaxed diaphragm. This action of the abdominal muscles decreases the vertical diameter of the thorax. The serratus posterior inferior, transversus thoracis, and the lateral and posterior parts of the internal intercostals act to depress the ribs and thereby to decrease the transverse and anteroposterior diameters of the thorax.

## 17.14 Movements of the Pelvis

The movements of the pelvis are forward tilt, backward tilt, lateral tilt, and rotation. None of the muscles that perform these movements are, strictly speaking, muscles of the pelvis, but rather muscles of the hip joint or of the trunk. This is true because the movements of the pelvis take place at the lumbar spine, the lumbosacral junction, and the hip joints. In fact, all the muscles of the trunk and of the hip joint, which attach to the pelvic bones or to the sacrum, act in some way either to initiate or to control the movements of the pelvis.

*Forward tilt* of the pelvis is associated with hyperextension of the lumbar spine and flexion of the hip joints. This movement is assisted especially by the anterior thigh muscles attaching to the front of the pelvis and is associated with any increase in the lumbar curvature.

*Backward tilt* of the pelvis is associated with flexion of the lumbar spine and extension of the hip joints. This movement is brought about both by the downward pull of the extensor muscles of the hip, especially the hamstrings, and by the upward pull on the pubis of the anterolateral musculature of the abdominal wall, especially the rectus abdominis.

*Lateral tilting* of the pelvis tends to occur when the weight is put upon one leg. The sagging of the pelvis on the unsupported side is opposed by the passive checking action of the fascia lata, particularly the iliotibial tract, and by the active contraction of the gluteus medius and minimus. With both feet on the ground, lateral tilt of the pelvis is associated with lateral tilt of the lumbar spine.

*Rotation* of the pelvis and trunk as a whole upon one femoral head, as in walking, is brought about mostly by certain of the rotators of the thigh, assisted also by the anterolateral abdominal muscles.

The primary conditioning problems of the trunk are those concerned with the flexibility of the trunk movements, and with the strength, power, and endurance of the trunk muscles.

### 17.15 Conditioning Problems of the Trunk

### Flexibility of the Trunk

Exercises designed to stretch the muscles and connective tissues of the trunk are illustrated in Figure 17-8.

### Isometric Measurements of Strength

The Clark Cable-Tension Strength Tests for the flexors, extensors, and lateral flexors of the trunk are illustrated in Figures 17-9 through 17-11.

### Isotonic Exercises and Measurements

Some isotonic exercises that can also be used to measure the strength, power, and endurance of the thigh and hip muscles are illustrated in Figure 17-12.

Fig. 17-8. Some flexibility exercises for the movement of the trunk. In *A* the girl seated in the chair is stretching the rotators of her trunk.

A

B

Fig. 17-9. The Clark Cable-Tension Strength Test for the trunk flexors. This test was modified by the authors by placing the strap over the arms.

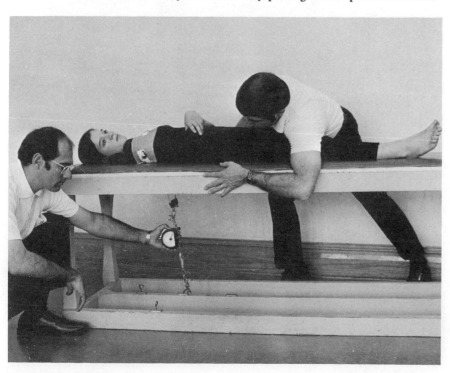

Fig. 17–10.  The Clark Cable-Tension Strength Test for the trunk extensors.

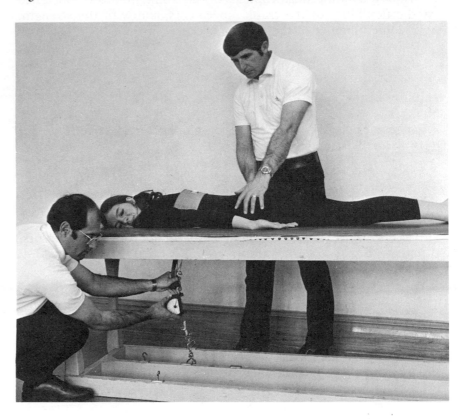

Fig. 17–11.  The Clark Cable-Tension Strength Test for the lateral flexors of the trunk.

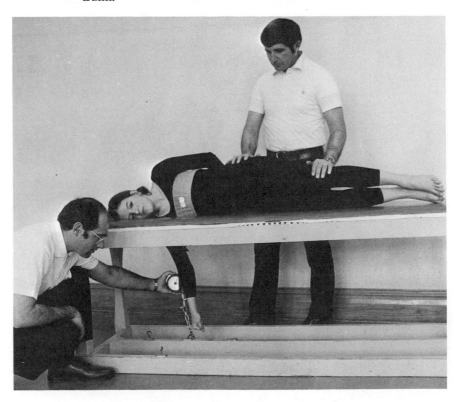

Fig. 17-12. Some isotonic exercises that can also be used to measure the strength, power, and endurance of the trunk muscles.

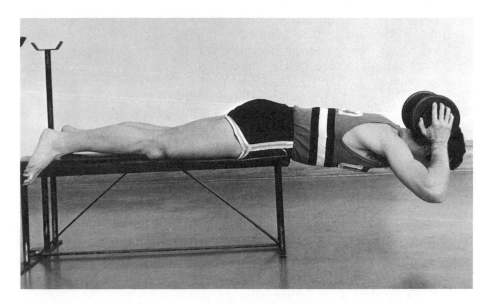

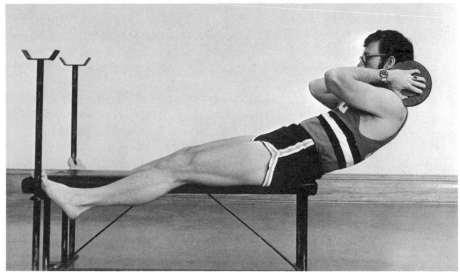

## Postural Problems

The major postural problems of the trunk are those concerned with the proper alignment of (1) the pelvis, (2) the lumbar vertebrae, (3) the thoracic vertebrae, and (4) the cervical vertebrae and the head.

*The Pelvis.* The normal alignment of the pelvis, when viewed from the side, is one in which the anterior superior iliac spine and the symphysis pubis are vertically aligned. When viewed from the front, the normal position of the pelvis is characterized by a horizontal alignment of the anterosuperior iliac spines. The vertical alignment may be checked with a plumb line, and the horizontal alignment may

**17.16 Postural and Pathological Problems of the Trunk**

be checked by the horizontal lines on a grid screen. If the anterior superior iliac spines are not aligned horizontally, a *lateral tilt* of the pelvis is indicated.

*Forward tilt* of the pelvis is present when the anterior superior iliac spine is forward of the symphysis pubis; *backward tilt* is present when the anterior superior iliac spine is behind the symphysis pubis.

Forward tilt of the pelvis is produced by the hip flexors and the extensors of the lumbar vertebrae. Backward tilt, on the other hand, is produced by the hip extensors and the flexors of the lumbar vertebrae. In the properly aligned, balanced position, equal tension is produced by each of these opposite groups. If, however, greater tension is exerted by one of these groups, either forward or backward tilt will result.

Since the rectus femoris and the hamstrings are two-joint muscles, their pulley actions, as discussed in Chapter 15, will affect the positioning of the pelvis. Flexion of the knees, for example, results in lengthening the rectus femoris, which then produces a downward pull on the anterior aspect of the pelvis. This downward pull causes a forward tilt of the pelvis. Stretching of the hamstrings, on the other hand, creates a downward pull on the posterior aspect of the pelvis, thereby producing backward tilt.

***The Lumbar Vertebrae.*** The normal lumbar vertebrae alignment, when viewed laterally, is characterized by a moderate anterior hyperextension curve. A marked increase in this curve is called a hollow back, or lumbar *lordosis*; a marked decrease in the curve is called a flat back, or lumbar *kyphosis.*

Because of the fixed position of the sacrum in the pelvic girdle, any movement of the pelvis will have a direct relationship on the position of the lumbar vertebrae. It is impossible, therefore, to separate the curve of the lumbar vertebrae from the inclination of the pelvis. Thus, lumbar lordosis is associated with forward tilt of the pelvis, and lumbar kyphosis is associated with backward tilt of the pelvis.

Also associated with lumbar lordosis and forward tilt of the pelvis is visceral *ptosis,* which is an anterior displacement or sagging of the abdominal vicera. Strong, well-developed abdominal muscles are responsible for preventing all three of these conditions. That is, these muscles pull up on the pelvis, thereby reducing forward tilt and lumbar lordosis, while also pressing backward on the abdominal viscera.

***The Thoracic Vertebrae.*** The normal thoracic curve is characterized by a moderate posterior flexion curve when viewed laterally. A marked increase in this curve is called "round upper back," or *thoracic kyphosis.* This condition is most commonly combined with lumbar lordosis.

The lumbar and thoracic vertebrae, when viewed from behind, should be vertically aligned. Any lateral deviation of the vertebrae is called *scoliosis.*

***The Cervical Vertebrae and Head.*** The normal cervical spine is characterized by a moderate anterior hyperextension curve when viewed laterally. A marked increase in this curve is called "poke neck," or cervical *lordosis;* a decrease in the curve is called "flat neck" or cervical *kyphosis.*

The balanced position of the head is one in which the vertical alignment passes through the midpoint of the shoulder and the lobe of the ear. If the lobe of the ear is anterior to the line, the head position is called "forward head," and if the lobe of the ear is posterior to the line, the head position is called "back head." A "forward head" is associated with cervical kyphosis, and "back head" is associated with cervical lordosis.

## Pathological Problems

The primary pathological problems of the trunk are (1) spondylolisthesis, (2) Scheuermann's disease, (3) spina bifida, (4) Pott's disease, and (5) wryneck.

Spondylolisthesis is an anterior displacement of the fifth lumbar vertebra on the sacrum. This condition usually manifests itself as lumbar lordosis, and it causes pressure on spinal nerves. Kyphosis of affected vertebrae is a characteristic of Scheuermann's disease, which is a condition confined to the vertebral epiphysis. This condition is also known as *osteochondritis deformans juvenilis dorsi.*

Spina bifida is a defect in which there is incomplete closure of the vertebral lamina. This defect is most common in the lumbosacral area. Pott's disease is characterized by the development of an abnormal prominence at some level of the vertebral column. This localized kyphosis usually occurs in the thoracic area, but it can also occur in the cervical and lumbar regions.

Because of muscular imbalance of the sternocleidomastoid muscle, the head is sometimes laterally flexed and rotated to one side. This condition is known as wryneck.

The chief traumatic problems of the (1) abdomen, (2) thorax, (3) back, (4) head and neck, and (5) pelvis will be discussed separately in this section.

**17.17 Traumatic Problems of the Trunk**

## The Abdomen

The major traumatic problems of the abdomen are muscle contusions and injuries to internal abdominal organs. Strong abdominal muscles give good protection to the abdomen when they are tensed, but they are easily damaged, when they are relaxed. The rectus abdominis seems to be most prone to bruising.

A blow to a relaxed abdomen can cause contusion of the solar plexus (sympathetic celiac plexus), which, in turn, causes a transitory paralysis of the diaphragm. Paralysis of the diaphragm results in a stoppage of breathing and in hypoxia.

Other internal organs sometimes injured by a severe blow to the lower abdomen are the bladder or urethra, spleen, and kidney. The so-called "stitch in the side," which is a cramplike pain that develops on either the left or the right costal angle during running, is probably caused by ischemia of either the diaphragm or the intercostals.

## The Thorax

The primary traumatic problems of the thorax (Fig. 17-13) are (1) fractures of the ribs and sternum, (2) costochondral separation and dislocation, (3) muscle contusions, and (4) injuries to internal thoracic organs.

**Fig. 17-13. Major injuries of the thorax.**

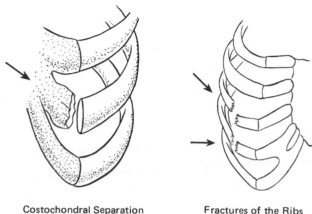

Costochondral Separation          Fractures of the Ribs

Rib injuries are quite common in athletics, especially in contact sports. Fractures of the ribs occur as a result of either a direct blow or a general compression of the rib cage as may occur in football. Fractures of the sternum, however, occur infrequently in athletics.

Costochondral separations and dislocations actually occur more frequently than do rib fractures. The most common condition is a fracture-separation at the costochondral junction.

All the muscles that attach to the thorax are subject to bruising, with the intercostals being perhaps the most assailable. Internal complications of the thorax, like injury to the lungs and heart, are rare in athletics.

## The Back

Back injuries, particularly those to the lower back, are next to foot problems in order of incidence. The most common injuries to the back are (1) strains and sprains, (2) contusions, (3) fractures, and (4) dislocations.

Strains and sprains of the back occur most often in the lower back and are the most frequent type of injury. One of the most common sprains of the back occurs during lifting activities. Improper lifting techniques with the lumbar vertebrae in a position that places undue pressure on the anterior portion of the intervertebral disks, especially when the lumbar curvature is reversed, may cause the disk to herniate posteriorly (Fig. 17-14). The improper lifting technique increases the pressure of the nucleus pulposus, which forces it through the anulus fibrosus and causes pressure to be applied on the posterior longitudinal ligament. This posterior protrusion of the disk, sometimes called a slipped disk, places pressure on the nerve roots, which, in turn, may result in pain in the lower back and legs.

Back contusions rank second to strains and sprains in incidence. Because of its large surface area, the back is quite liable to bruising.

Fractures and dislocations of the vertebral column, in terms of bone and joint injury, are not serious in themselves; but they pose dangers when related to spinal cord damage. Therefore, all injuries to the back should be considered fractures until proven differently. The athlete should be removed from the playing area face down on a stretcher, so that the normal spinal curve is maintained.

Compression of the vertebrae is the most frequent cause of fracture. This can result from a violent hyperflexion or jackknifing of the trunk, falling from a height and landing on the feet or buttock, or from a direct blow. The vertebrae in the dorsolumbar curves are fractured most often.

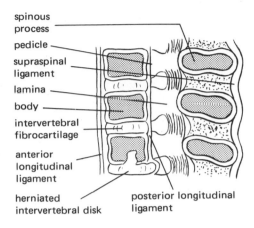

**Fig. 17–14. Herniation of the intervertebral disks (a slipped disk).**

spinous process
pedicle
supraspinal ligament
lamina
body
intervertebral fibrocartilage
anterior longitudinal ligament
herniated intervertebral disk
posterior longitudinal ligament

## The Head and Neck

Most traumas suffered by the head are the result of direct or indirect blows and may be classified as concussion injuries. The word "concussion" means agitation. Therefore, any agitation or jarring of the head and brain is defined as a concussion.

Severe neck injuries are relatively uncommon in sports, because of the free mobility of the cervical vertebrae compared with that of the thoracic and lumbar areas. The neck, however, has been known to be broken (fractured) and dislocated, especially in football and diving. Any severe force that either hyperextends, compresses, or twists the neck can cause cervical fracture. Cervical dislocations most often occur at the fourth, fifth, or sixth vertebra.

## The Pelvis

The major injuries of the pelvic region are (1) hernias, (2) scrotum contusion, (3) injuries to the pelvis and (4) the hip pointer, which is a contusion of the iliac crest.

A hernia is a protrusion of abdominal viscera through a potential opening of the abdominal wall. Most hernias occurring in athletics are found in the groin area with the inguinal type being the most prevalent. The inguinal hernia results from an abnormal enlargement of the opening of the inguinal canal through which the vessels and nerves of the male reproductive system pass.

Contusion of the scrotum is a very common injury in athletics. The cause of the injury is most often a direct blow to the area.

The most common fractures of the pelvic girdle are of one or both rami and of the ilium. Sprains of the sacroiliac joint are not uncommon. An iliac crest contusion, commonly known as a hip pointer (Fig. 17–15), occurs most often in contact sports, particularly football. Due to the soft-tissue damage in the area, this injury is quite painful and is one of the most handicapping in athletics.

**Fig. 17–15. The hip pointer.**

## 17.20 Study Guidelines

## 17.21 Movements of the Cervical Spine and Atlantooccipital Joint

A. Specific Student Objectives

1. Name the four muscles that produce flexion of the cervical spine and of the atlantooccipital joint.
2. Name the six muscles that produce extension of the cervical spine and of the atlantooccipital joint.
3. Name the nine muscles that produce lateral flexion of the cervical spine and of the atlantooccipital joint.
4. Name the five muscles that produce rotation of the cervical spine and of the atlantooccipital joint. Identify the two muscles that rotate to the opposite side and the three muscles that rotate to the same side.

## 17.22 Movements of the Thoracic and Lumbar Spine

A. Specific Student Objectives

1. Name the four muscles that produce flexion of the thoracic and lumbar spine.
2. Name the three muscles that produce extension and hyperextension of the thoracic and lumbar spine.
3. Name the nine muscles that produce lateral flexion of the thoracic and lumbar spine.
4. Name the five muscles that produce rotation of the thoracic and lumbar spine. Identify the three muscles that rotate to the opposite side and the two muscles that rotate to the same side.

## 17.23 Movements of the Thorax in Respiration

A. Specific Student Objectives

1. Name the three muscles involved in normal inhalation.
2. Name the seven additional muscles involved in vigorous inhalation.
3. Name the seven muscles involved in vigorous exhalation.

## 17.24 Movements of the Pelvis

A. Specific Student Objectives

1. Identify and define the fundamental movements of the pelvic girdle.
2. Identify the muscle groups involved in forward and backward tilt, lateral tilt, and rotation of the pelvis.

B. Study Hints

1. In his study of the muscles that produce the movements of the trunk, and pelvis, the student is advised to do a minimal amount of pure memorizing.

   It is much better for the student to study muscle-produced joint actions along with the actual exercises which employ these actions. Exercises of this type are presented in section 17.15.

**17.25  Conditioning Problems of the Trunk**

A. Specific Student Objectives

1. Identify the specific structures of the trunk that are stretched in the flexibility exercises presented in Figure 17–8.
2. Identify the specific muscles being tested by the Clark Cable-Tension Strength Tests in Figures 17–9 through 17–11.
3. Identify the specific muscles being exercised in Figure 17–12.

B. Study Hints

1. The strength tests and the exercises presented in this section are excellent for studying muscles in a way in which they can best be palpated. The palpation instructions presented in Table 17–2 should be used to locate the muscles producing the joint actions demonstrated in the measurements and exercises presented in this section.

**17.26  Postural and Pathological Problems of the Trunk**

A. Specific Student Objectives

1. *Postural Problems*

   a. Identify the normal alignment of the pelvis.
   b. State how the pulley actions of two-joint muscles affect the positioning of the pelvis.
   c. Identify the normal alignment of the lumbar vertebrae.
   d. Define lumbar lordosis and lumbar kyphosis.
   e. Define visceral ptosis.
   f. Identify the normal alignment of the thoracic vertebrae.
   g. Define scoliosis.
   h. Identify the normal alignment of the cervical vertebrae and head.

2. *Pathological Problems*

   a. Identify the primary pathological problems of the trunk.
   b. Define spondylolisthesis.

**17.27  Traumatic Problems of the Trunk**

A. Specific Student Objectives

1. Identify and define the major traumatic problems of the abdomen.
2. Identify and define the major traumatic problems of the thorax.

3. Identify and define the major traumatic problems of the back.
4. Describe the causes for a slipped disk.
5. Identify and define the major traumatic problems of the head and neck.
6. Identify and define the major traumatic problems of the pelvis.

**17.30 Recommended Supplementary Readings**

The student should consult any recent kinesiology text for supplementary readings on the movements and problems of the trunk. A list of selected kinesiology texts is given in Appendix B. The following readings are especially recommended.

Campbell, E. J. M.: "An Electromyographic Study of the Role of the Abdominal Muscles in Breathing," *J. Physio.*, **117**: 222–33, 1952.

Flint, M. M.: "Effect of Increasing Back and Abdominal Muscle Strength on Low Back Pain," *Res. Quart., Am. Assoc. Health Phys. Educ.*, **29**:160–71, 1958.

———: "An Electromyographic Comparison of the Function of the Iliacus and the Rectus Abdominis Muscles," *J. Am. Phys. Ther. Assoc.*, **45**:248–52, 1965.

Gough, Joseph G., and Koepke, George H.: "Electromyographic Determination of Motor Root Levels in Erector Spinae Muscles," *Arch. Phys. Med. Rehabil.*, **47**:9–11, 1966.

Jonsson, B.: "Morphology, Innervation, and Electromyographic Study of the Erector Spinae, *Arch. Phys. Med. Rehabil.*, **50**:638–41, 1969.

Keagy, R. D., and others: "Direct Electromyography of the Psoas Major Muscle in Man," *J. Bone Joint Surg.*, **48A**:1377–82, 1966.

Morris, J. M., and others: "An Electromyographic Study of the Intrinsic Muscles of the Back in Man," *J. Anat.*, **96**:509–20, 1962.

Partridge, M. J., and Walters, E. Etta: "Participation of the Abdominal Muscles in Various Movements of the Trunk in Man," *Phys. Ther. Rev.*, **39**:791–800, 1959.

Sheffield, F. J.: "Electromyographic Study of the Abdominal Muscles in Walking and Other Movements," *Am. J. Phys. Med.*, **41**:142–47, 1962.

Walters, C. E., and Partirdge, M. J.: "Electromyographic Study of the Differential Action of the Abdominal Muscles During Exercise," *Am. J. Phys. Med.*, **36**:259–68, 1957.

# Part VIII

# Structural
# Kinesiology
# of the
# Shoulder and Arm

# 18

# Structure
# of the
# Shoulder and Arm

**General Student Objective**

*In his study of the basic concepts of this chapter the student should become familiar with*

    *18.11  Bones of the Shoulder and Arm*
    *18.12  Joints of the Shoulder Region*
    *18.13  Muscles of the Shoulder*
    *18.14  Muscles of the Arm*

The skeleton of the upper extremity (Fig. 18–1) is divided into the shoulder girdle and the skeleton of the upper limb. The shoulder girdle is composed of the scapula or shoulder blade, and the clavicle or collarbone. The bones of the free upper limb consist of those in the arm, forearm, wrist, and hand. The three bones with which we will be concerned in this chapter are the two bones of the shoulder girdle, i.e., the scapula and clavicle, and the one bone of the arm, i.e., the humerus.

**18.11  Bones of the Shoulder and Arm**

## The Shoulder Girdle

The scapula (Figs. 18–2 and 18–3) is located on the posterior aspect of the thorax to which it is attached only by means of muscles. It lies between the levels of the second and seventh ribs with its medial border about 2 in. lateral to the vertebral column. In thin subjects it can easily be palpated throughout its extent. Some of the important markings on the scapula are

Fig. 18–1. The bones of the upper extremity.

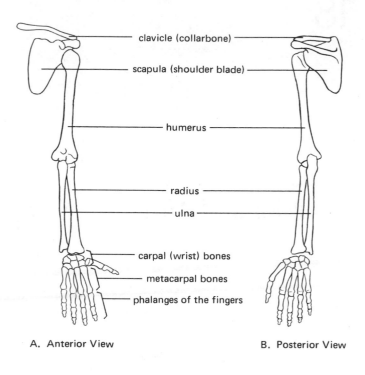

A. Anterior View        B. Posterior View

A. *Two surfaces*

1. *Posterior surface*

a. *Spine:* a prominent ridge located on the posterior surface of the bone.
b. *Acromion* (ah-cro'me-on): a pronounced overhanging projection that marks the lateral termination of the spine.
c. *Supraspinous* (su"prah-spi'nus) *fossa:* the area superior to the spine.
d. *Infraspinous fossa:* the area inferior to the spine.
e. *Great scapular notch:* located at the lateral border of the spine where the two fossa come together.

2. *Anterior or costal surface*

a. *Subscapular fossa:* a somewhat shallow depression located on the anterior surface of the bone.

B. *Three borders*

1. *Vertebral* or *medial border:* the longest of the three borders.
2. *Superior border* is sharp and thin.

a. *Lesser scapular notch:* located on the lateral aspect of the superior border.
b. *Coracoid* (kor'ah-koid) *process:* a thick, hooklike process located on the superior border.

**Fig. 18–2. Posterior view of the left scapula.**

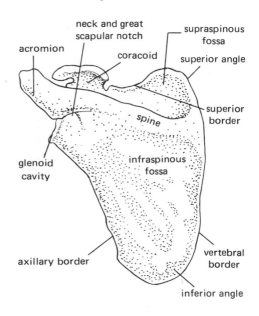

3. *Axillary* (ak′si-lar″e) or *lateral border* is thicker than the other borders. It is called axillary because of its relation to the axilla (ak-sil′ah) or armpit.

    a. *Infraglenoid tuberosity:* located at the upper end of the axillary border slightly inferior to the glenoid cavity.

C. *Three angles*

1. *Superior angle* is formed at the junction of the vertebral and superior borders.
2. *Inferior angle* is formed at the junction of the vertebral and axillary borders
3. *Lateral* or *external angle*, sometimes called the *head*, is located at the junction of the superior and axillary borders

    a. *Glenoid* (gle′noid) *fossa* or *cavity:* an articular surface for the reception of the head of the humerus, located on the lateral angle.

    b. *Supraglenoid tubercle:* a small eminence located superior to the glenoid cavity and lateral to the base of the coracoid process.

    c. *Neck:* separates the body of the bone from the head, and is located on the lateral angle.

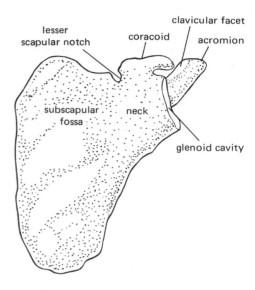

**Fig. 18–3. Anterior view of the left scapula.**

**Fig. 18–4. The left clavicle.**

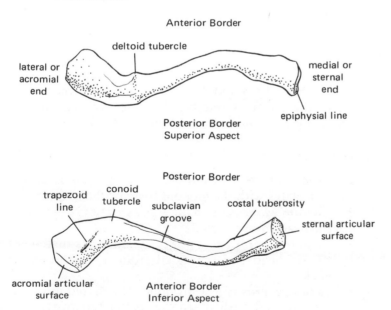

The clavicle (Fig. 18–4) is an f-shaped bone located horizontally at the upper and anterior part of the thorax, just above the first rib. It consists of a middle portion, the body or shaft, and two extremities. Some of the markings on the clavicle are

A. The *medial* or *sternal extremity:* articulates with the clavicular notch of the sternum.
B. The *lateral* or *acromial extremity:* the larger of the two extremities.

**Fig. 18–5.** Anterior view of the left humerus.

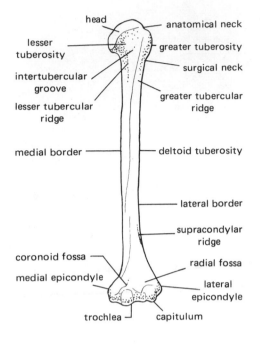

C. The *shaft*

 1. *Two surfaces*

   a. Superior surface is subcutaneous and comparatively smooth and can easily be palpated throughout its extent.

   b. *Inferior surface*

   (1) *Costal tuberosity:* a roughened area near the sternal end.

   (2) *Subclavian* (sub-kla′ve-an) *groove:* located lateral to the costal tuberosity and extends to beyond the middle one third of the shaft.

   (3) *Conoid tubercle:* a well-marked eminence located near the posterior border, slightly beyond the lateral termination of the subclavian groove.

   (4) *Trapezoid* (trap′e-zoid) *line:* a more or less prominent ridge that runs forward obliquely and laterally from the conoid tubercle.

 2. *Two borders*

   a. *Anterior border:* medial two thirds is convex and the lateral one third is concave.

   (1) *Deltoid tubercle:* a slight projection near the acromial extremity.

   b. *Posterior border*

## The Arm

The *humerus* (Figs. 18–5 and 18–6) or arm bone is the longest and largest bone of the upper extremity. It presents a shaft and two extremities. Some of the important markings on the humerus are

A. *The superior or proximal extremity*

 1. *Head:* a large hemispherical articular prominence which articulates with the glenoid fossa of the scapula.

 2. *Anatomical neck:* a shallow constriction which separates the head from the shaft.

 3. *Greater tuberosity:* a large prominence situated anterior to the head and separated from it by the anatomical neck.

 4. *Lesser tuberosity:* a prominence situated inferiorly, anteriorly, and medially to the greater tuberosity.

 5. *Greater tubercular* (tu-ber′ku-lar) *ridge:* a prominent ridge passing inferiorly from the greater tuberosity on the anterolateral surface of the superior extremity.

 6. *Lesser tubercular ridge:* a less prominent ridge passing inferiorly from the lesser tuberosity medial to the greater tubercular ridge.

 7. *Intertubercular* (in″ter-tu-ber′ku-lar) *or bicipital groove:* a rather deep groove that separates the greater and lesser tuberosities. The lips of this groove are formed by the

**Fig. 18–6.** Posterior view of the left humerus.

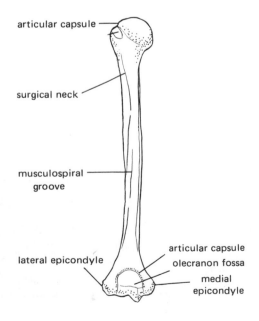

greater and lesser tubercular ridges. The greater tubercular ridge is often called the lateral lip of the bicipital groove and the lesser tubercular ridge is often called the *medial lip.*

8. *Surgical neck:* a constriction of the bone slightly inferior to the tuberosities. It receives its name from the fact that the bone is easily fractured at this point.

B. *The shaft*

1. *Deltoid tuberosity:* a large, elevated, roughened area located near the middle of the lateral aspect of the shaft.
2. *Three surfaces:* inferior to the deltoid tuberosity the shaft is slightly twisted, and becomes three sided so that three surfaces, namely, the *anteromedial, anterolateral,* and *posterior,* can be recognized.
3. *Three borders:*

   a. *The anterior border,* which descends on the front of the shaft to the distal or inferior extremity of the bone, separates the two anterior surfaces.
   b. The *medial and lateral borders* are sharp, terminating inferiorly in the *medial and lateral supracondylar ridges.*

4. *Musculospiral groove* is a shallow groove on the lateral aspect at about the middle of the shaft. It winds in a spinal direction from above downward and from the medial to the lateral aspect.

C. *The inferior or distal extremity*

1. *Capitulum* (ka-pit'u-lum): articulates with the fovea on the head of the radius.
2. *Trochlea:* a medial pulley-shaped surface that articulates with the semilunar notch of the ulna.
3. *Radial fossa:* a slight depression located superior to the capitulum on the anterolateral surface, which accommodates the circumference of the head of the radius during extreme flexion.
4. *Coronoid fossa:* located superior to the trochlea on the anteromedial surface. It receives the coronoid process of the ulna during flexion of the forearm.
5. *Olecranon* (o'lek'rah-non) *fossa:* a large and rather deep pit located on the posterior surface in a position corresponding to the radial and coronoid fossas. It serves for the reception of the olecranon process of the ulna in extreme extension.
6. *Lateral and medial epicondyles:* processes projecting from the sides of the distal extremity. The medial is the more prominent and serves as a landmark in the region of the elbow as it can easily be palpated. It forms the so-called "crazy bone" because a blow upon it results in the characteristic tingling sensation in the hand, due to stimulation of the ulnar nerve which is in close proximity.

**18.12 Joint of the Shoulder Region**

The joints of the shoulder region include the shoulder joint and the three joints of the shoulder girdle.

### The Shoulder Girdle

The three joints of the shoulder girdle (Fig. 18–7) are

A. *The Sternoclavicular Joint* (sliding joint): articulation between the medial or sternal end of the clavicle, the clavicular notch of the manubrium and the cartilage of the first rib.

B. *The Acromioclavicular Joint* (sliding joint): articulation between the acromial extremity of the clavicle and the medial edge of the acromion process of the scapula.

C. *The Coracoclavicular Union* (syndesmoses): the coracoclavicular ligament connects the clavicle with the coracoid process of the scapula.

*Movements:* The movements of the scapula and clavicle are closely associated with one another since the position of the scapula does not permit its movement independently. The scapula moves upon the lateral extremity of the clavicle, and the clavicle, in turn, moves upon the sternum at the sternoclavicular articulation. As a result of this arrangement, the scapula moves in the arc of a circle, the center of which is at the sternoclavicular joint, with the clavicle as the radius. During these movements, the scapula glides across the posterior thoracic wall to which it remains closely applied by the action of muscles.

The movements of the shoulder girdle, expressed in terms of the movements of the scapula are *elevation* (hunching the shoulders), *depression* (return from the position of elevation), *abduction* or *protraction* (a lateral movement of the scapula away from the spinal column), *adduction* or *retraction* (a medial movement of the scapula toward the spinal column), *upward rotation* (a rotation of the scapula so that the glenoid fossa faces somewhat upward), *downward rotation* (return from the position of upward rotation), *upward tilt* (a forward rotation of the scapula so that its posterior surface faces slightly upward and the inferior angle protrudes from the back), and *reduction of upward tilt* (the return movement from upward tilt). The rolling of the shoulders is called *circumduction*.

The movements of the clavicle permitted at the sternoclavicular joint are elevation, depression, abduction, adduction and circumduction, and a slight amount of rotatory movement. The movements of the scapula permitted at the acromioclavicular joint are gliding and rotation.

*Ligaments:* The principal ligaments of the shoulder girdle are

A. *The Sternoclavicular Joint* (Fig. 18–8)

1. *The capsular ligament or articular capsule:* completely surrounds the joint. It is attached to the margins of the articular surfaces.

2. *Anterior and posterior sternoclavicular ligaments:* reinforces the articular capsule on its anterior and posterior surfaces.

Fig. 18-7. The shoulder girdle.

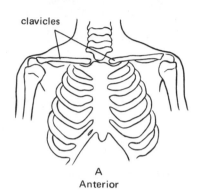

A
Anterior

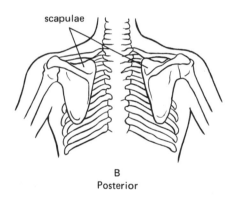

B
Posterior

Fig. 18-8. Anterior view of the sternoclavicular joints.

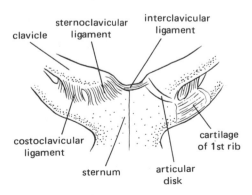

3. *Interclavicular ligament:* passes across the jugular notch of the manubrium. It is attached to the sternal ends of both clavicles, while the lowest fibers extend to the jugular notch. It serves to prevent displacement of the clavicles from the clavicle notches.

4. *Costoclavicular ligament:* attached above to the costal tuberosity of the clavicle and below to the superior border of the first costal cartilage and rib.

B. *The Acromioclavicular Joint* (Fig. 18–9)

1. *Capsular ligament:* completely surrounds the joint and is attached to the articular margins of the bones.

2. *Acromioclavicular ligament:* reinforces the capsule on its superior surface. It is attached to the superior surfaces of the acromial extremity of the clavicle and to the adjoining part of the acromion.

3. *Articular disk:* occupies, when present, only the upper part of the joint. It is generally incomplete and only partially separates the articular surfaces.

Fig. 18–9. The acromioclavicular joint and the coracoclavicular union.

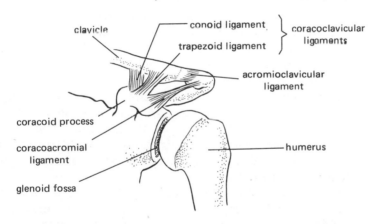

C. *The Coracoclavicular Union* (Figs. 18–9 and 18–10)

1. *Coracoclavicular ligament:* connects the clavicle with the coracoid process of the scapula. It is divisible into two parts: the *conoid* and *trapezoid ligaments,* which are attached to the conoid tubercle and trapezoid line, respectively, of the clavicle.

2. *Coracoacromial ligament:* extends between the coracoid process and the acromion, where it forms, with the coracoid and acromion processes, an arch which serves to protect the shoulder joint.

## The Shoulder Joint

The shoulder joint (Fig. 18–10) is a ball-and-socket joint formed by the head of the humerus and the glenoid fossa of the scapula.

*Movements.* Owing to the looseness and the large size of the head of the humerus compared with the depth of the glenoid fossa, the range of movement in this joint is greater than in any other joint. The range of movement of the humerus is also increased by the mobility of the shoulder girdle.

The movements of the shoulder joint and, therefore, of the humerus are *flexion* (swinging forward), *hyperflexion* (flexion continued beyond 180°), *extension* (return from flexion), *hyperextension* (swinging backward beyond the anatomical position), *abduction* (swinging sideward), *adduction* (return from abduction), *outward* or *lateral rotation,* and *inward* or *medial rotation* (rotation around the vertical axis of the humerus), *horizontal flexion-adduction* (a forward, side-arm movement of the abducted humerus in a horizontal plane), *horizontal extension-abduction* (a backward, sideward movement of the flexed humerus in a horizontal plane). Swinging the arms in a circle is called *circumduction.*

**Fig. 18–10. The shoulder joint.**

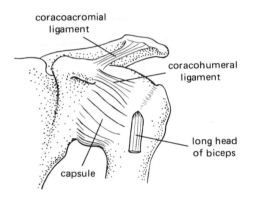

coracoacromial ligament

coracohumeral ligament

long head of biceps

capsule

*Ligaments.*   The primary ligaments of the shoulder joint (Fig. 18–10) are

A. *Glenoid lip or ligament:*   a narrow, fibrocartilaginous rim that surrounds and is attached to the margin of the glenoid fossa. It serves to deepen the fossa and to protect its edges.

B. *The articular capsule:*   completely surrounds the articulation. It is attached to the scapula round the margin of the glenoid fossa, reaching as far as the neck of the bone, and to the humerus at the anatomical neck. It is so lax that it is insufficient in itself to keep the bones in contact, thus allowing extreme freedom of movements.

C. *Superior, middle,* and *inferior glenohumeral bands:*   reinforces the anterior aspect of the capsule. The superior, also called the *glenohumeral ligament,* extends from the root of the coracoid process to a depression above the lesser tuberosity of the humerus.

D. *Coracohumeral ligament:*   a strong, broad band attached to the root and lateral border of the coracoid process and passing obliquely over the capsule, with which it is intimately connected, to the greater tuberosity of the humerus.

E. *Transverse humeral ligament:* a strong band of fibrous tissue that passes from the lesser to the greater tuberosity of the humerus and converts the intertubercular or bicipital groove into a canal for the passage of the long tendon of the biceps brachii.

**18.13   Muscles of the Shoulder Region**

The muscles of the upper extremity include those of the shoulder, arm, forearm, and hand. The muscles located in the shoulder region are

A. Muscles of the shoulder region with proximal attachments on the trunk

1. Anterior (Fig. 18–11)

a. Pectoralis (pek″to-ra′lis) major

**Fig. 18–11.** The anterior muscles of the shoulder.

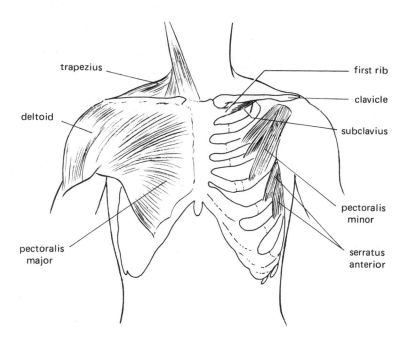

b. Pectoralis minor
c. Subclavius (sub-kla′ve-us)
d. Serratus (ser-ra′tus) anterior

2. Posterior (Fig. 18–12)

a. Trapezius (trah-pe′ze-us)
b. Rhomboids (rom′boids) major and minor
c. Levator scapulae
d. Latissimus dorsi (lah-tis′i-mus dor′si)

B. Muscles of the shoulder region with proximal attachments on the scapula

1. Anterior (Fig. 18–13)

a. Subscapularis (sub″skap-u-la′ris)

2. Posterior (Fig. 18–12)

a. Deltoids
b. Supraspinatus (su″prah-spi-na′tus)
c. Infraspinatus (in″frah-spi-na′tus)
d. Teres (te′rez) major
e. Teres minor

## Anterior Muscles of the Shoulder Region with Proximal Attachments on the Trunk (Fig. 18–11)

The anterior muscles of the shoulder region with proximal attachments on the trunk include the pectoralis major and minor, the subclavius, and the serratus anterior.

**Fig. 18–12. The posterior muscles of the shoulder.**

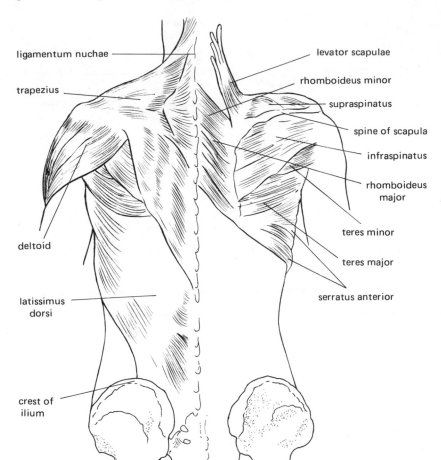

**Fig. 18–13. The subscapularis.**

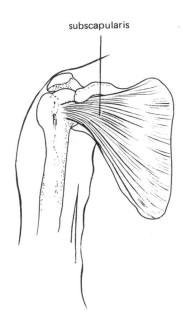

The *pectoralis* major is a large fan-shaped muscle of the chest that is divided into two parts, a clavicular and a sternal, corresponding to its proximal attachments. The medial two thirds of the clavicle is the proximal attachment of the clavicular part, whereas the anterior surface of the sternum, cartilages of the first six ribs, and slips from the aponeurosis of the external oblique abdominal muscle serve as the proximal attachments of the sternal part. It attaches laterally to the lateral lip of the bicipital groove of the humerus by a round tendon, which twists on itself in such a way that the fibers coming from the lower portion of the muscle terminate in the higher attachment, and vice versa.

The muscle as a whole brings the arm forward (flexion) and medially across the chest (horizontal flexion). Since the tendon of the muscle crosses over the front of the arm to attach to the lateral lip of the bicipital groove, it will tend to move the lateral lip medially upon contraction and, thus, produce inward rotation. The clavicular portion will produce abduction when the arm is above the horizontal, since in this position the line of pull of the muscle is above the axis of movement. The action of the sternal portion, however, is adduction.

Because of the attachment of the humerus to the scapula at the shoulder joint, the action of the pectoralis major in producing adduction and horizontal flexion of this joint also produces abduction of the shoulder girdle. These combined actions of the shoulder joint and shoulder girdle are termed protraction. The opposite combined action is retraction.

The *pectoralis minor* is located underneath the pectoralis major. It has its lower attachments on the anterior surface of the third, fourth, and fifth ribs, near their cartilages. Its upper attachment is on the tip of the coracoid process of the scapula. Its action at the thorax is elevation of the third, fourth, and fifth ribs. At the shoulder girdle it serves to depress, abduct, and downward rotate the scapula.

The *subclavius* is located below the clavicle, and its fibers run almost parallel with the long axis of the bone. It has a slight downward and strong medialward pull. The proximal attachment of the subclavius is on the upper surface of the first rib at the junction with the cartilage. Its distal attachment is on the underside of the middle half of the clavicle. It acts to depress the clavicle and to stabilize the sternoclavicular joint.

The *serratus anterior* is made up of separate bands or bundles of fibers attached to the ribs in a sawtooth arrangement. It attaches proximally to the outer surfaces of the upper nine ribs at the side of the chest. It attaches distally to the anterior surface of the vertebral border and inferior angle of the scapula. Its upper fibers, which attach to the vertebral border, act to abduct the scapula, whereas its lower fibers, which attach to the inferior angle, act to upward rotate the scapula.

**Posterior Muscles of the Shoulder Region with Proximal Attachments on the Trunk** (Fig. 18–12)

The posterior muscles of the shoulder region with proximal attachments on the trunk include the trapezius, rhomboid major and minor, levator scapulae, and the latissimus dorsi.

The *trapezius* (Fig. 18–14) is a superficial muscle located directly under the skin. The muscle consists of four parts. Parts I and II comprise the upper trapezius, part III the middle, and part IV the lower. The proximal attachments of the trapezius are on the occipital bone, ligamentum nuchae, spinous processes of seventh cervical, and all thoracic vertebrae. The distal attachments are as follows:

Part   I:   Posterior border of lateral third of clavicle
Part  II:   Top of acromion process
Part III:   Upper border of spine of scapula
Part IV:   Root of spine of scapula

The actions of the four portions on the scapula are

Part   I:   Elevation
Part  II:   Elevation, upward rotation, assist in adduction
Part III:   Adduction
Part IV:   Depression, upward rotation, assist in adduction

The *rhomboids* may be regarded as one muscle, in spite of the fact that they are usually described as two. There is no important dif-

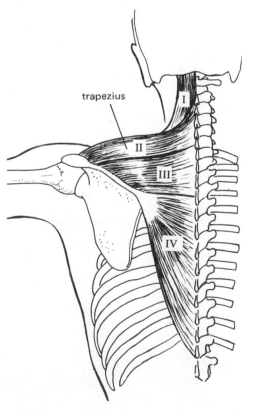

Fig. 18–14. The trapezius.

**Fig. 18–15. The latissimus dorsi.**

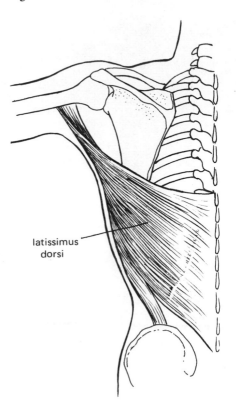

latissimus
dorsi

ference in function between the two. They have their proximal attachments on the spinous processes of the seventh cervical and first five thoracic vertebrae. Their distal attachment is on the vertebral border of the scapula from the spine to the inferior angle. Their actions are adduction, downward rotation, and elevation of the shoulder girdle.

The *levator scapulae* is attached proximally to the transverse processes of the first four cervical vertebrae and distally to the vertebral border of the scapula between the superior angle and the spine. It acts to elevate and downward rotate the scapula.

The *latissimus dorsi* (Fig. 18–15) is a broad sheet of muscle that covers the lower and middle portions of the back. It attaches proximally to the spinous processes of the lower six thoracic and all lumbar vertebrae, posterior surface of the sacrum, crest of ilium, and lower three ribs. Its distal attachment is on the medial lip of the bicipital groove of the humerus. Its actions are adduction, extension, horizontal extension, and inward rotation of the arm.

## Muscles of the Shoulder Region with Proximal Attachments on the Scapula

The *subscapularis* is attached on the entire anterior surface of the scapula. It occupies the subscapula fossa and is the only muscle in this classification that attaches to the anterior or costal surface of the scapula. Its distal attachment is on the lesser tuberosity of the humerus. Its actions are inward rotation and horizontal flexion, and its lower fibers aid in adduction when the arm is above the horizontal.

The *posterior* muscles of the shoulder with proximal attachments on the scapula include the deltoids, supraspinatus, infraspinatus, teres major, and the teres minor.

The *deltoid* muscle consists of three parts: an anterior, a middle, and a posterior. The proximal attachments of these three parts are

Anterior:  Anterior border of the lateral third of the clavicle
Middle:  Acromion process and lateral end of the clavicle
Posterior:  Lower margin of the scapula spine

The three parts have a common tendon of distal attachment on the deltoid tuberosity located on the lateral aspect of the humerus, near the midpoint. The actions of the three parts are

Anterior:  Flexion, horizontal flexion, inward rotation
Middle:  Abduction
Posterior:  Extension, horizontal extension, outward rotation, adduction

The *supraspinatus* is attached proximally on the medial two thirds of the supraspinatus fossa above the spine of the scapula. Distally it attaches to the top of the greater tuberosity of the humerus. It abducts at the shoulder joint and serves to lift the capsule out of the way.

The *infraspinatus and teres minor* are functionally one muscle. They are attached proximally to the axillary border and posterior surface of the scapula below the scapula spine. Distally they are attached to the posterior aspect of the greater tuberosity of the humerus. They act to outward rotate and horizontally extend the shoulder joint.

The *teres major* is often referred to as the latissimus dorsi's "little helper." Its proximal attachment is on the posterior surface of the inferior angle of the scapula. Distally it is attached to the medial lip of the bicipital groove of the humerus along with the tendon of the latissimus dorsi. Its actions are adduction, extension, horizontal extension, and inward rotation.

The muscles of the arm are divided into two groups, namely, anterior and posterior. The arm muscles have their main action on the forearm, but the two joint muscles may also act on the shoulder joint. The muscles of the arm are

**18.14 Muscles of the Arm**

    A. Anterior or flexor group (Figs. 18–16 and 18–17)

       1. Biceps brachii
       2. Coracobrachialis (kor″ah-ko-bra″ke-a′lis)
       3. Brachialis (bra″ke-a′lis)

    B. Posterior or extensor group (Fig. 18–18)

       1. Triceps brachii
       2. Anconeus (an-ko′ne-us)

**Muscles of the Anterior Arm**

The muscles in the anterior group are the biceps brachii, the coracobrachialis, and the brachialis. The *biceps brachii* (Fig. 18–16), as its name implies, is formed by the union of two distinct heads, the long head and the short head. The long head arises from the upper margin of the glenoid fossa, and the short head from the coracoid process of the scapula. The tendon of the long head passes downward from its proximal attachment through the articular capsule and through the bicipital groove of the humerus. The short head is

Fig. 18–16. The biceps brachii and coracobrachialis.

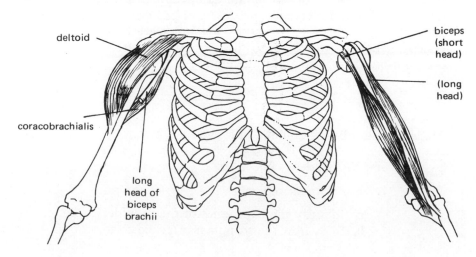

**Fig. 18–17. The brachialis.**

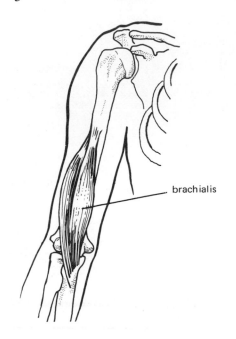

brachialis

flattened and is adherent to the coracobrachialis muscle. These two heads form a common tendon attached distally on the tuberosity of the radius, also known as the bicipital tuberosity. The biceps brachii is the chief flexor of the forearm at the elbow and is the strongest supinator of the forearm at the radioulnar articulations. Both heads are so situated at the shoulder joint as to be able to flex the arm at the shoulder. The long head may also assist in abduction.

The *coracobrachialis* (Fig. 18–16) lies alongside the short head of the biceps. It receives its name from the fact that it extends from the coracoid process to the arm (brachium). More precisely, it attaches distally to the medial surface of the humerus near its midpoint opposite the deltoid attachment. It acts as a flexor and an adductor of the humerus at the shoulder. It assists, along with the biceps, in extreme abduction by keeping the head of the humerus in the glenoid fossa.

The *brachialis* (Fig. 18–17) lies lateral to the biceps on the anterior surface of the lower half of the humerus. It attaches distally on the anterior surface of the coronoid process of ulna. Its only action is flexion of the forearm.

**Muscles of the Posterior Arm** (Fig. 18–18)

To the posterior group belong the triceps brachii and the anconeus. The *triceps brachii,* as its name implies, has three distinct heads, which occupy the entire posterior surface of the humerus. The three heads are designated the long head, the medial head, and the lateral head. The long head arises from the infraglenoid tuberosity of the scapula, whereas both the lateral and medial heads arise from the humerus. The lateral head occupies the posterior surface of the upper half of the humerus, and the medial head occupies the posterior surface of the lower two thirds of the humerus. Distally the three heads fuse to form the main belly of the muscle, which terminates in a common tendon attaching to the olecranon of the ulna. The muscle acting as a whole extends the forearm. The long head also serves to extend and adduct the humerus at the shoulder joint and to pull upward on the humerus, thus tending to hold its head in the glenoid fossa.

The *anconeus* is a small, flat, triangular muscle that extends from the posterior surface of the lateral epicondyle of the humerus to the lateral side of the olecranon process and posterior surface of upper part of ulna. Since its function and innervation is similar to the triceps, it belongs in reality to the arm musculature. Its only action is extention of the forearm at the elbow.

**18.20  Study Guidelines**

**18.21  Bones of the Shoulder and Arm**

A.  Specific Student Objectives

1.  *The Scapula*

a.  Identify the two bones of the shoulder girdle.
b.  State how the scapula is attached to the thorax.

c. The scapula is located between what two ribs?

d. Locate a scapula on a mounted skeleton and identify the following:

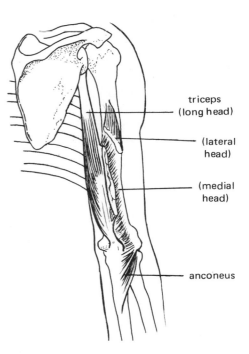

Fig. 18–18. The triceps brachii and the anconeus.

| | |
|---|---|
| posterior surface | coracoid process |
| spine | axillary border |
| acromion process | infraglenoid tuberosity |
| supraspinous fossa | superior angle |
| infraspinous fossa | inferior angle |
| greater scapular notch | lateral angle |
| anterior surface | head |
| subscapular fossa | glenoid fossa |
| vertebral border | supraglenoid tubercle |
| superior border | neck |
| lesser scapular notch | |

e. Locate the scapula on the back of a friend and identify the following:

| | |
|---|---|
| posterior surface | axillary border |
| spine | superior angle |
| acromion process | inferior angle |
| vertebral border | lateral angle |
| superior border | |

2. *The Clavicle*

a. The clavicle is shaped like which letter of the alphabet?

b. The clavicle is located just below which rib?

c. Locate a scapula on a mounted skeleton and identify the following:

| | |
|---|---|
| sternal extremity | subclavian groove |
| acromial extremity | conoid tubercle |
| the shaft | trapezoid line |
| superior surface | anterior border |
| inferior surface | deltoid tubercle |
| costal tuberosity | posterior border |

d. Locate the clavicle in your own shoulder and identify the following:

| | |
|---|---|
| sternal extremity | inferior surface |
| acromial extremity | anterior border |
| the shaft | posterior border |
| superior surface | |

3. *The Humerus*

a. Locate a humerus on a mounted skeleton and identify the following:

| | |
|---|---|
| superior extremity | lesser tubercular ridge |
| head | intertubercular groove |
| anatomical neck | surgical neck |
| greater tuberosity | the shaft |
| lesser tuberosity | deltoid tuberosity |
| greater tubercular ridge | anteromedial surface |

anterolateral surface          musculospiral groove
posterior surface              inferior extremity
anterior border                capitulum
medial border                  trochlea
lateral border                 radial fossa
medial supracondylar           coronoid fossa
  ridge              olecranon fossa
lateral supracondylar          lateral epicondyle
  ridge              medial epicondyle

b. Locate the humerus in your own arm and identify the following:

head                           lateral epicondyle
greater tuberosity             medial epicondyle

B. Study Hints

1. The use of actual bones is quite beneficial in the study of specific osteology, and there is no substitute for independent study of a mounted skeleton in learning the specific markings on a bone.
2. Locating bony landmarks in the student's body is also a valuable aid to learning.

### 18.22 Joints of the Shoulder Region

A. Specific Student Objectives

1. *The Sternoclavicular Joint*

   a. What type of joint is this?
   b. Describe the bony articulations involved in this joint.
   c. What movements are allowed at this joint? Describe these movements.
   d. Describe the ligamentous reinforcements of this joint.

2. *The Acromioclavicular Joint*

   a. What type of joint is this?
   b. Describe the bony articulations involved in this joint.
   c. What movements are allowed at this joint? Describe these movements.
   d. Describe the ligamentous reinforcements of this joint.

3. *The Coracoclavicular Union*

   a. What type of joint is this?
   b. Describe the bony articulations involved in this joint.
   c. Describe the ligamentous reinforcements of this joint.

4. *The Shoulder Girdle*

   a. Identify and describe the movements of the shoulder girdle, expressed in terms of the movements of the scapula.

5. *The Shoulder Joint*

   a. What type of joint is this?
   b. Describe the bony articulations involved in this joint.

    c. What movements are allowed at this joint? Describe these movements.

    d. Describe the ligamentous reinforcements of this joint.

B. Study Hints

  1. The student should study each joint on a mounted skeleton, where he can visualize the bony articulations and ligamentous reinforcements involved in the joint.

  2. The student should also identify each joint in his shoulder and perform the movements of that joint according to the descriptions presented in the text. It is important that he learn to identify the movements by their proper names whenever he sees them performed.

## 18.23  Muscles of the Shoulder Region

A. Specific Student Objectives

  1. *Anterior Muscles of the Shoulder Region with Proximal Attachments on the Trunk*

    a. Identify the four muscles in this group.

    b. Give the proximal and distal attachments of each of these muscles.

    c. Give the joint actions produced by the contraction of each of these muscles.

    d. Locate each of these muscles in your own shoulder.

  2. *Posterior Muscles of the Shoulder Region with Proximal Attachments on the Trunk*

    a. Identify the four muscles in this group.

    b. Give the proximal and distal attachments of each of these muscles.

    c. Give the joint actions produced by the contraction of each of these muscles.

    d. Locate each of these muscles in your shoulder or in the shoulder of a friend.

  3. *Muscles of the Shoulder Region with Proximal Attachments on the Scapula*

    a. Identify the only *anterior* muscle of the shoulder with a proximal attachment on the scapula.

    b. Give the proximal and distal attachments of this muscle.

    c. Give the joint actions produced by the contraction of this muscle.

    d. Identify the five *posterior* muscles of the shoulder with proximal attachments on the scapula.

    e. Give the proximal and distal attachments of each of these muscles.

    f. Give the joint actions produced by the contraction of each of these muscles.

    g. Locate each of these muscles in the shoulder of a friend.

## 18.24  Muscles of the Arm

A.  Specific Student Objectives

1.  *Anterior Muscles of the Arm*

   a.  Identify the three anterior muscles of the arm.
   b.  Give the proximal and distal attachments of each of these muscles.
   c.  Give the joint actions produced by the contraction of each of these muscles.
   d.  Locate each of these muscles in your own arm.

2.  *Posterior Muscles of the Arm*

   a.  Identify the two posterior muscles of the arm.
   b.  Give the proximal and distal attachments of each of these muscles.
   c.  Give the joint actions produced by the contraction of each of these muscles.
   d.  Locate each of these muscles in your arm.

B.  Study Hints

1.  Table 18–1 is presented here to aid in the mastery of specific muscle actions and attachments.
2.  Instructions as to where the muscles of the shoulder and arm can be palpated are presented in Table 18–2. The student should perform the movements of the shoulder girdle and shoulder joint and attempt to locate through palpation each of the muscles listed.

Table 18–1.  **The Attachments and Actions of the Shoulder and Arm Muscles**

| Location | Name | Proximal Attachment | Illustration | Distal Attachment | Action |
|---|---|---|---|---|---|
| Shoulder, proximal attachment on trunk, anterior group | Pectoralis major | Clavicular part: medial two thirds of clavicle. Sternal part: anterior surface of sternum, cartilages of first six ribs, slips from aponeurosis of external oblique | Fig. 18–11 | Lateral lip of bicipital groove of humerus | Whole muscle; flexion, horizontal flexion, and inward rotation. Clavicular: abduction; Sternal: adduction of shoulder joint |
| | Pectoralis minor | Anterior surface of third, fourth, and fifth ribs, near cartilages | Fig. 18–11 | Tip of coracoid process of scapula | Depression, abduction, and downward rotation of scapula |
| | Subclavius | Upper surface of first rib at junction with cartilage | Fig. 18–11 | Undersurface of middle half of clavicle | Depression of clavicle |
| | Serratus anterior | Outer surfaces of upper nine ribs at side of chest. | Fig. 18–11 | Anterior surface of vertebral border and inferior angle of scapula | Upper fibers: abduction of scapula; lower fibers: upward rotation of scapula |

**Table 18-1. The Attachments and Actions of the Shoulder and Arm Muscles (continued)**

| Location | Name | Proximal Attachment | Illustration | Distal Attachment | Action |
|---|---|---|---|---|---|
| posterior group | Trapezius | Occipital bone, ligamentum nuchae, spinous processes of seventh cervical, and all thoracic vertebrae. | Fig. 18-14 | I. Posterior border of lateral third of clavicle<br>II. Top of acromion process<br>III. Upper border of spine of scapula.<br>IV. Root of spine of scapula | I. Elevation<br>II. Elevation, upward rotation, adduction<br>III. Adduction<br>IV. Depression, upward rotation, adduction |
| | Rhomboids | Spinous processes of seventh cervical and first five thoracic vertebrae | Fig. 18-12 | Vertebral border of scapula from spine to inferior angle | Adduction, downward rotation, and elevation |
| | Levator scapulae | Transverse processes of first four cervical vertebrae | Fig. 18-12 | Vertebral border of scapula from superior angle to spine | Elevation and downward rotation of scapula |
| | Latissimus dorsi | Spinous processes of lower six thoracic and all lumbar vertebrae, posterior surface of sacrum, crest of ilium, and lower three ribs | Fig. 18-15 | Medial lip of bicipital groove of humerus | Adduction, extension, horizontal extension, and inward rotation of arm |
| Shoulder, proximal attachment on scapula, anterior muscle | Subscapularis | Subscapula fossa on entire anterior surface of scapula | Fig. 18-13 | Lesser tuberosity of humerus | Inward rotation, horizontal flexion and lower fibers: adduction of arm |
| posterior group | Deltoid | Anterior: anterior border of the lateral third of clavicle Middle: acromion process and lateral end of clavicle. Posterior: lower margin of the scapula spine | Fig. 18-12 | Deltoid tuberosity located on lateral aspect of humerus near midpoint | Anterior: flexion, horizontal flexion, and inward rotation. Middle: abduction. Posterior: extension, horizontal extension, outward extension and adduction |
| | Supraspinatus | Medial two thirds of supraspinatus fossa | Fig. 18-12 | Top of greater tuberosity of humerus | Abduction of arm |
| | Infraspinatus and teres minor | Axillary border and posterior surface of scapula below scapula spine | Fig. 18-12 | Posterior aspect of the greater tuberosity of humerus | Outward rotation and horizontal extension of arm |
| | Teres major | Posterior surface of inferior angle of scapula | Fig. 18-12 | Medial lip of bicipital groove of humerus | Adduction, extension, horizontal extension, and inward rotation |
| Arm anterior group | Biceps brachii | Long head: upper margin of glenoid fossa; short head: coracoid process of scapula | Fig. 18-16 | Tuberosity of radius | Flexion and supination of forearm and flexion of arm. Long head: abduction |

**Table 18–1. The Attachments and Actions of the Shoulder and Arm Muscles (continued)**

| Location | Name | Proximal Attachment | Illustration | Distal Attachment | Action |
|---|---|---|---|---|---|
| | Coracobrachia-lis | Coracoid process of scapula | Fig. 18–16 | Medial surface of humerus near midpoint opposite the deltoid attachment | Flexion and adduction of arm |
| | Brachialis | Anterior surface of lower half of humerus | Fig. 18–17 | Anterior surface of coronoid process of ulna | Flexion of forearm |
| posterior group | Triceps brachii | Long head: infraglenoid tuberosity of scapula; lateral head: posterior surface of upper half of humerus; medial head: posterior surface of lower two thirds of humerus | Fig. 18–18 | Olecranon process of ulna | Extension of forearm. Long head: extension and adduction of arm |
| | Anconeus | Posterior surface of lateral epicondyle of humerus | Fig. 18–18 | Lateral side of olecranon process and posterior surface of upper part of ulna | Extension of forearm |

**Table 18–2. Instructions for Palpating the Muscles of the Shoulder and Arm**

| Name of Muscle | Where the Muscle Can Be Palpated |
|---|---|
| A. Muscles of the shoulder region with proximal attachments on the trunk | |
| 1. Anterior (Fig. 18–11) | |
| a. Pectoralis major | *Clavicular:* Just below the medial two thirds of the clavicle. *Sternal:* Lateral to the sternum, below clavicular portion. *Both:* Anterior border of axilla. |
| b. Pectoralis minor | This muscle cannot be palpated when the pectoralis major is not relaxed. It may be palpated halfway between clavicle and nipple when the arm is hyperextended as far as possible. |
| c. Subclavius | Cannot be palpated. |
| d. Serratus anterior | On well-developed individuals this muscle can be palpated on the anterolateral surface of upper thorax where it attaches to the ribs. |
| 2. Posterior | |
| a. Trapezius | This is the kite-shaped muscle in the upper back and neck. |
| b. Rhomboids | This muscle is difficult to palpate. |
| c. Levator scapulae | This muscle is difficult to palpate. |
| d. Latissimus dorsi | This muscle can be palpated on the posterior border of the axilla just below the teres major. |

Table 18-2. **Instructions for Palpating the Muscles of the Shoulder and Arm** (continued)

| Name of Muscle | Where the Muscle Can Be Palpated |
|---|---|
| B. Muscles of the shoulder region with proximal attachments on the scapula. | |
| 1. Anterior (Fig. 18-13) | |
| a. Subscapularis | Cannot be palpated. |
| 2. Posterior (Fig. 18-14) | |
| a. Deltoids | *Anterior:* 2 or 3 in. in front of and below the head of the humerus. *Middle:* Lateral surface of upper third of arm. *Posterior:* Below the scapular spine on the lateral portion of the posterior surface of the scapula. |
| b. Supraspinatus | Above the spine of the scapula. |
| c. Infraspinatus and teres minor | These muscles can be palpated on the posterior surface of the scapula slightly medial and inferior to the posterior deltoid muscle. |
| d. Teres major | This muscle can be palpated on the posterior border of the axilla just above the latissimus dorsi. |
| C. Muscles of the arm | |
| 1. Anterior (Figs. 18-16 and 18-17) | |
| a. Biceps brachii | Anterior surface of lower two thirds of arm about 3 or 4 in. above elbow. |
| b. Coracobrachialis | Anterior surface of arm, medial to short head of the biceps brachii. |
| c. Brachialis | This muscle can be palpated just lateral to the biceps brachii. |
| 2. Posterior (Fig. 18-18) | |
| a. Triceps brachii | Posterior surface of arm. |
| b. Anconeus | Lateral margin of olecranon process on back of elbow. |

The student should consult any recent basic anatomy text for supplementary readings on the structure of the shoulder and arm. A list of selected anatomy texts is given in Appendix B.

**18.30 Recommended Supplementary Readings**

# 19

# Movements and Problems
of the
Shoulder and Arm

**General Student Objective**

*In his study of the basic concepts of this chapter the student should
become familiar with*

19.11   *Movements of the Shoulder Girdle*
19.12   *Movements of the Shoulder Joint*
19.13   *Movements of the Shoulder Complex*
19.14   *Conditioning Problems of the Shoulder and Arm*
19.15   *Postural and Pathological Problems of the Shoulder and
        Arm*
19.16   *Traumatic Problems of the Shoulder and Arm*

The movements of the shoulder girdle are elevation and depression, abduction and adduction, and upward and downward rotation.

**19.11 Movements of the Shoulder Girdle**

**Elevation and Depression**

The muscles that produce elevation and depression of the shoulder girdle are

     A. *Elevation* (Fig. 19–1)

         1. Levator scapulae
         2. Trapezius, parts I and II
         3. Rhomboids

     B. *Depression* (Fig. 19–2)

         1. Trapezius, part IV
         2. Pectoralis minor
         3. Subclavius

**Fig. 19–1. The elevators of the shoulder girdle.**

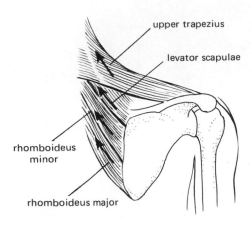

**Fig. 19–2. The depressors of the shoulder girdle.**

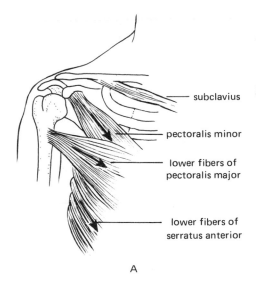

A

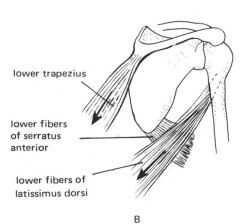

B

4. Pectoralis major, lower fibers
5. Serratus anterior, lower fibers
6. Latissimus dorsi, lower fibers

The *elevators* of the scapula are the levator scapulae, the rhomboids, and parts I and II of the trapezius. Only the trapezius is capable of elevating the lateral angle of the scapula; the levator scapulae and the rhomboids are responsible for elevating the medial angle.

The *depressors* of the shoulder girdle are the pectoralis minor, subclavius, part IV of the trapezius, and the lower fibers of the pectoralis major, serratus anterior, and latissimus dorsi. The subclavius is the weakest of the depressors because of its size and oblique position. The rest of the depressors tend to produce additional actions that must be neutralized. The pectoralis minor, for instance, tends to downward rotate the scapula while acting as a depressor, but the serratus anterior neutralizes this action with its tendency to upward rotate the scapula. The lower trapezius and the lower fibers of the latissimus dorsi tend to adduct the scapula, whereas the pectoralis major tends to abduct it.

## Abduction and Adduction

The muscles that produce abduction and adduction of the shoulder girdle are

A. *Abduction* (Fig. 19–3)

1. Serratus anterior
2. Pectoralis minor
3. Pectoralis major

B. *Adduction* (Fig. 19–4)

1. Rhomboids
2. Middle trapezius, part III
3. Trapezius, parts II and IV
4. Latissimus dorsi, upper fibers

*Abduction* of the scapula is brought about by the pectoralis minor, the pectoralis major, and the serratus anterior. *Adduction*, on the other hand, is due to the actions of the middle fibers of the trapezius and the rhomboids with assistance from the upper fibers of the latissimus dorsi and parts II and IV of the trapezius.

## Upward and Downward Rotation

The muscles that produce upward and downward rotation of the shoulder girdle are

A. *Upward rotation* (Fig. 19–5)

1. Trapezius II and IV
2. Serratus anterior

B. *Downward rotation* (Fig. 19-6)

1. Rhomboids
2. Pectoralis minor
3. Levator scapulae
4. Pectoralis major, lower part
5. Latissimus dorsi

*Upward rotation* of the scapula is carried out by the combined actions of the serratus anterior and parts II and IV of the trapezius.

*Downward rotation* is produced by the actions of the rhomboids and the levator scapulae in raising the medial border of the scapula, while the latissimus dorsi, pectoralis minor and pectoralis major pull downward on the lateral angle.

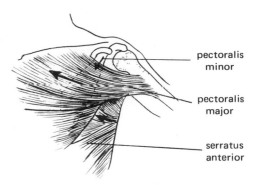

Fig. 19-3. The abductors of the shoulder girdle.

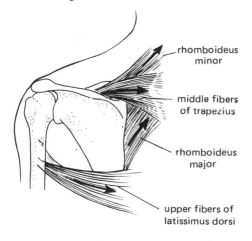

Fig. 19-4. The adductors of the shoulder girdle.

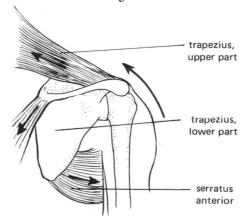

Fig. 19-5. The upward rotators of the shoulder girdle.

Fig. 19-6. The downward rotators of the shoulder girdle.

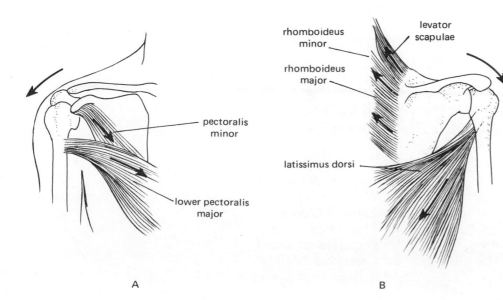

A

B

## 19.12 Movements of the Shoulder Joint

Since the shoulder joint is a ball-and-socket joint, which allows movement in all three planes, it allows flexion and extension, abduction and adduction, and inward and outward rotation. The special movements of horizontal flexion and horizontal extension are also allowed.

### Flexion and Extension

The muscles that produce flexion and extension of the shoulder joint are

A. *Flexion* (Fig. 19–7)

    1. Anterior deltoid
    2. Pectoralis major, clavicular portion
    3. Coracobrachialis
    4. Biceps brachii, short head

B. *Extension* (Fig. 19–8)

    1. Posterior deltoid
    2. Latissimus dorsi
    3. Teres major
    4. Pectoralis major, sternal portion
    5. Triceps brachii, long head

*Flexion* at the shoulder joint is brought about by the anterior deltoid, clavicular portion of the pectoralis major, coracobrachialis, and the short head of the biceps brachii. Of these muscles, the anterior deltoid is the most important.

*Extension* at the shoulder joint is brought about by the posterior deltoid, latissimus dorsi, teres major, the sternal portion of the pectoralis major, and the long head of the triceps brachii.

**Fig. 19–7. The flexors of the shoulder joint.**

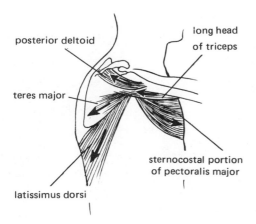

coracobrachialis

anterior deltoid

clavicular head of pectoralis major

biceps brachii

### Abduction and Adduction

The muscles that produce abduction and adduction of the shoulder joint are

A. *Abduction* (Fig. 19–9)

    1. Muscle deltoid
    2. Supraspinatus

B. *Adduction* (Fig. 19–10)

    1. Anterior deltoid
    2. Posterior deltoid
    3. Latissimus dorsi
    4. Teres major
    5. Pectoralis major
    6. Coracobrachialis
    7. Triceps brachii, long head

**Fig. 19–8. The extensors of the shoulder joint.**

posterior deltoid

long head of triceps

teres major

latissimus dorsi

sternocostal portion of pectoralis major

*Abduction* is produced primarily by the supraspinatus and the middle deltoid. The anterior and posterior deltoids, however, can contribute to the movement when the humerus is rotated either inward or outward.

In *adduction,* the anterior and posterior deltoids can assist in the movement. The chief adductors of the shoulder joint, however, are the latissimus dorsi, teres major, and the pectoralis major. These muscles are assisted to a small extent by the coracobrachialis and the long head of the triceps brachii.

**Fig. 19-9. The abductors of the shoulder joint.**

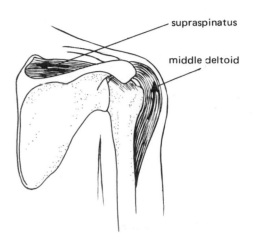

### Inward and Outward Rotation

The muscles that produce inward and outward rotation of the shoulder joint are

A. *Inward rotation* (Figs. 19–11 and 19–12)

 1. Latissimus dorsi
 2. Teres major
 3. Subscapularis
 4. Pectoralis major
 5. Anterior deltoid

B. *Outward rotation* (Figs. 19–11 and 19–13)

 1. Infraspinatus and teres minor
 2. Posterior deltoid

*Inward rotation* is brought about primarily by the subscapularis. The latissimus dorsi, teres major, pectoralis major, and the anterior deltoid assist in the movement. *Outward rotation,* on the other hand, is brought about primarily by the infraspinatus and teres minor with some help from the posterior deltoid when extension and outward rotation are combined.

**Fig. 19–10. The adductors of the shoulder joint.**

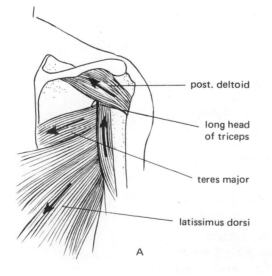

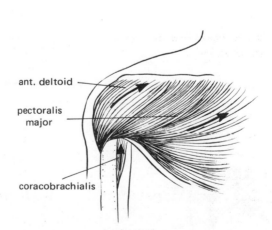

**Fig. 19–11. The inward and outward rotators of the shoulder joint.**

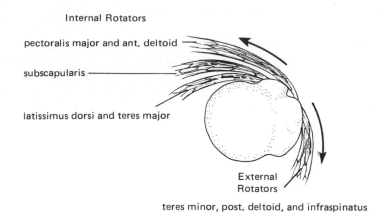

Internal Rotators

pectoralis major and ant. deltoid

subscapularis

latissimus dorsi and teres major

External Rotators

teres minor, post. deltoid, and infraspinatus

**Fig. 19–12. The inward rotators of the shoulder joint.**

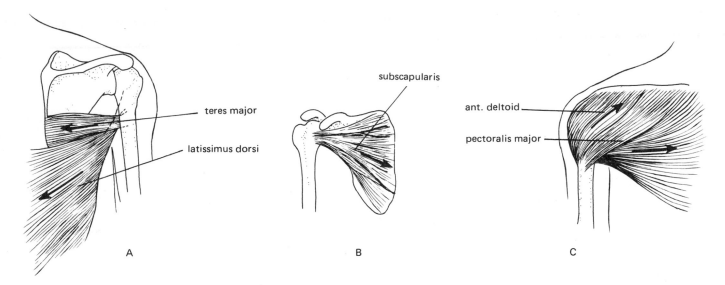

teres major

latissimus dorsi

subscapularis

ant. deltoid

pectoralis major

A

B

C

## Horizontal Flexion and Extension

**Fig. 19–13. The outward rotators of the shoulder joint.**

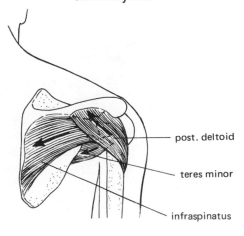

post. deltoid

teres minor

infraspinatus

The muscles that produce horizontal flexion and extension of the shoulder joint are

A. *Horizontal flexion* (Fig. 19–14)

1. Pectoralis major
2. Anterior deltoid
3. Subscapularis
4. Coracobrachialis
5. Biceps brachii, short head

B. *Horizontal extension* (Fig. 19–15)

1. Latissimus dorsi
2. Teres major
3. Posterior deltoid
4. Infraspinatus and teres minor

**Fig. 19-18.** Some isotonic exercises that can also be used to measure the strength, power, and endurance of the shoulder girdle elevators is shown in (A), and an exercise for the adductors is shown in (B).

A

B

**Table 19-1. Martin Breaking Strength Tests\* for the Muscles Producing the Movements of the Shoulder**

1. *Muscles that adduct the arm in front of the body*

    The subject stands with the middle of the back pressed firm against an upright post and with the hand of the arm that is not being tested grasping a post. The adjuster faces and stands directly in front of him. He places the loop in front of and just above the elbow of the arm to be tested. With one hand the adjuster holds the loop in its position, and with the other hand grasps lightly the subject's hand or wrist. The adjuster, keeping the subject's arm straight, draws it across the subject's body as far as possible, keeping it as close to the body as possible and still giving clearance for the loop. At the command "Hold back," the subject attempts to hold the arm from being drawn downward, sideward, and backward. The operator holds the dynamometer in a line downward, sideward, and backward from the subject's elbow so that as the arm is drawn downward, sideward, and backward, it will just clear the subject's body. At the command "Hold back," the operator develops sufficient tension to draw the arm down to the side of the body. The command "Stop" must be given, and the pulling discontinued before the arm has been drawn beyond the vertical line.

2. *Muscles that abduct the arm behind the body*

    The subject stands with the middle of the abdomen pressed firm against an upright post and with the hand of the arm that is not being tested grasping a post. With the fist closed, and with the dorsum of the hand toward the back, the arm, just clearing the trunk, is drawn as far as possible across the back of the body. The strap is placed just above the elbow, and the pull is horizontal and outward anteriorly at a 30° angle to the lateral plane.

3. *Muscles that horizontally flex the arm*

    The subject stands with the middle of the back pressed firm against an upright post and with the hand of the arm that is not being tested grasping a support that the shoulders are not elevated. The arm being tested is raised to the level of the shoulders and brought forward to an angle of 30° from the lateral plane of the trunk. The strap is placed just above the elbow, and the pull is backward and downward, establishing a 60° angle with the upper arm. This angle is maintained until the arm gives.

4. *Muscles that horizontally extend the arm*

    The position of the subject is the same as for the preceding test. The arm to be tested is raised to the level of the shoulders posteriorly at a 30° angle to the lateral plane of the trunk. The strap is placed just above the elbow, and the pull is forward and downward, establishing a 60° angle with the upper arm. This angle is maintained until the arm gives.

\*E. G. Martin: "Tests of Muscular Efficiency," *Phys. Rev.*, 1:454–75, 1921.

When the midpoint of the shoulder is anterior of the vertical reference line, the condition is called "round or forward shoulders." This condition gives the appearance of increasing the thoracic curve, which frequently results in the faulty assumption that forward shoulders and round upper back are synonymous.

One cause of round or forward shoulders is the habitual use of the hands and arms in front of the body. Continuous use of this position could result in a shortening of the anterior muscles, which would pull the shoulders forward and abduct the scapulae. Because of the forward position of the shoulders, the chest will appear sunken or shallow.

**Fig. 19-14.** The horizontal flexors of the shoulder joint.

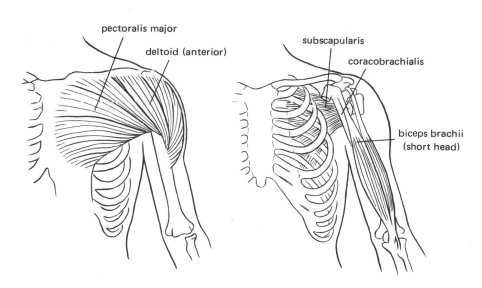

*Horizontal flexion* is produced by the anteriorly located pectoralis major, anterior deltoid, subscapularis, coracobrachialis, and the short head of the biceps brachii. *Horizontal extension* is brought about by the posteriorly located latissimus dorsi, teres major, posterior deltoid infraspinatus, and teres minor.

**Fig. 19-15.** The horizontal extensors of the shoulder joint.

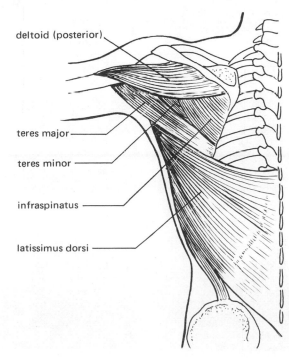

**19.13 Movements of the Shoulder Complex**

The above movements of the shoulder joint are ordinarily accompanied by movements of the shoulder girdle. The movements of the scapula increase not only the force of arm movements, but also, by tilting the glenoid cavity in the desired direction, the range of arm movements. As the arm is abducted, for instance, there is an accompanying upward rotation of the glenoid cavity, more marked as the arm reaches and passes the horizontal plane. Likewise, bringing the arm back to the side, adduction, is accompanied by downward rotation of the glenoid cavity. When the arms are used in front of the body, the glenoid cavity is abducted; when the arms are moved backward, the glenoid cavity is adducted.

**19.14 Conditioning Problems of the Shoulder and Arm**

The conditioning problems of the shoulder and arm are those concerned with the flexibility of the shoulder girdle and shoulder joint and with the strength, power, and endurance of the shoulder and arm muscles.

**Flexibility of the Shoulder**

Flexibility exercises for the movements of the shoulder girdle and shoulder joint are illustrated in Figure 19–16.

Fig. 19–16. Some flexibility exercises for the movements of the shoulder girdle and shoulder joint.

Fig. 19–17. The Clark Cable-Tension Strength Test for the flexors (*A*), extensors (*B*), and adductors (*C*) of the shoulder joint. In testing the flexors of the shoulder joint, both the shoulder and elbow on the side tested are flexed to 90°. In testing the extensors of the shoulder joint, the shoulder on the side being tested in flexed to 90°. In testing the adductors of the shoulder joint, the shoulder being tested is adducted to 110°.

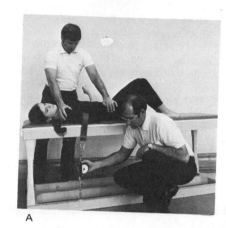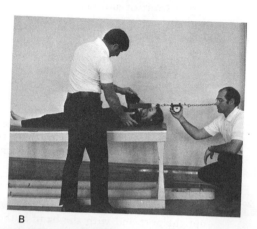

A                          B

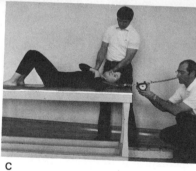

C

**Isometric Measurements of Strength**

The Clark Cable-Tension Strength Tests for the flexors and adductors of the shoulder joint are illustrated in Figure 19–17. The Martin Breaking Strength Tests for shoulder joint muscles are described in Table 19–1.

**Isotonic Exercises and Measurements**

Some isotonic exercises that can also be used to measure the strength, power, and endurance of the muscles of the shoulder girdle and shoulder joint are illustrated in Figures 19–18 and 19–19.

The normal alignment of the shoulders is horizontal with the midpoint of the shoulder directly above the midpoint of the hip. The vertical alignment of the shoulders may be checked through the use of a plumb line.

**19.15 Postural Problems**

Fig. 19–19. Some isotonic exercises that can also be used to measure the strength, power, and endurance of the shoulder joint muscles.

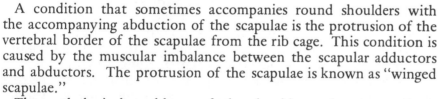

A condition that sometimes accompanies round shoulders with the accompanying abduction of the scapulae is the protrusion of the vertebral border of the scapulae from the rib cage. This condition is caused by the muscular imbalance between the scapular adductors and abductors. The protrusion of the scapulae is known as "winged scapulae."

The pathological problems of the shoulder and arm are those normally associated with such conditions as multiple sclerosis, polio, or muscular dystrophy.

The major traumatic problems of (1) the shoulder girdle, (2) the shoulder joint, and (3) the arm will be discussed separately in this section.

**19.16 Traumatic Problems of the Shoulder and Arm**

## The Shoulder Girdle

The principal traumatic injuries of the shoulder girdle (Fig. 19–20) are (1) clavicular fractures, (2) fractures of the scapula, and (3) sprains of the clavicle.

Clavicular fractures are one of the most frequent fractures in athletics and occur most often to the middle third of the bone. Fracture of the scapula, on the other hand, is an infrequent injury in athletics. Falling on an outstretched hand or on the elbow or tip of the shoulder is the most frequent cause of clavicular and scapula fractures.

Sternoclavicular sprains are rare, but in this injury the clavicle is displaced upward and slightly anteriorly. Acromioclavicular sprains are much more frequent and are caused by a direct blow to the tip of

**Fig. 19-20. Major injuries of the shoulder girdle.**

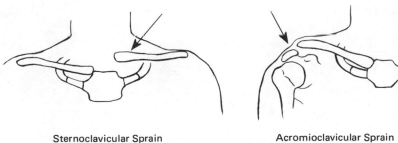

Sternoclavicular Sprain          Acromioclavicular Sprain

the shoulder, pushing the acromion process downward, or by an upward force exerted against the long axis of the humerus.

**Fig. 19-21. Major injuries of the shoulder joint.**

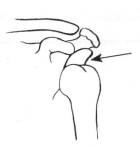

Anterior Glenohumeral Dislocation

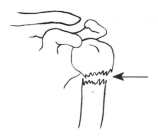

Fracture of the Humerus

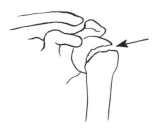

Epiphyseal Fracture

## The Shoulder Joint

The major traumatic problems of the shoulder joint (Fig. 19-21) are (1) dislocations, (2) contusions, (3) strains, and (4) sprains.

Dislocations of the shoulder joint are second only to finger dislocations in order of incidence in athletics. The two types of shoulder joint dislocations are the anterior glenohumeral dislocation and the downward glenohumeral dislocation.

In the anterior glenohumeral dislocation, the head of the humerus is forced out of its articular capsule in a forward direction past the glenoid lip and then upward to rest under the coracoid process. In the downward glenohumeral dislocation, the head of the humerus is forced into a position below the glenoid cavity. The anterior displacement is the most frequently encountered of the two.

Contusions of the shoulder joint most often affect the deltoid muscle, which is also the most frequently strained muscle. The rotator cuff muscles, which include the subscapularis, supraspinatus, infraspinatus, and teres minor, are also frequently subject to strains. The principal rotator cuff tendon strained is the supraspinatus. The shoulder joint, like all joints, is also subject to sprains.

## The Arm

The major injuries of the arm (Fig. 19-22) are (1) fractures, (2) contusions, and (3) strains. Fractures of the upper humerus can involve various parts of the bone, such as the anatomical neck, the tuberosities, or the surgical neck. The greatest number of fractures occur at the surgical neck. Epiphyseal fractures of the head of the humerus are much more common in the young athlete than are bone fractures. Fractures of the humeral shaft are usually transverse, and deformity is often produced because the bone fragments override each other as a result of strong muscular pull.

Although any muscle of the arm is subject to bruising, the area most often affected is the lateral aspect, primarily the brachialis and portions of the biceps and triceps brachii muscles. The muscles particularly involved in strains are the biceps and triceps brachii.

## 19.21  Movements of the Shoulder Girdle

A. Specific Student Objectives

1. Name the three muscles that produce elevation of the shoulder girdle.
2. Name the six muscles that produce depression of the shoulder girdle.
3. Name the three muscles that produce abduction of the shoulder girdle.
4. Name the four muscles that produce adduction of the shoulder girdle.
5. Name the two muscles that produce upward rotation of the shoulder girdle.
6. Name the five muscles that produce downward rotation of the shoulder girdle.

## 19.22  Movements of the Shoulder Joint

A. Specific Student Objectives

1. Name the four muscles that produce flexion of the shoulder joint.
2. Name the five muscles that produce extension of the shoulder joint.
3. Name the two muscles that produce abduction of the shoulder joint.

Fig. 19-22. Major injuries of the arm.

4. Name the seven muscles that produce adduction of the shoulder joint.
5. Name the five muscles that produce inward rotation of the shoulder joint.
6. Name the two muscles that produce outward rotation of the shoulder joint.
7. Name the five muscles that produce horizontal flexion of the shoulder joint.
8. Name the four muscles that produce horizontal extension of the shoulder joint.

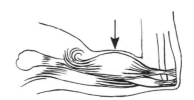

Biceps Brachii Rupture

## 19.23  Movements of the Shoulder Complex

A. Specific Student Objectives

1. State how movements of the scapula facilitate the movements of the shoulder joint.
2. State the movement of the scapula that accompanies shoulder joint abduction.
3. State the movement of the scapula that accompanies shoulder joint adduction.
4. State the movement of the scapula that accompanies shoulder joint flexion.

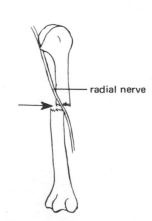

radial nerve

Fracture of the Humerus

B. Study Hints

1. In his study of the muscles that produce the movements of the shoulder girdle and the shoulder joint, the student is advised to do a minimal amount of pure memorizing.

   It is much better for the student to study muscle-produced joint actions along with the actual exercises that employ these actions. Exercises of this type are presented in Section 19.14.

### 19.24 Conditioning Problems of the Shoulder and Arm

A. Specific Student Objectives

1. Identify the specific shoulder structures stretched in the flexibility exercises presented in Figures 19–16 and 19–17.
2. Identify the specific muscles being tested by the Clark Cable-Tension Strength Tests in Figure 19–18.
3. Identify the specific muscles being exercised in Figures 19–18 and 19–19.

B. Study Hints

1. The strength tests and the exercises presented in this section are excellent for studying muscles in a way in which they can best be palpated. The palpation instructions presented in Table 18–2 should be used to locate the muscles producing the joint actions demonstrated in the measurements and exercises presented in this section.

### 19.25 Postural and Pathological Problems of the Shoulder and Arm

A. Specific Student Objectives

1. Identify the postural and pathological problems of the shoulder.

### 19.26 Traumatic Problems of the Shoulder and Arm

A. Specific Student Objectives

1. Identify and define the major traumatic problems of the shoulder girdle.
2. Identify and define the major traumatic problems of the shoulder joint.
3. Identify and define the major traumatic problems of the arm.

The student should consult any recent kinesiology text for supplementary readings on the movements and problems of the shoulder and arm. A list of selected kinesiology texts is given in Appendix B. The following readings are especially recommended.

**19.30 Recommended Supplementary Readings**

Bearn, J. G.: "An Electromyographic Study of the Trapezius, Deltoid, Pectoralis Major, Biceps and Triceps Muscles During Statis Loading of the Upper Limb," *Anat. Rec.,* **140**:103–107, 1961.

———: "Function of Certain Shoulder Muscles in Posture and in Holding Weights," *Ann. Phys. Med.,* **6**:100–104, 1961.

———: "Direct Observations on the Function of the Capsule of the Sterno-clavicular Joint in Clavicular Support," *J. Anat.,* **101**:159–70, 1967.

Dempster, Wilfrid T.: "Mechanisms of Shoulder Movement," *Arch. Phys. Med. Rehab.,* **46**:49–70, 1965.

Inman, V. T., and others: "Observations on the Function of the Shoulder Joint," *J. Bone Joint Surg.,* **26**:1–30, 1944.

———: "The Shoulder as a Functional Unit," *Arch. Phys. Med. Rehab.,* **44**:67, 1963.

Marmor, L, and others: "Pectoralis Major Muscle," *J. Bone Joint Surg.,* **43A**: 81–87, 1961.

Reeder, Thelma: "Electromyographic Study of the Latissimus Dorsi Muscle," *J. Bone Joint Surg.,* **43**:165–72, 1963.

Shevlin, M. G., and others: "Electromyographic Study of the Function of Some Muscles Crossing the Glenohumeral Joint," *Arch. Phys. Med. Rehab.,* **50**: 264–70, 1969.

Slaughter, Duane R.: "Electromyographic Studies of Arm Movements," *Res. Q.,* **30**:326–37, 1959.

Wiedenbauer, M. M., and Mortensen, O. A., "An Electromyographic Study of the Trapezius Muscle," *Am. J. Phys. Med.,* **31**:363–73, 1952.

# Part IX

# Structural Kinesiology of the Forearm and Hand

# 20

## Structure of the Elbow, Forearm, Wrist, and Hand

The two bones of the forearm are the ulna and the radius. The *ulna* (Figs. 20–1 and 20–2), or elbow bone, is the medial of the two bones and is slightly longer than the radius. It is composed of a shaft and two extremities. Some of the important markings on the ulna are

**20.11 Bones of the Forearm**

A. *Superior or proximal extremity*

1. *Anterior aspect*

   a. *Semilunar notch*: articulates with trochlea of the humerus.
   b. *Coronoid process*: projects horizontally forward from the anterior part of the semilunar notch.
   c. *Tuberosity of the ulna*: a rough eminence located on the anterior surface and base of the coronoid process.

2. *Posterior aspect*

   a. *Olecranon process*: the "tip of the elbow" located on the posterior portion of the semilunar notch. It is readily palpated.

**Fig. 20–1. Anteromedial view of left ulna and radius.**

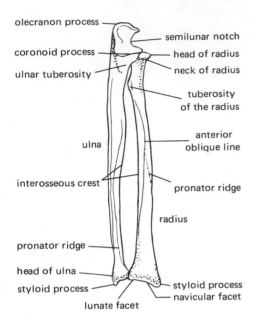

**Fig. 20–2. Posterolateral view of left ulna and radius.**

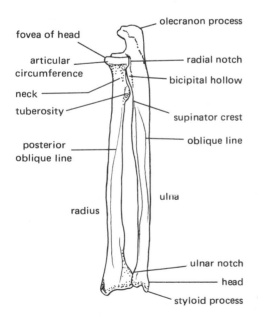

3. *Lateral aspect*

   a. *Radial notch:* serves for the reception of the articular circumference of the head of the radius and is located on the lateral side of the base of the coronoid process.

   b. *Supinator crest:* a rough longitudinal ridge located inferior to the radial notch on the lateral aspect of the ulna.

   c. *Bicipital hollow:* a triangular depression that accommodates the tuberosity of the radius during pronation of the forearm. Its posterior boundary is formed by the supinator crest.

B. *Shaft*

   1. *Three surfaces* known as the *anterior, medial,* and *posterior.*

   2. *Oblique line:* a line on the upper part of the posterior surface, which extends inferiorly from the supinator crest to the posterior border.

   3. *Three borders* known as the volar, dorsal, and lateral. The lateral border is also known as the *interosseous crest.*

C. *The distal* or *inferior extremity* (also known as the *head*)

   1. *Semilunar facets:* a more or less flattened facet upon which the articular disk of the wrist plays. It is the distal of the two articular surfaces of the head.

   2. *Articular circumference:* a lateral, convex facet which is received into the ulnar notch of the radius.

   3. *Styloid process:* projects downward from the medial and dorsal part of the head and appears to be a continuation of the dorsal border

The *radius* (Figs. 20–1 and 20–2) is placed on the lateral side of the ulna and is shorter and smaller than the ulna. It presents a shaft and two extremities. Some of the important markings on the radius are

A. *Proximal* or *superior extremity*

   1. *Head:* a disk-shaped structure located on the superior extremity.

   2. *Fovea:* a depression located on the summit of the head, which articulates with the capitulum of the humerus.

   3. *Articular circumference:* the convex rim that comprises the margin of the head, which articulates with the radial notch of the ulna.

   4. *Neck:* the somewhat constricted part of the bone inferior to the head.

B. *The shaft*

   1. *Three surfaces* known as the *lateral, volar,* and *posterior.*

   2. *Tuberosity of the radius,* also called the bicipital tuberosity: located inferior to the neck on the volar surface of the bone.

3. *Anterior oblique line*: a line that extends inferiorly and laterally from the tuberosity.

4. *Pronator ridge*: a line that marks the inferior limit of the anterior oblique line.

5. *Posterior oblique line*: a line that marks the posterior surface at the junction of its proximal and middle thirds.

6. *Three borders* known as the *anterior* or *volar*, *dorsal* or *posterior*, and the *medial* or *interosseous crest*. The latter is a prominent ridge separating the volar from the dorsal surface.

C. *The distal or inferior extremity*

1. *Lunate facet*: the medial of the two facets of the distal extremity. It articulates with the lunate bone.

2. *Navicular facet*: the lateral of the two facets of the distal extremity. It articulates with the navicular bone.

3. *Styloid process*: a blunt eminence located on the lateral surface of the distal extremity. It can easily be palpated and serves as a landmark in the region of the wrist.

4. *Ulnar notch*: located on the medial surface and articulates with the head of the ulna.

The *carpus* or *wrist* (Fig. 20–3) is composed of eight short carpal bones arranged in proximal and distal rows with four bones in each. Passing from the radial to the ulnar side, the bones of the proximal row are the navicular, lunate, triquetral, and the pisiform. Because it actually sits upon the triquetral bone, the pisiform can be observed only on the anterior surface of the wrist. Passing in the same direc-

**20.12 Bones of the Wrist and Hand**

Fig. 20–3. Anterior view of the wrist bones.

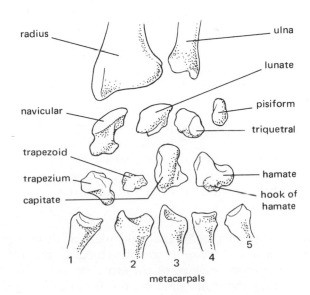

tion, the bones of the distal row are the trapezium, trapezoid, capitate, and the hamate. The anterior surface of the hamate shows a hooklike process called *hook of the hamate.*

The *metacarpus*, or body of the hand (Fig. 20–4) consists of five metacarpal bones numbered from the radial or thumb side to the ulnar or little finger side of the hand. Each bone consists of a proximal extremity or *base*, a *shaft*, and a distal extremity or *head.*

The *phalanges* (Fig. 20–4) are the bones of the digits or fingers. Each digit has three phalanges with the exception of the thumb, which has only two. The phalanges are called the first or proximal, the second or middle, and the third or distal. Each phalanx presents a proximal extremity or *base*, a *shaft*, and a distal extremity or *trochlea.* The distal extremity or each terminal phalanx is flattened to form the *ungual tuberosity.* Pollicis is another name for the thumb or first digit.

**Fig. 20–4. Posterior view of the left hand.**

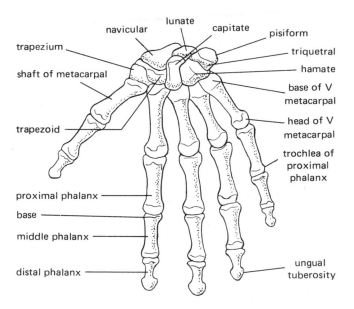

### 20.13 The Elbow and Radioulnar Joints

**The Elbow Joint**

The elbow joint is a hinge joint formed by the articulation of the semiulnar notch of the ulna with the trochlea of the humerus, and the fovea on the head of the radius with the capitulum of the humerus.

*Movements.* The movements that take place at this hinge joint are flexion and extension. *Flexion* is the movement of the anterior forearm toward the anterior surface of the arm. *Extension* is the reverse of flexion. During these movements, the fovea on the head of the radius glides upon the capitulum, and the semiulnar notch of the ulna glides upon the trochlea of the humerus.

*Ligaments.* The major ligaments of the elbow (Fig. 20–5) are

A. *Anterior Ligament*: covers the anterior surface of the joint.
B. *Posterior Ligament*: forms a membranous covering for the posterior surface of the joint.
C. *Ulnar Collateral Ligament*: a thick, strong, triangular ligament. It is attached superiorly to the medial epicondyle and inferiorly to the medial margin of the semilunar notch.
D. *Radial Collateral Ligament*: attached superiorly to the lateral epicondyle of the humerus and inferiorly to the neck of the radius.

## The Radioulnar Joints

The radioulnar joints include three separate articulations: the superior radioulnar joint, the inferior radioulnar joint, and the radioulnar union. The *superior radioulnar joint* (pivot joint): the articulation between the circumference of the head of the radius and the radial notch of the ulna. The *inferior radioulnar joint* (pivot joint): formed by the head of the ulna, which is received into the ulnar notch of the radius. The *radioulnar union* (syndesmoses): formed by the thin interosseous membrane, which occupies the interval between the shafts of the radius and ulna.

*Movements.* The movements permitted at these joints are pronation (a rotation of the forearm so that the palm of the hand faces downward when the arm is horizontal), and supination (a rotation of the forearm so that the palm of the hand faces upward when the arm is horizontal). These movements principally involve the radius, since the ulna cannot rotate at the elbow.

*Ligaments.* The major ligaments of the radioulnar joints (Fig. 20–6) are

A. *Superior Radioulnar Joint*

  1. *Annular ligament*: encircles the head of the radius and holds it in the radial notch of the ulna.

B. *Inferior Radioulnar Joint*

  1. *Anterior* and *posterior radioulnar ligaments*: reinforce the capsule.

C. *Radioulnar Union*

  1. Interosseous membrane.

The joints of the wrist and hand are

A. The Radiocarpal or Wrist Joint
B. The Intercarpal Joints
C. The Carpometacarpal Joints
D. The Intermetacarpal Joints
E. The Metacarpophalangeal Joints
F. The Interphalangeal Joints

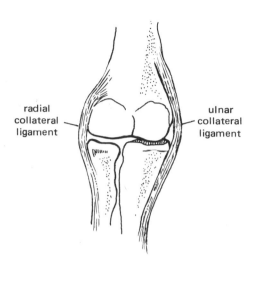

**Fig. 20–5. The radial and ulnar collateral ligaments.**

radial collateral ligament

ulnar collateral ligament

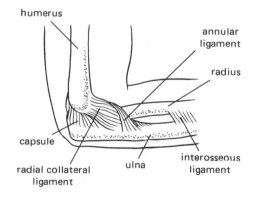

**Fig. 20–6. The superior radioulnar joint and the radioulnar union.**

humerus

annular ligament

radius

capsule

radial collateral ligament

ulna

interosseous ligament

**20.14 Joints of the Wrist and Hand**

**The Radiocarpal or Wrist Joint**

The radiocarpal or wrist joint is a condyloid joint formed by the distal end of the radius and the articular disk superiorly, and the navicular, lunate, and triquetral bones inferiorly.

*Movements.* The movements of the wrist joint are *flexion* (movement of the palmar surface of the hand toward the anterior surface of the forearm), *extension* (return from flexion), *hyperextension* (movement of the dorsal surface of the hand toward the posterior surface of the forearm), *abduction* or *radial flexion* (bending the hand laterally), *adduction* or *ulnar flexion* (bending the hand medially), and *circumduction* (a movement of the hand at the wrist whereby the fingertips describe a circle, and the hand as a whole describes a cone).

**Fig. 20–7. The ligaments of the wrist or radiocarpal joint.**

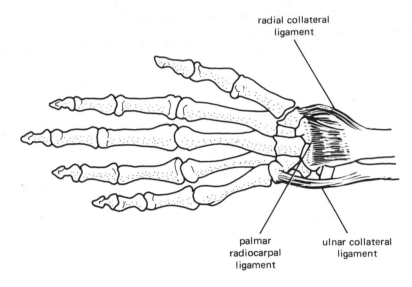

radial collateral
ligament

palmar
radiocarpal
ligament

ulnar collateral
ligament

*Ligaments.* The ligaments of the wrist joint (Fig. 20–7) are

A. *Articular disk*: separates the head of the ulna from the triquetral bone of the carpus and serves to bind the inferior extremities of the radius and ulna.
B. *Articular capsule*: completely surrounds the joint and is divided into the following ligaments:

1. Palmar radiocarpal
2. Dorsal radiocarpal
3. Ulnar collateral
4. Radial collateral

**The Intercarpal Joints**

The intercarpal joints are sliding joints located between the individual carpal bones. The gliding movements possible at these joints complement those of the wrist joint.

*Ligaments.* The dorsal, volar, and interosseous intercarpal ligaments bind the bones of each row of carpal bones together. The dorsal and volar ligaments extend transversely across the bones of each row on the dorsal and volar surfaces, respectively, whereas the interosseous ligaments are attached to the contiguous surfaces of the bones.

### The Carpometacarpal Joints

The carpometacarpal joints are the articulations between the bases of the metacarpals and the distal row of carpal bones. The medial four articulations are sliding joints, whereas that of the thumb is a saddle joint.

*Movements.* The medial four articulations (fingers) permit only slight amounts of flexion and extension, which supplement the movements of the wrist.

The saddle joint at the thumb allows *abduction* (a forward movement of the thumb at right angles to the palm), *adduction* (return movement from abduction), *hyperadduction* (a backward movement of the thumb at right angles to the hand), *extension* (a lateral movement of the thumb away from the index finger), *flexion* (return movement from extension), *hyperflexion* (a medialward movement of the thumb from a position of slight abduction, i.e., the thumb slides across the front of the palm), *circumduction* (a combination of all the above movements, performed in sequence in either direction), and *opposition* (touching the tip of the thumb to the tip of any of the four fingers). Opposition is a movement unique to human beings.

*Ligaments.* All five carpometacarpal joints (Figs. 20–8 and 20–9) are reinforced by the *dorsal, volar,* and *interosseous carpometacarpal ligaments.*

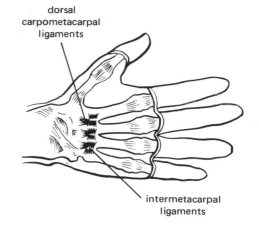

**Fig. 20–8. The carpometacarpal and intermetacarpal joints.**

**Fig. 20–9. Ligaments of the left hand.**

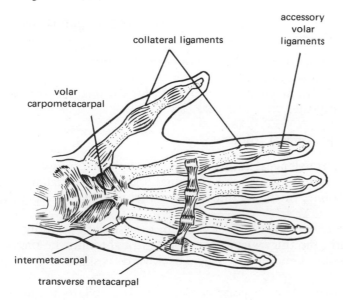

## The Intermetacarpal Joints

The intermetacarpal joints are sliding joints located between the adjacent sides of the bases of the medial four metacarpal bones. These sliding joints permit only slight amounts of flexion and extension, which supplement the movements of the wrist.

*Ligaments.* The ligaments of the intermetacarpal joints (Fig. 20–9) are

A. *Dorsal, volar,* and *interosseous intermetacarpal ligaments:* connect the base of each metacarpal bone, with the exception of the first, with the bases of the adjacent metacarpals.
B. *Transverse metacarpal ligament:* connects the heads of the four medial metacarpals on their volar surfaces.

## The Metacarpophalangeal Joints

The metacarpophalangeal joints are formed when the rounded head of each metacarpal bone is received into a concavity in the base of the first or proximal phalanx. The medial four articulations are condyloid joints, whereas that of the thumb is a hinge joint.

*Movements.* Since the metacarpophalangeal joint of the thumb is a hinge joint, it permits only flexion and extension.

The movements allowed at the metacarpophalangeal joints of the four fingers are *flexion* (movement of the anterior surface of the finger toward the palmar surface of the hand), *extension* (return movement from flexion), *hyperextension* (a slight movement of the posterior surface of the fingers toward the dorsal surface of the hand), and *circumduction* (a circular movement of the fingers).

*Abduction* of the fourth, fifth, and index fingers is a movement of these fingers away from the middle finger, and *adduction* is the reverse movement. *Abduction* of the middle finger, also called *radial flexion*, is a movement of this finger laterally, whereas *adduction* or *ulnar flexion* is the movement of the middle finger medially.

*Ligaments.* The ligaments of the metacarpophalangeal joints (Fig. 20–9) are

A. *Capsular Ligament:* connects the margins of the articular surfaces of the bones.
B. *Collateral* and *Accessory Volar Ligaments:* reinforce the capsule.

## The Interphalangeal Joints

The interphalangeal joints are the hinge joints between the heads or distal extremities of the proximal and middle phalanges and the adjacent bones of the middle and terminal phalanges, respectively.

*Movements.* Being hinge joints, these articulations allow only *flexion* (curling the fingers) and *extension* (straightening the fingers). Hyperextension (bending the fingers backward) is slight, if present at all.

*Ligaments.* The articular capsule and the collateral and accessory volar ligaments (Fig. 20–9) reinforce these joints.

The muscles of the forearm have an anterior and posterior group. The muscles in each of these groups may, in turn, be arranged into a superficial and a deep subdivision as follows:

**20.15 Muscles of the Forearm**

A. *Anterior*: comprised mostly of the flexors of the wrist and fingers and the pronators of the forearm.

    1. *Superficial subdivision* (Figs. 20–10 and 20–11)

        a. Pronator teres
        b. Flexor carpi radialis
        c. Palmaris longus
        d. Flexor digitorum superficialis
        e. Flexor carpi ulnaris

    2. *Deep subdivision* (Figs. 20–11 and 20–12)

        a. Flexor digitorum profundus
        b. Flexor pollicis longus
        c. Pronator quadratus

B. *Posterior*: comprised mostly of the extensors of the hand and fingers and the supinators of the forearm.

    1. *Superficial subdivision* (Figs. 20–13 and 20–14)

        a. Brachioradialis
        b. Extensor carpi radialis longus
        c. Extensor carpi radialis brevis
        d. Extensor digitorum
        e. Extensor digiti minimi
        f. Extensor carpi ulnaris

    2. *Deep subdivision* (Fig. 20–15)

        a. Supinator
        b. Abductor pollicis longus
        c. Extensor pollicis brevis
        d. Extensor pollicis longus
        e. Extensor indicis

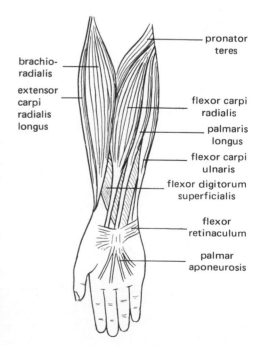

Fig. 20–10. The muscles of the superficial subdivision of the anterior forearm muscles. The muscles with labels on the left of the illustration are posterior muscles visible from the anterior side.

brachio-radialis

extensor carpi radialis longus

pronator teres

flexor carpi radialis

palmaris longus

flexor carpi ulnaris

flexor digitorum superficialis

flexor retinaculum

palmar aponeurosis

**Superficial Muscles of the Anterior Forearm** (Figs. 20–10 and 20–11)

All five muscles in this group arise by a common tendon from the medial epicondyle of the humerus and are, named in order from the lateral to the medial side, pronator teres, flexor carpi radialis, palmaris longus, flexor digitorum superficialis, and flexor carpi ulnaris. In addition to attachments on the medial epicondyle, the pronator teres has a second head, which arises from the medial side of the coronoid process of the ulna, and the flexor carpi ulnaris has a second head, which arises from the medial border of the olecranon process of the ulna. The flex digitorum superficialis also has two heads.

The *pronator teres*, as mentioned above, arises from the medial epicondyle of the humerus and by a second head from the coronoid process of the ulna. It attaches distally to the pronator ridge of the radius. Because it is wrapped around the radius, its chief action is to roll the radius medially and, thus, to pronate the forearm. By

**Fig. 20–11. The anterior muscles of the forearm.**

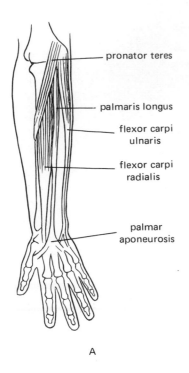

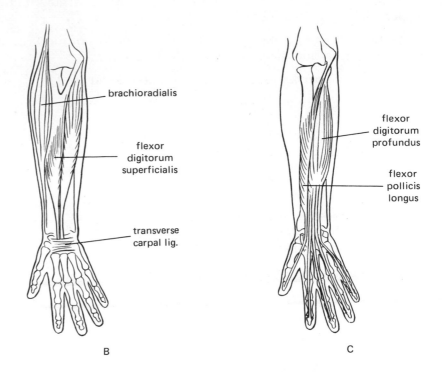

A                    B                    C

virtue of its relatively high attachment on the humerus, it is also a weak flexor at the elbow.

The *flexor carpi radialis* occupies a median position in the forearm. Coming from the medial epicondyle of the humerus, it passes to the base of the second metacarpal. It acts as a flexor and radial flexor (abductor) of the hand at the wrist and, because of its obliquity, it assists in pronation.

The middle muscle of the superficial group is the *palmaris longus,* which is situated medial to and parallel with the flexor carpi radialis. It passes from the medial epicondyle of the humerus to the palmar aponeurosis in the hand. This muscle is absent on one or both sides in about 12 per cent of the population. When present, it aids in flexion at the wrist and may also assist in pronation.

The *flexor digitorum superficialis* is covered proximally by all the other muscles of the superficial group. Some authors, therefore, classify this muscle as forming an intermediate layer between the superficial and deep groups. It arises by two heads: a humeroulnar head from the medial epicondyle of the humerus and the coronoid process of the ulna and a radial head from the upper half of the radius below the radial tuberosity. Distally, the muscle is superficial and can easily be made out between the flexor carpi ulnaris and the palmaris longus, and on each side of the flexor carpi radialis. Its distal attachment is by four tendons to the four fingers. Each tendon splits to attach to the sides of the base of the middle phalanx. It acts to flex the middle phalanges of the fingers and assists in flexion of the first phalanges and the wrist.

The *flexor carpi ulnaris* is the most medially situated muscle of the superficial anterior group. It arises by two heads, from the medial epicondyle of the humerus and from the medial border of the olecranon process and upper two thirds of ulna. Its distal attachment is on the pisiform and hamate bones and on the fifth metacarpal. It is a flexor and an ulnar flexor (adductor) of the hand at the wrist.

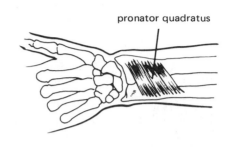

Fig. 20–12. The pronator quadratus.

pronator quadratus

### Deep Muscles of the Anterior Forearm (Figs. 20–11 and 20–12)

The deep subdivision consists of the flexor digitorum profundus, the flexor pollicis longus, and the pronator quadratus.

The *flexor digitorum profundus* is a broad thick muscle that lies beneath the superficialis. It has an extensive proximal attachment from the upper two thirds or more of the ulna. Like the superficialis, this muscle also ends in four tendons. These tendons pass through the split tendons of the superficialis and attach to the base of the distal phalanges of the four medial digits. It flexes the terminal phalanges of the fingers and aids in flexing the hand at the wrist.

The *flexor pollicis longus* is a long spindle-shaped muscle that lies parallel with and lateral to the flexor digitorum profundus. It arises from much of the anterior surface of the radius and gives off a large rounded tendon, which passes to the terminal phalanx of the thumb. Its actions are flexion of both phalanges of the thumb, flexion of the wrist, and assistance in adduction of the thumb metacarpal.

The *pronator quadratus* (Fig. 20–12) is a flat, quadrangular muscle passing from the ulna to the radius almost transversely, but inclined slightly distally. It is located on the anterior surfaces of the lower one fourth of the ulna and the radius. Its only action is pronation of the forearm.

### Superficial Muscles of the Posterior Forearm (Figs. 20–13 and 20–14)

The superficial subdivision of the posterior or extensor forearm muscles consists of the following muscles, named from the lateral to the medial side, the brachioradialis, the extensors carpi radialis longus and brevis, the extensor digitorum, the extensor digiti minimi, and the extensor carpi ulnaris.

The majority of these muscles take their proximal attachments from a common tendon attached to the lateral epicondyle of the humerus, the exceptions being the brachioradialis and the extensor carpi radialis longus, which arise from the lateral supracondylar ridge, and the extensor carpi ulnaris, one head of which originates from the middle third of the posterior border of the ulna.

The *brachioradialis* is the most anterior member of the superficial group because it lies along the radial border of the anterior aspect of the forearm. It attaches distally to the styloid process of the radius. Because of its high attachment on the humerus and its course across the front of the elbow joint, it is flexor of the elbow. It may also supinate or pronate slightly, if the hand is already in marked pronation or supination.

Under the brachioradialis is the *extensor carpi radialis longus*. The *extensor carpi radialis brevis* is closely associated with the longus in both location and function. The brevis lies along the lateral surface of the radius adjacent and medial to the longus. It attaches distally

Fig. 20–13. The superficial muscles of the posterior forearm.

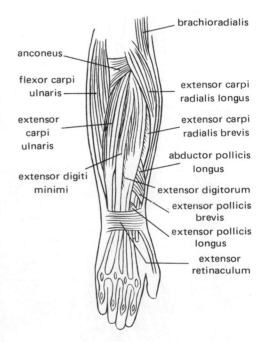

brachioradialis

anconeus

flexor carpi ulnaris

extensor carpi ulnaris

extensor digiti minimi

extensor carpi radialis longus

extensor carpi radialis brevis

abductor pollicis longus

extensor digitorum

extensor pollicis brevis

extensor pollicis longus

extensor retinaculum

**Fig. 20-14. Muscles of the superficial subdivision of the posterior forearm muscles, excluding the brachioradialis.**

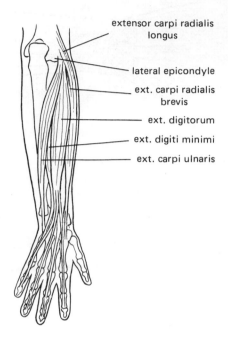

extensor carpi radialis longus

lateral epicondyle

ext. carpi radialis brevis

ext. digitorum

ext. digiti minimi

ext. carpi ulnaris

**Fig. 20-15. The deep subdivision of the posterior forearm muscles.**

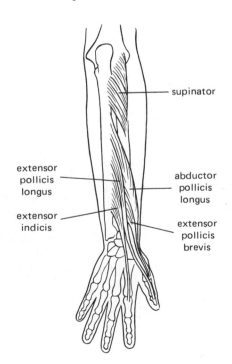

extensor pollicis longus

extensor indicis

supinator

abductor pollicis longus

extensor pollicis brevis

to the base of the third metacarpal. These two muscles extend and perhaps help slightly to radial flex (abduct) the wrist. They also assist in flexion and supination of the forearm.

The *extensor digitorum* occupies much of the posterior surface of the forearm. It arises from the humerus and splits into four tendons as it reaches the wrist. The four tendons are attached distally to the four fingers. Each tendon divides into three slips, the middle one attaching to the dorsal surface of the second phalanx and the other two uniting and attaching to the dorsal surface of the base of the distal phalanx. It acts to extend the proximal phalanges of the fingers and assists in extension of the second and third phalanges and of wrist.

The *extensor digiti minimi* is a thin, slender muscle that appears to be a part of the extensor digitorum. Its distal attachment is on the base of the proximal phalanx of the little finger. It extends and abducts the little finger.

The *extensor carpi ulnaris* is situated along the posterior surface of the ulna and is attached distally to the base of the fifth metacarpal. It is an extensor and ulnar flexor (adductor) of the hand at the wrist.

## Deep Muscles of the Posterior Forearm (Fig. 20-15)

The deep posterior muscles are the supinator, three thumb muscles—the abductor pollicis longus, extensor pollicis brevis, and extensor pollicis longus—and the extensor indicis.

The *supinator* is the most proximal of the deep group. It arises from the lateral epicondyle of the humerus and the supinator crest of the ulna and passes obliquely downward and laterally across the arm to attach on the radius superior to the oblique line that is almost on the anterior surface. As its name indicates, it supinates the forearm.

The *abductor pollicis longus* arises from the middle third of the posterior surfaces of the radius and ulnar inferior to the posterior oblique lines of these bones and extends to the base of the first metacarpal. It acts to abduct and extend the thumb metacarpal, and, by its position at the wrist, it is also both a radial flexor (abductor) and a flexor of the hand.

The *extensor pollicis brevis* is a slender muscle that lies medial and inferior to the abductor. It arises from the posterior surface of the radius and ulna below the attachment of the abductor and extends to the base of the first phalanx of the thumb. It acts to extend the metacarpophalangeal joint of the thumb and to abduct the metacarpal. It also assists in radial flexion (abduction) of the wrist.

The *extensor pollicis longus* is a long, slender muscle that lies medial and inferior to the brevis. It arises from the posterior surface of the middle third of the ulna and attaches distally to the base of the distal phalanx of the thumb. It extends and abducts the thumb. It also assists in radial flexion (abduction) of the hand at the wrist joint.

The *extensor indicis* is a long, slender muscle that lies medial to the extensor pollicis longus and is completely covered by the extensor digitorum. It arises from the posterior surface of the lower half of the ulna and extends to the base of the first phalanx of the index finger. It extends and adducts the index finger and assists in the extension of the wrist.

The intrinsic muscles of the hand lie entirely within the hand and are concerned with movements of the digits. They are arranged in the following divisions:

**20.16  Muscles of the Hand**

A. *Muscles of the thumb* (Fig. 20–16): These muscles form a prominence called the thenar eminence, which forms the proximal and lateral boundary of the palm.

    1. Abductor pollicis brevis
    2. Opponens pollicis
    3. Flexor pollicis brevis
    4. Adductor pollicis

B. *Muscles of the little finger* (Fig. 20–17): These muscles form a prominence called the hypothenar eminence, which forms the medial border of the palm.

    1. Abductor digiti minimi
    2. Flexor digiti minimi
    3. Opponens digiti minimi

C. *The lumbricales* (Fig. 20–18)
D. *The interosseous muscles* (Fig. 20–19)

    1. The palmar interossei
    2. The dorsal interossei

**The Muscles of the Thumb** (Fig. 20–16)

The *abductor pollicis brevis* is a flat muscle arising from the transverse carpal ligament and trapezium bone and attaching distally on the radial side of the base of the first phalanx of the thumb. This muscle is a true abductor of the thumb in that it moves the thumb almost perpendicularly away from the plane of the palm. It also assists in flexion of the proximal phalanx of the thumb.

The *opponens pollicis* is largely covered by the short abductor. It, like the abductor, arises from the transverse carpal ligament and

**Fig. 20–16. The muscles of the thumb.**

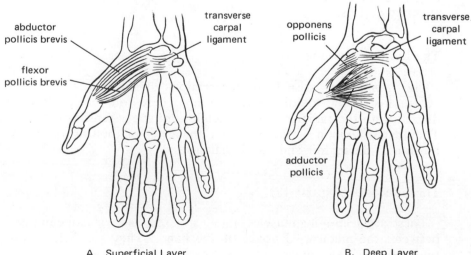

A. Superficial Layer        B. Deep Layer

trapezium bone, but it attaches distally along most of the length of the first metacarpal. It thus draws the first metacarpal across the palm of the hand, rotating this bone as it contracts and producing the movement known as opposition of the thumb.

The *flexor pollicis brevis* like the muscles already discussed arises from the transverse carpal ligament and trapezium, but it also has a deep head that arises from the ulnar side of the first metacarpal bone. The two heads unite to form a common tendon to attach distally near the attachment of the short abductor on the radial side of the base of the proximal phalanx of the thumb, but more on the palmar surface than does the abductor. It not only flexes the proximal phalanx, but also aids in adduction and opposition of the thumb.

The *adductor pollicis* also has two heads, a transverse and an oblique one. The transverse head arises primarily from the palmar surface of the third metacarpal. The oblique head arises from the deep carpal ligaments, capitate bone, and bases of the second and third metacarpal bones. The two heads come together to attach into the ulnar side of the palmar surface of the base of the proximal phalanx of the thumb. The muscles act to adduct and flex the thumb.

### The Muscles of the Little Finger (Fig. 20–17)

The most superficial of the little finger muscles on the ulnar border of the palm is the *abductor digiti minimi*, which has its proximal attachment largely on the pisiform bone. It attaches distally on the ulnar aspect of the base of the proximal phalanx. The *flexor digiti minimi brevis* arises from the hook of the hamate bone and adjacent parts of the transverse carpal ligament. It attaches distally, along with the abductor on the proximal phalanx, but more on the palmar side. The *opponens digiti minimi* is located deeper than the other two muscles. It, like the flexor, arises from the hook of the hamate bone and adjacent parts of the transverse carpal ligament, but it attaches distally into the ulnar border of almost the entire length of the body of the fifth metacarpal.

The abductor and short flexor aid in both abduction and flexion of the little finger. The opponens aids in opposition of the little finger to the thumb and, therefore, also in cupping the hand and in grasping objects.

### The Lumbricales (Fig. 20–18)

The *lumbricales* arise from the tendons of the flexor digitorum profundus in the middle of the palm. These four muscles attach distally into the radial side of the tendons of the extensor digitorum. They act in flexion of the proximal phalanges of the fingers and extension of the middle and distal phalanges.

### The Interossei (Fig. 20–19)

These are deep-lying muscles largely situated, as their name implies, between the metacarpal bones of the hand. They are divided into two groups, three palmar and four dorsal.

**Fig. 20-17. The muscles of the little finger.**

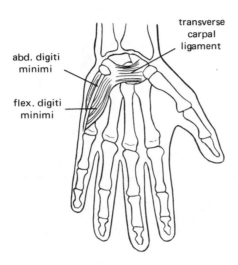

transverse
carpal
ligament

abd. digiti
minimi

flex. digiti
minimi

A. Superficial Layer

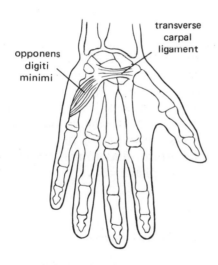

transverse
carpal
ligament

opponens
digiti
minimi

B. Deep Layer

The proximal attachments of the *palmar interossei* are as follows:

First:     Ulnar side of second metacarpal bone

Second:  Radial side of fourth metacarpal bone

Third:     Radial side of fifth metacarpal bone

These muscles cross over the metacarpophalangeal joints and attach to the proximal phalanges of the index, ring, and little fingers. The tendons then pass dorsally to join the expansions of the extensor digitorum tendons to these fingers. On attaching to the phalanges, the first attaches to the ulnar side of the base of the proximal phalanx of the index finger, whereas the second and third attach to radial

**Fig. 20-18. The lumbricales.**

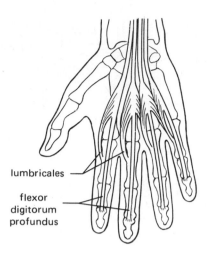

lumbricales

flexor
digitorum
profundus

sides of the phalanges of the fourth and fifth fingers. These muscles act to adduct and flex the second, fourth, and fifth fingers at the metacarpophalangeal joints and to extend the second and third phalanges of these fingers.

The four *dorsal interossei* arise by two heads from the adjacent sides of the metacarpal bones in each interspace. They attach distally to the base of the proximal phalanx and aponeurosis of the extensor muscles on each side of the middle finger, on the thumb side of the index finger, and on the ulnar side of the fourth finger. They act to abduct the index and fourth fingers and to radial and ulnar flex the middle finger. They also act to flex the proximal row of phalanges of the second, third, and fourth fingers and to extend the middle and distal rows of phalanges.

**Fig. 20-19. The palmar and dorsal interossei.**

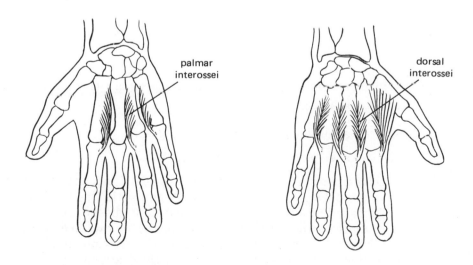

palmar
interossei

dorsal
interossei

## 20.21 Bones of the Forearm

A. Specific Student Objectives

1. *The Ulna*

    a. Identify the two bones of the forearm.
    b. State which bone is located on the medial side of the forearm.
    c. What is the longest bone of the forearm?
    d. Locate an ulna on a mounted skeleton and identify the following:

    | | |
    |---|---|
    | superior extremity | oblique line |
    | semilunar notch | volar border |
    | coronoid process | dorsal border |
    | tuberosity of the ulna | lateral border |
    | olecranon process | interosseous crest |
    | radial notch | inferior extremity |
    | supinator crest | head |
    | bicipital hollow | semilunar facets |
    | anterior surface | articular circumference |
    | medial surface | styloid process |
    | posterior surface | |

    e. Locate the ulna in your own forearm and identify the following:

    olecranon process
    styloid process

2. *The Radius*

    a. Locate a radius on a mounted skeleton and identify the following:

    | | |
    |---|---|
    | proximal extremity | pronator ridge |
    | head | posterior oblique line |
    | fovea | anterior border |
    | articular circumference | posterior border |
    | neck | interosseous crest |
    | lateral surface | lunate facet |
    | volar surface | navicular facet |
    | posterior surface | styloid process |
    | tuberosity of the radius | ulnar notch |
    | anterior oblique line | |

    b. Locate the radius in your own forearm and identify the following:

    head
    styloid process

## 20.22 Bones of the Wrist and Hand

A. Specific Student Objectives

1. State the technical name of the wrist.
2. Identify the two rows of carpal bones.

3. Locate the wrist on a mounted skeleton and identify the following:

| | |
|---|---|
| navicular | trapezoid |
| lunate | capitate |
| triquetral | hamate |
| pisiform | hook of the hamate |
| trapezium | |

4. Locate the wrist in your own body and identify the following:

   pisiform
   navicular

5. State the technical name of the body of the hand.
6. State the technical name of the bones of the hand.
7. Locate the hand on a mounted skeleton and identify the following:

   base of the third metacarpal bone
   shaft of the first metacarpal bone
   head of the fifth metacarpal bone

8. Locate the metacarpal bones in your own hand and identify the following:

   base of the second metacarpal bone
   head of the fourth metacarpal bone

9. State the technical name of the fingers.
10. State the technical name of the bones of the fingers.
11. Locate the fingers on a mounted skeleton and identify the following:

   proximal phalanx of the thumb
   distal phalanx of the second finger
   middle phalanx of the third finger
   ungual tuberosity
   trochlea of the proximal phalanx of the thumb

12. Locate the phalanges in your own fingers and identify the following:

   proximal phalanx of the little finger
   distal phalanx of the middle finger
   head of the middle phalanx of the ring finger

B. Study Hints

1. The use of actual bones is quite beneficial in the study of specific osteology, and there is no substitute for independent study of a mounted skeleton in learning the specific markings on a bone.
2. Locating bony landmarks in the student's body is also a valuable aid to learning.

## 20.23  The Elbow and Radioulnar Joints

A.  Specific Student Objectives

1.  *The Elbow Joint*

    a.  What type of joint is this?
    b.  Describe the bony articulations involved in this joint.
    c.  What movements are allowed at this joint?  Describe these movements.
    d.  Describe the ligamentous reinforcements of this joint.

2.  *The Radioulnar Joints*

    a.  Identify the three radioulnar joints by name and by type.
    b.  Describe the bony articulations involved in these joints.
    c.  What movements are allowed at these joints?  Describe these movements.
    d.  Describe the ligamentous reinforcements of this joint.

## 20.24  Joints of the Wrist and Hand

A.  Specific Student Objectives

1.  *The Radiocarpal or Wrist Joint*

    a.  What type of joint is this?
    b.  Describe the bony articulations involved in this joint.
    c.  What movements are allowed at this joint?  Describe these movements.
    d.  Describe the ligamentous reinforcements of this joint.

2.  *The Intercarpal Joints*

    a.  What type of joints are these?
    b.  Describe the bony articulations involved in these joints.
    c.  What movements are allowed at these joints?
    d.  Describe the ligamentous reinforcements of these joints.

3.  *The Carpometacarpal Joints*

    a.  What type of joints are these?
    b.  What are the bony articulations involved in these joints?
    c.  What movements are allowed at these joints?  Describe these movements.
    d.  Describe the ligamentous reinforcements of these joints.

4.  *The Intermetacarpal Joints*

    a.  What type of joints are these?
    b.  Describe the bony articulations involved in these joints.
    c.  What movements are allowed at these joints?

d. Describe the ligamentous reinforcements of these joints.

5. *The Metacarpophalangeal Joints*

a. What type of joints are these?
b. What are the bony articulations involved in these joints?
c. What movements are allowed at these joints? Describe these movements.
d. Describe the ligamentous reinforcements of these joints.

6. *The Interphalangeal Joints*

a. What type of joints are these?
b. What are the bony articulations involved in these joints?
c. What movements are allowed at these joints? Describe these movements.
d. Describe the ligamentous reinforcements of these joints.

B. Study Hints

1. The student should study each joint on a mounted skeleton where he can visualize the bony articulations and ligamentous reinforcements involved in the joint.
2. The student should also identify each joint in his own body and perform the movements of that joint according to the descriptions presented in the text. It is important that he learn to identify the movements by their proper names whenever he sees them performed.

## 20.25  Muscles of the Forearm

A. Specific Student Objectives

1. *Anterior Muscles of the Forearm*

a. Identify the two subdivisions of anterior forearm muscles.
b. Identify by name and by subdivision each of the eight anterior muscles of the forearm.
c. Give the proximal and distal attachments of each of these muscles.
d. Give the joint actions produced by the contraction of each of these muscles.
e. Locate each of the superficial muscles in your own forearm.
f. Name the five muscles of the superficial layer in order from the lateral to the medial side.
g. Name the common proximal attachment of all five superficial muscles.

2. *Posterior Muscles of the Forearm*

   a. Identify the two subdivisions of posterior forearm muscles.

   b. Identify by name and by subdivision each of the eleven posterior muscles of the forearm.

   c. Give the proximal and distal attachments of each of these muscles.

   d. Give the joint actions produced by the contraction of each of these muscles.

   e. Locate each of the superficial muscles in your own forearm.

   f. Name the six muscles of the superficial layer in order from the lateral to the medial side.

   g. Name the common proximal attachment of a majority of the superficial muscles.

B. Study Hints

   1. Table 20–1 is presented to aid in the mastery of specific muscle actions and attachments.

**Table 20–1. The Attachments and Actions of the Forearm Muscles**

| Location | Name | Proximal Attachment | Illustration | Distal Attachment | Action |
|---|---|---|---|---|---|
| Anterior group Superficial subdivision | Pronator teres | Two heads, one from the medial epicondyle of the humerus and the other from the coronoid process of the ulna | Figs. 20–10 and 20–11 | Pronator ridge of the radius | Flexion of elbow and pronation of forearm |
| | Flexor carpi radialis | Medial epicondyle of humerus | Figs. 20–10 and 20–11 | Base of the second metacarpal | Flexion and abduction of wrist and assistant in pronation of forearm |
| | Palmaris longus | Medial epicondyle of humerus | Figs. 20–10 and 20–11 | Palmar aponeurosis in the hand | Assistant in flexion of wrist and pronation of forearm |
| | Flexor digitorum superficialis | Humeroulnar head: medial epicondyle of humerus and the coronoid process of the ulna. Radial head: upper half of the radius below radial tuberosity | Figs. 20–10 and 20–11 | By four tendons to the four fingers. Each tendon splits to attach to the sides of the bases of the middle phalanx | Flexion of the first and second phalanges of four fingers and of wrist |
| | Flexor carpi ulnaris | Two heads, one from the medial epicondyle of the humerus and the other from the medial border of the olecranon process and upper two thirds of the ulna | Figs. 20–10 and 20–11 | Palmar surface of the pisiform and hamate bones and on fifth metacarpal | Flexion and adduction of wrist |

**Table 20–1. The Attachments and Actions of the Forearm Muscles (continued)**

| Location | Name | Proximal Attachment | Illustration | Distal Attachment | Action |
|---|---|---|---|---|---|
| Anterior group Deep subdivision | Flexor digitorum profundus | Upper two thirds of ulna | Fig. 20–11 | By four tendons to the distal phalanges of the four medial fingers | Flexion of the four medial fingers and of the wrist |
| | Flexor pollicis longus | Anterior surface of middle half of radius | Fig. 20–11 | Base of distal phalanx of the thumb | Flexion and adduction of thumb and flexion of wrist |
| | Pronator quadratus | Anterior surface of lower one fourth of ulna | Fig. 20–12 | Anterior surface of lower one fourth of radius | Pronation of forearm |
| Posterior group Superficial subdivision | Brachio-radialis | Upper two thirds of the lateral supracondyloid ridge of humerus | Figs. 20–10 and 20–11 | Styloid process of the radius | Flexion of elbow. Reduction of extreme supination and pronation to midposition |
| | Extensor carpi radialis longus | Lower third of the lateral supracondyloid ridge of humerus | Figs. 20–13 and 20–14 | Base of second metacarpal | Extension and abduction of wrist and forearm supination |
| | Extensor carpi radialis brevis | Lateral epicondyle of humerus | Figs. 20–13 and 20–14 | Base of third metacarpal | Extension and abduction of wrist, and forearm supination |
| | Extensor digitorum | Lateral epicondyle of humerus | Figs. 20–13 and 20–14 | By four tendons to four fingers. Each tendon splits into three slips, the middle one attaches to the dorsal surface of middle phalanx and other two unite to attach to base of distal phalanx | Extension of fingers and wrist |
| | Extensor digiti minimi | Tendon of extensor digitorum | Figs. 20–13 and 20–14 | Tendon of extensor digitorum at the proximal phalanx of little finger | Extension and abduction of little finger |
| | Extensor carpi ulnaris | Lateral epicondyle of humerus and middle third of the posterior border of ulna | Figs. 20–13 and 20–14 | Base of fifth metacarpal | Extension and adduction of wrist |
| Posterior group Deep subdivision | Supinator | Lateral epicondyle of humerus and supinator crest of ulna | Fig. 20–15 | On radius superior to the oblique line | Supination of forearm |
| | Abductor pollicis longus | Middle third of posterior surfaces of radius and ulnar inferior to posterior oblique line of these bones | Figs. 20–14 and 20–15 | Base of the first metacarpal | Abduction and extension of thumb and abduction and flexion of wrist |

Table 20-1. The Attachments and Actions of the Forearm Muscles (continued)

| Location | Name | Proximal Attachment | Illustration | Distal Attachment | Action |
|----------|------|---------------------|--------------|-------------------|--------|
| | Extensor pollicis brevis | Posterior surface of the radius and ulna below attachment of the abductor | Figs. 20-14 and 20-15 | Base of the first phalanx of the thumb | Extension and abduction of thumb and abduction of the wrist |
| | Extensor pollicis longus | Posterior surface of the middle third of ulna | Figs. 20-14 and 20-15 | Base of the distal phalanx of the thumb | Extension and abduction of thumb and abduction of wrist |
| | Extensor indicis | Posterior surface of the lower half of the ulna | Fig. 20-15 | Base of the first phalanx of the index or second finger | Extension and adduction of index finger |

2. Instructions as to where the muscles of the forearm can be palpated are presented in Table 20-2. The student should perform the movements of the elbow, forearm, and wrist and attempt to locate through palpation each of the muscles listed.

Table 20-2. Instructions for Palpating the Muscles of the Forearm

| Name of Muscle | Where the Muscle Can Be Palpated |
|----------------|----------------------------------|

A. *Anterior*

  1. Superficial subdivision (Figs. 20-10 and 20-11)

| | |
|---|---|
|     a. Pronator teres | Cannot be palpated. |
|     b. Flexor carpi radialis | Anterior surface of wrist, just lateral to the tendon of the palmaris longus. |
|     c. Palmaris longus | Anterior surface of the wrist in the exact center. It is the most prominent of the flexor tendons. |
|     d. Flexor digitorum superficialis | Palm of hand. |
|     e. Flexor carpi ulnaris | Anterior surface of ulnar side of forearm. The tendon may be palpated on the medial side of anterior surface of wrist, just proximal to the pisiform bone. |

  2. Deep subdivision (Fig. 20-15)

| | |
|---|---|
|     a. Flexor digitorum profundus | Cannot be palpated. |
|     b. Flexor pollicis longus | Cannot be palpated. |
|     c. Pronator quadratus | Cannot be palpated. |

Table 20–2. Instructions for Palpating the Muscles of the Forearm (continued)

| Name of Muscle | Where the Muscle Can Be Palpated |
|---|---|
| B. *Posterior* | |
| 1. Superficial subdivision (Figs. 20–13 and 20–14) | |
| a. Brachioradialis | On anterolateral surface of upper half of forearm. |
| b. Extensor carpi radialis longus | The tendon can be felt on the dorsal surface of wrist in line with the index finger. The muscular portion can be felt in the center of the dorsal surface of forearm about 2 in. below the elbow when forearm is in pronated position. |
| c. Extensor carpi radialis brevis | This muscle can also be palpated on the dorsal surface of the forearm slightly below the extensor carpi radialis longus. |
| d. Extensor digitorum | Dorsal surface of hand and forearm. |
| e. Extensor digiti minimi | Cannot be palpated. |
| f. Extensor carpi ulnaris | This muscle can be palpated halfway between the elbow and wrist on the ulnar margin of the posterior surface of forearm. |
| 2. Deep subdivision (Fig. 20–15) | |
| a. Supinator | Cannot be palpated. |
| b. Abductor pollicis longus | The tendon of this muscle can be palpated just anterior to the tendon of the extensor pollicis brevis at the base of the first metacarpal. These two tendons lie side by side. |
| c. Extensor pollicis brevis | If the first phalanx is extended against resistance, the tendon stands out between the wrist and first metacarpophalangeal joint. |
| d. Extensor pollicis longus | If the hand is placed palm down on a table and the thumb raised as high as possible, the tendon may be clearly seen and palpated on the dorsal surface of the thumb and radial side of hand. |
| e. Extensor indicis | Cannot be palpated. |

## 20.26 Muscles of the Hand

A. Specific Student Objectives

1. *Muscles of the Thumb*

   a. Identify the four muscles of the thumb.
   b. Give the proximal and distal attachments of each of these muscles.
   c. Give the joint actions produced by the contraction of each of these muscles.
   d. Locate each of these muscles in your own thumb.

2. *Muscles of the Little Finger*

   a. Identify the three muscles of the little finger.
   b. Give the proximal and distal attachments of each of these muscles.
   c. Give the joint actions produced by the contraction of each of these muscles.
   d. Locate each of these muscles in your own little finger.

3. *The Lumbricales*

   a. Give the proximal and distal attachments of the lumbricales.
   b. Give the joint actions produced by the contraction of these muscles.

4. *The Interossei*

   a. Identify the two interossei muscles.
   b. Give the proximal and distal attachments of each of these muscles.
   c. Give the joint actions produced by the contraction of each of these muscles.

B. Study Hints

   1. Table 20-3 is presented to aid in the mastery of specific muscle actions and attachments.

Table 20-3. **The Attachments and Actions of the Muscles of the Hand**

| Location | Name | Proximal Attachment | Illustration | Distal Attachment | Action |
|---|---|---|---|---|---|
| Muscles of the thumb | Abductor pollicis brevis | Transverse carpal ligament and trapezium bone | Fig. 20–16 | Radial side of the base of the first phalanx of the thumb | Abduction of thumb and assistant in flexion of first phalanx |
| | Opponens pollicis | Transverse carpal ligament and trapezium bone | Fig. 20–16 | Along most of the length of the first metacarpal | Opposition of thumb |
| | Flexor pollicis brevis | Transverse carpal ligament and trapezium bone and second head on ulnar side of first metacarpal | Fig. 20–16 | The radial side of the base of the proximal phalanx of the thumb | Flexion of proximal phalanx and assistant in adduction and opposition |
| | Adductor pollicis | Transverse head: palmar surface of the third metacarpal. Oblique head: deep carpal ligaments, capitate bone, and bases of second and third metacarpals | Fig. 20–16 | Ulnar side of the palmar surface of the base of the proximal phalanx of the thumb | Adduction and flexion of thumb |
| Muscles of the little finger | Abductor digiti minimi | Pisiform bone | Fig. 20–17 | Ulnar aspect of the base of proximal phalanx of little finger | Flexion and abduction of little finger |
| | Flexor digiti minimi brevis | Hook of hamate bone and adjacent parts of transverse carpal ligament | Fig. 20–17 | Palmar aspect of the base of proximal phalanx of little finger | Flexion and abduction of little finger |

**Table 20–3. The Attachments and Actions of the Muscles of the Hand (continued)**

| Location | Name | Proximal Attachment | Illustration | Distal Attachment | Action |
|---|---|---|---|---|---|
| | Opponens digiti minimi | Hook of the hamate bone, adjacent parts of the transverse carpal ligament | Fig. 20–17 | Ulnar border of almost entire length of the body of fifth metacarpal | Opposition |
| Lumbricales division | Lumbricales | Tendons of flexor digitorum profundus | Fig. 20–18 | Radial side of the tendons of extensor digitorum | Flexion of proximal phalanges of fingers and extension of the others |
| Interossei | Palmar interossei | 1st: Ulnar side of second metacarpal<br>2nd: Radial side of fourth metacarpal<br>3rd: Radial side of fifth metacarpal | Fig. 20–19 | Proximal phalanges of the index, ring, and little fingers. First attaches on ulnar side of the base of proximal phalanx of index finger. Second and third attach on radial side of fourth and fifth fingers | Adduction and flexion of second, fourth, and fifth fingers at metacarpophalangeal joints and extension of second and third phalanges of these fingers |
| | Dorsal interossei | By two heads from adjacent sides of the metacarpal bones | Fig. 20–19 | Base of the proximal phalanx and aponeurosis of extensor muscles on each side of middle finger, on thumb side of index finger, and on ulnar side of fourth finger | Abduction of index and fourth fingers and radial and ulnar flexion of middle finger. Flexion of proximal row of phalanges of second, third, and fourth fingers and extension of the middle and distal rows of phalanges |

2. Instructions as to where the muscles of the hand can be palpated are presented in Table 20–4. The student should perform the movements of the fingers and attempt to locate through palpation each of the muscles listed.

**Table 20–4. Instructions for Palpating the Muscles of the Hand**

| Name of Muscle | Where the Muscle Can Be Palpated |
|---|---|
| A. *Muscles of the thumb* (Fig. 20–16) | |
| 1. Abductor pollicis brevis | Anterior surface of thenar eminence. |
| 2. Opponens pollicis | This muscle can be palpated along the lateral margin of the thenar eminence, close to the metacarpal bone when the thumb is pressed hard against the middle finger. |

Table 20-4. Instructions for Palpating the Muscles of the Hand (continued)

| Name of Muscle | Where the Muscle Can Be Palpated |
| --- | --- |
| 3. Flexor pollicis brevis | The superficial head can be palpated along the medial margin of the anterior surface of the thenar eminence. |
| 4. Adductor pollicis | This muscle can easily be palpated when the thumb is pressed against one of the fingers. It is located on the inner anterior surface of the metacarpophalangeal joint of the thumb. |
| B. *Muscles of the little finger* (Fig. 20-17) | |
| 1. Abductor digiti minimi | Ulnar border of hand. |
| 2. Flexor digiti minimi | In palm of hand just beside abductor digiti minimi. |
| 3. Opponens digiti minimi | Cannot be palpated. |
| C. *The lumbricales* (Fig. 20-18) | Cannot be palpated. |
| D. *The interosseous muscles* (Fig. 20-19) | |
| 1. The palmar interossei | Cannot be palpated. |
| 2. The dorsal interossei | Cannot be palpated. |

The student should consult any recent basic anatomy text for supplementary readings on the structure of the elbow, forearm, wrist, and hand. A list of selected anatomy texts is given in Appendix B.

**20.30  Recommended Supplementary Readings**

# 21

# Movements and Problems of the Elbow, Forearm, Wrist, and Hand

The movements of the elbow and the muscles that produce them are

**21.11   Movements of the Elbow Joint**

A.  *Flexion* (Fig. 21–1)

1.  Biceps brachii
2.  Brachialis
3.  Brachioradialis
4.  Pronator teres

B.  *Extension* (Fig. 21–2)

1.  Triceps brachii
2.  Anconeus

351

**Fig. 21–1. The flexors of the elbow joint.**

**Fig. 21–2. The extensors of the elbow joint.**

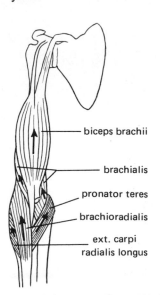

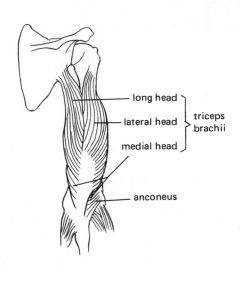

*Flexion* of the elbow is produced principally through the actions of the biceps brachii and the brachialis. The brachioradialis is also a good flexor because of its high attachment on the humerus and its line of pull, which is well in front of the elbow joint. It is, however, the only muscle on the extensor side of the forearm that is of any importance in flexion with the possible exception of the extensor carpi radialis longus. Of the flexor group of forearm muscles, the pronator teres has the highest attachment on the humerus and, is therefore, the only one that contributes significantly to elbow flexion. The other muscles of the forearm are probably unimportant as flexors.

*Extension* of the elbow is produced by the triceps brachii, which is perhaps aided slightly by the tiny anconeus.

## 21.12 Movements of the Radioulnar Joints

The movements of the radioulnar joints and the muscles that produce them are

A. *Pronation* (Fig. 21–3)

   1. Pronator quadratus
   2. Pronator teres
   3. Brachioradialis
   4. Flexor carpi radialis
   5. Palmaris longus

B. *Supination* (Fig. 21–4)

   1. Supinator
   2. Biceps brachii
   3. Brachioradialis
   4. Extensor carpi radialis longus

**Fig. 21-3. The pronators of the forearm.**     **Fig. 21-4. The supinators of the forearm.**

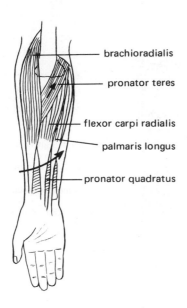

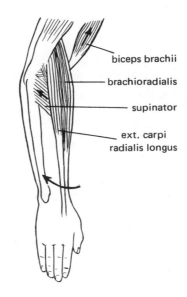

*Pronation* is produced principally by the action of the pronator quadratus, the pronator teres, and the flexor carpi radialis. The palmaris longus contracts when the movement is forceful, and the brachioradialis tends to reduce supination and return the forearm to a neutral position.

*Supination* is a much stronger movement than is pronation. It is produced by the supinator, biceps brachii, and the extensor carpi radialis longus. The biceps is a particularly strong supinator, but is effective only when the forearm is flexed. The brachioradialis tends to reduce pronation and return the forearm to a neutral position.

The movements of the wrist are flexion and extension, and abduction or radial flexion, and adduction or ulnar flexion.

**21.13  Movements of the Wrist**

### Flexion and Extension

The muscles that produce flexion and extension of the wrist are

    A. *Flexion* (Fig. 21-5)

        1. Flexor carpi ulnaris
        2. Flexor carpi radialis
        3. Palmaris longus
        4. Abductor pollicis longus
        5. Flexor pollicis longus
        6. Flexor digitorum profundus
        7. Flexor digitorum superficialis

**Fig. 21-5. The flexors of the wrist.**     **Fig. 21-6. The extensors of the wrist.**

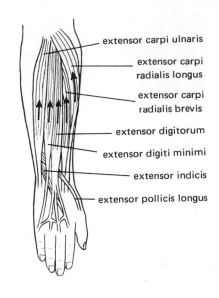

flexor carpi radialis

palmaris longus

flexor carpi ulnaris

flexor digitorum
superficialis

flexor digitorum
profundus

flexor pollicis longus

abductor pollicis
longus

extensor carpi ulnaris

extensor carpi
radialis longus

extensor carpi
radialis brevis

extensor digitorum

extensor digiti minimi

extensor indicis

extensor pollicis longus

B. *Extension* (Fig. 21-6)

1. Extensor carpi ulnaris
2. Extensor carpi radialis longus
3. Extensor carpi radialis brevis
4. Extensor digitorum
5. Extensor digiti minimi
6. Extensor indicis
7. Extensor pollicis longus

*Flexion* at the wrist is produced primarily through the flexor carpi ulnaris and the flexor carpi radialis. Also assisting in this action are the palmaris longus and the abductor pollicis longus. The flexor pollicis longus, flexor digitorum profundus, and the flexor digitorum superficialis assist in wrist flexion only when the fingers are kept extended because their range of action is too short to allow them to flex the fingers and wrist at the same time.

*Extension* at the wrist is mainly produced by the extensor carpi ulnaris, and the extensors carpi radialis longus and brevis. The extensors of the fingers and the long extensor of the thumb can assist in this movement if the fist is clenched.

**Abduction and Adduction**

The muscles that produce abduction and adduction of the wrist are

A. *Abduction or radial flexion* (Fig. 21-7)

1. Extensor carpi radialis longus
2. Extensor carpi radialis brevis
3. Flexor carpi radialis
4. Abductor pollicis longus
5. Extensor pollicis longus
6. Extensor pollicis brevis

**Fig. 21–7. The radial and ulnar flexors of the wrist.**

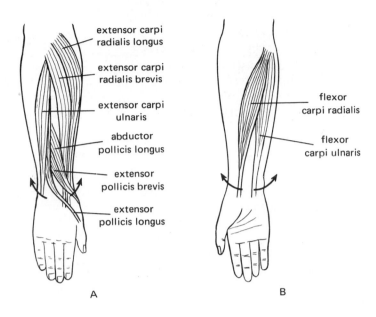

extensor carpi
radialis longus

extensor carpi
radialis brevis

extensor carpi
ulnaris

abductor
pollicis longus

extensor
pollicis brevis

extensor
pollicis longus

flexor
carpi radialis

flexor
carpi ulnaris

A

B

B. *Adduction or ulnar flexion* (Fig. 21–7)

    1.  Extensor carpi ulnaris
    2.  Flexor carpi ulnaris

*Radial flexion* or abduction is brought about chiefly by the abductor pollicis longus and the extensor pollicis brevis. The extensors carpi radialis longus and brevis, the flexor carpi radialis, and the extensor pollicis longus may also assist in the movement.

*Ulnar flexion* or adduction is brought about by the combined actions of the extensor carpi ulnaris and the flexor carpi ulnaris.

**21.14 Movements of the Digits**

The movements of the fingers and thumb are flexion and extension, abduction and adduction, opposition of the thumb, and radial and ulnar flexion of the middle finger.

**Flexion and Extension**

The muscles that produce flexion and extension of the thumb and fingers are

    A. *Flexion* (Fig. 21–8)

        1. *Thumb*

            a.  Flexor pollicis longus
            b.  Flexor pollicis brevis
            c.  Adductor pollicis
            d.  Abductor pollicis brevis

2. *Fingers*

    a. Flexor digitorum superficialis
    b. Flexor digitorum profundus
    c. Lumbricales
    d. Flexor digiti minimi brevis
    e. Abductor digiti minimi
    f. Palmar interossei
    g. Dorsal interossei
    h. Opponens digiti minimi

**Fig. 21–8. The chief flexors of the digits.**

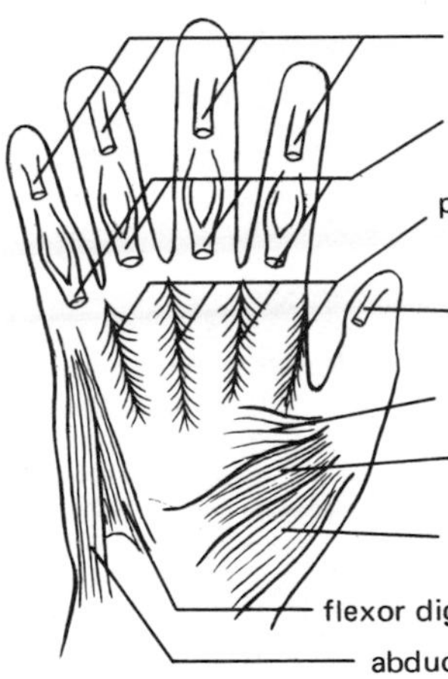

**Fig. 21–9. The extensors of a typical digit.**

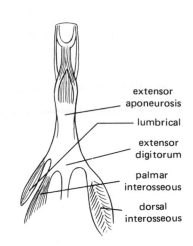

flexor digitorum profundus
flexor digitorum superficialis
palmar and dorsal interossei
flexor pollicis longus
abductor pollicis
flexor pollicis brevis
abductor pollicis brevis
flexor digiti minimi brevis
abductor digiti minimi

extensor aponeurosis
lumbrical
extensor digitorum
palmar interosseous
dorsal interosseous

B. *Extension* (Fig. 21–9)

    1. *Thumb*

        a. Extensor pollicis longus
        b. Extensor pollicis brevis
        c. Abductor pollicis longus

    2. *Fingers*

        a. Extensor digitorum
        b. Extensor indicis
        c. Extensor digiti minimi
        d. Lumbricales
        e. Palmar interossei
        f. Dorsal interossei
        g. Abductor digiti minimi

*Flexion* of the distal phalanx of the thumb can be brought about only by the flexor pollicis longus. The flexor pollicis brevis and the adductor pollicis produce flexion at the metacarpophalangeal joint of the thumb. The abductor pollicis brevis aids in flexion of this joint.

Flexion of the distal interphalangeal joints is produced by the flexor of the proximal interphalangeal joints. Ordinarily, flexion of the metacarpophalangeal joints is brought about by the lumbricales and the palmar and dorsal interossei. The profundus and superficialis are assisted in flexing the little finger, of course, by the flexor digiti minimi brevis, abductor digiti minimi, and the opponens digiti minimi. Perhaps it would be of value to emphasize that although the tendons of the profundus and superficialis may act across all the more proximal joints, each of the three joints of a finger has its own special flexor. That is, the profundus acts on the distal interphalangeal joint, the superficialis acts on the proximal interphalangeal joint, and the interossei and lumbricales act on the metacarpophalangeal joint.

The flexor digitorum profundus and the superficialis, which are so essential to the gripping strength of the fingers and hand, are at a mechanical advantage only when the wrist is extended. Flexion of the wrist, therefore, markedly interferes with flexion of the fingers.

*Extension* at the interphalangeal joint of the thumb is produced by the extensor pollicis longus, whereas the extensor pollicis brevis acts primarily at the metacarpophalangeal joint. The carpometacarpal joint is extended mainly by the abductor pollicis longus.

The sole extensors of the metacarpophalangeal joints of the fingers are the extensor digitorum and the special extensors of the index and little fingers. The interphalangeal joints are extended by the extensor digitorum, the lumbricales, and the interossei. It should be remembered that the lumbricales and the interossei act as flexors at the metacarpophalangeal joints only; because of their attachments on the extensor aponeurosis of each finger, they act as extensors of the interphalangeal joints.

### Abduction and Adduction

The muscles that produce abduction and adduction of the thumb and fingers are

 A. *Abduction* (Fig. 21–10)

  1. *Thumb*

   a. Abductor pollicis longus
   b. Abductor pollicis brevis
   c. Extensor pollicis brevis
   d. Flexor pollicis brevis

  2. *Fingers*

   a. Dorsal interossei
   b. Abductor digiti minimi
   c. Lumbricales

 B. *Adduction* (Fig. 21–11)

  1. *Thumb*

   a. Adductor pollicis
   b. Flexor pollicis longus
   c. Extensor pollicis

  2. *Fingers*

   a. Palmar interossei
   b. Opponens digiti minimi
   c. Lumbricales

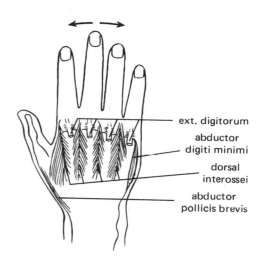

**Fig. 21-10. The chief abductors of the digits.**

ext. digitorum
abductor digiti minimi
dorsal interossei
abductor pollicis brevis

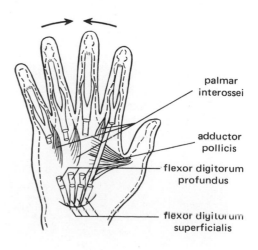

**Fig. 21-11. The chief adductors of the digits.**

palmar interossei
adductor pollicis
flexor digitorum profundus
flexor digitorum superficialis

*Abduction* of the thumb is brought about by the abductor pollicis brevis and the abductor pollicis longus with assistance from the extensor pollicis brevis and the flexor pollicis brevis.

Abduction of the fingers is brought about by the dorsal interossei, which act upon the middle three fingers, the abductor digiti minimi, which acts upon the little finger, and the lumbricales, which abduct the index finger. The abduction of the middle finger by the lumbricales will be discussed later in this section.

Pure *adduction* of the thumb can be brought about only through the combined actions of the adductor pollicis and the extensor pollicis longus. The flexor pollicis longus also assists in this movement.

Adduction of the fingers is produced by the palmar interossei. The lumbricales, parts three and four, aid in adduction of the ring and little fingers, and the opponens digiti minimi aids in the adduction of the little finger.

### Opposition of the Thumb

*Opposition* of the thumb is most easily carried out by the opponens, but it is aided by the combined action of the long and short flexors, the long and short extensors, and the adductor. In list form, the opposition muscles are

A. *Opposition of the thumb*

1. Opponens pollicis
2. Flexor pollicis longus
3. Flexor pollicis brevis
4. Abductor pollicis longus
5. Abductor pollicis brevis
6. Adductor pollicis

### Radial and Ulnar Flexion of the Middle Finger

*Radial flexion* of the middle finger is produced by the dorsal interossei and the lumbricales; *ulnar flexion* is produced by the dorsal interossei. In list form, these muscles are

A. *Radial and ulnar flexion of the middle finger*

1. Dorsal interossei
2. Lumbricales

## 21.15 Conditioning Problems of the Elbow, Forearm, Wrist, and Hand

The conditioning problems of the elbow, forearm, wrist, and hand are those concerned with the flexibility of the elbow, wrist, and finger joints and with the strength, power, and endurance of the arm, forearm, and hand muscles.

### Flexibility of the Elbow, Wrist, and Finger Joints

Flexibility exercises for the movements of the elbow, wrist, and finger joints are given in Figure 21–12.

Fig. 21-12. Some flexibility exercises for the movements of the wrist. The girl on the left is stretching her wrist extensors, and the girl on the right is stretching her wrist flexors.

### Isometric Measurements of Strength

The Clark Cable-Tension Strength Tests for the elbow flexors and extensors are illustrated in Figure 21-13. The Martin Breaking Strength Tests for the movements of the elbow, forearm, wrist, and fingers are described in Table 21-1.

### Isotonic Exercises and Measurements

Some isotonic exercises that can also be used to measure the strength, power, and endurance of the muscles of the arm, forearm, and hand are illustrated in Figure 21-14.

Since the upper limb is not normally involved in weight bearing, very little attention is generally given to the postural problems of the forearm, wrist, and hand. The proper alignment of these structures for force transmission or absorption is, however, an important topic. In this consideration, it is suggested that the student review the principles of mobility and stability presented in Chapter 9 and prac-

**21.16 Postural and Pathological Problems of the Elbow, Forearm, Wrist, and Hand**

Fig. 21–13. The Clark Cable-Tension Strength Tests for the elbow flexors (*A*) and extensors (*B*). In testing the elbow flexors, the elbow is flexed to 115°. In testing the elbow extensors, the elbow is flexed to 40°.

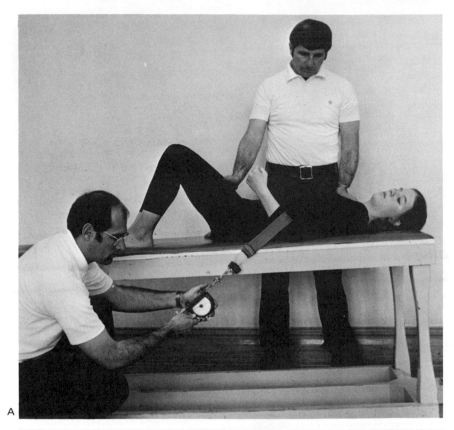

A

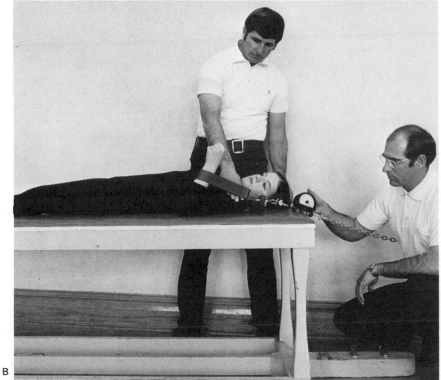

B

Fig. 21-14. Some isotonic exercises that can also be used to measure the strength, power, and endurance of the arm, forearm, and hand muscles. Exercises for the elbow flexors and extensors are shown in *A* and *B*, respectively. In *C* the subject is exercising his wrist flexors, and in *D* he is exercising his finger flexors.

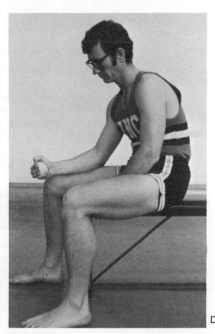

tice the application of these principles to the proper alignment of the forearm, wrist, and hand in performing, for example, a push-up.

No particular pathological problems are to be found in the bones, joints, and muscles of the forearm, wrist, and hand that are not typically found in such general conditions as arthritis, muscular dystrophy, or neurological involvements.

**Table 21-1. Martin Breaking Strength Tests\* for the Muscles Producing the Movements of the Elbow, Wrist, and Fingers**

1. *Muscles that extend the forearm*

   The subject lies on his back. The arm to be tested is at the side of the body, and the forearm is perpendicular to the table, against which the elbow rests. The hand, with the thumb pointing to the shoulder, is closed. The loop is behind the wrist. The operator stands at the head of the table. The adjuster stands at the side of the table, and, with one hand, braces the subject's elbow on the table, and, with the other hand at the subject's wrist, limits the extension of the forearm. The pull is horizontal. At the command of the adjuster, the extension of the forearm and the pull of the operator start together slowly. Extension is permitted for from 5 to 15° from the perpendicular and is overcome by the pull of the operator. The command "Stop" is given just as the forearm crosses the vertical line.

2. *Muscles that flex the forearm*

   The subject lies on his back, with his heels pressed firm against the cleat at the end of the table. The adjuster stands at the left of the subject. With his right hand, he holds the subject's elbow to the table. With his left hand, he flexes the subject's forearm about 15° and adjusts the loop about the wrist so that the upper edge of the loop is at the crease in the skin at the base of the hand. The operator stands at the foot of the table and exerts tension at the word of command. The command "Stop" should be given when the forearm reaches the vertical.

3. *Muscles that extend the wrist*

   The subject stands beside an upright post. His arm is elevated forward to the level of the shoulders. The front of the distal part of the forearm is against the post with the hand extended past the post to the styloid process of the ulna. With the palmar surface of the hand vertical and the fingers extended, the hand is put in maximum dorsiflexion. The adjuster encircles the wrist with his hand, bracing the subject's arm in position. The loop is placed across the dorsum of the hand, just distal to the metacarpals. The pull is exerted horizontally and at an angle slightly less than 90° to the hand, being deflected toward the wrist. The angle of pull must be constant: to secure this the operator swings the dynamometer through an arc as the hand gives. The accuracy of the reading depends upon maintaining the indicated direction of pull and upon placing the loop correctly. Both of these items are very important in this and the three following tests.

4. *Muscles that flex the wrist*

   The position of the subject is the same as in the preceding test except that the back of the forearm is against the post, with the hand projecting past the post to the styloid process of the ulna. A folded handkerchief or towel may be interposed between the forearm and the post. The adjuster stands directly in front of the subject's palm. With one hand, he holds the subject's wrist against the post, and, with the other hand, he adjusts and holds the loop. The loop is so placed that the middle of the loop is directly over the crease at the base of the fingers. Keeping the subject's fingers straight, the adjuster palmarflexes the subject's hand. The operator pulls at an angle just less than 90° from the plane of the subject's hand. At the command "Hold back," the subject holds the hand in extreme palmarflexion. The command "Stop" must be given as soon as the hand begins to yield.

5. *Muscles that extend the fingers*

   The subject stands beside an upright post. His arm is elevated forward to the level of the shoulders. The front of the forearm is against the post. The palmar surface of the hand is vertical. The adjuster braces against the post the palm of the subject's hand well below the palmar crease. A small loop of cloth is placed behind the middle phalanges. The pull is horizontal and at an angle slightly less than 90° to the extended fingers. The deflection of the angle is toward the wrist.

**Table 21-1. Martin Breaking Strength Tests\* for the Muscles Producing the Movements of the Elbow, Wrist, and Fingers (continued)**

6. *Muscles that flex the fingers*

The position of the subject and the bracing by the adjuster are the same as for the preceding test. The small loop of cloth is placed on the palmar surface of the middle phalanges. The dorsal surface of the hand is vertical against the post. The pull is horizontal and at an angle slightly less than 90° to the proximal phalanges. The deflection is toward the dorsum of the hand.

7. *Muscles that adduct the thumb*

The hand of the subject is held in a horizontal position, with the palmar surface directed downward. The adjuster braces, with one hand, the subject's extended fingers, and, with the other hand, the subject's wrist. The small loop is placed at the interphalangeal joint of the thumb. The subject adducts the thumb as far as possible under the palm. The pull is horizontal and at a right angle to the thumb joint. The call "Stop" is made by the adjuster just as the thumb appears from the hand.

8. *Muscles that abduct the thumb*

The position of the hand and the bracing by the adjuster are the same as for the preceding test. The subject abducts the thumb in the same horizontal plane as the hand. The position of the small loop is the same as in the preceding test, but the direction of the loop is reversed. The pull deflects downward from the horizontal just enough for the loop to escape the palmar surface of the hand. It is exerted at a right angle to the thumb.

---

\*E. G. Martin: "Tests of Muscular Efficiency," *Phys. Rev.,* **1**:454–75, 1921.

The major traumatic problems of the (1) elbow, (2) forearm, (3) wrist, and (4) hand will be discussed separately in this section.

**The Elbow**

The principal injuries of the elbow (Fig. 21–15) are (1) fractures, (2) dislocations, (3) contusions, (4) strains and sprains, and (5) epicondylitis humeri.

Elbow fractures are usually caused by a fall on the outstretched hand or the flexed elbow. The bones involved in the injury are the humerus above the condyles, the condyles proper, or the area between the condyles. The ulnar and radius may also be the recipients of trauma, and a direct force delivered to the ulna's olecranon process or a force transmitted to the head of the radius may cause a fracture.

In dislocations of the elbow, the bones of the ulna and radius may be displaced either backward, forward, or laterally. The most common dislocation is one in which both the ulna and the radius are forced backward.

Because of its lack of padding and its general vulnerability, the elbow often becomes contused in contact sports. Bone bruises arise from a deep penetration or a succession of blows to the sharp projections of the elbow.

**21.17 Traumatic Problems of the Elbow, Forearm, Wrist, and Hand**

**Fig. 21–15. Major injuries of the elbow.**

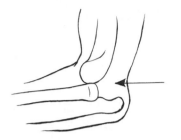

Dislocation of the Elbow

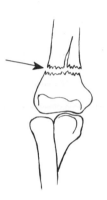

Fracture of the Elbow

**Fig. 21–16. Major injuries of the forearm.**

Fracture of the Forearm

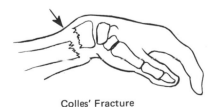

Colles' Fracture

Strains and sprains of the elbow usually are the result of the joint being forced into hyperextension. These two types of injury are difficult to separate, because nearly all traumas of the elbow involve some degree of ligamentous and tendinous involvement.

Epicondylitis humeri is sometimes also called the tennis elbow, or the pitcher's elbow, and it affects athletes who execute repeated forearm pronation and supination movements. The condition results in minute tears of the proximal attachments of either the extensor carpi radialis or the extensor digitorum.

## The Forearm

The major injuries of the forearm (Fig. 21–16) are (1) fractures, (2) contusions, and (3) forearm splints.

Fractures of the forearm are particularly common among active young people, and they usually occur as the result of a blow or fall. Fractures of the ulna and radius singly are much more rare than simultaneous fractures of both. If there is a break in the upper third of the bone, the pronator teres has a tendency to pull the forearm into an abduction deformity, whereas this deformity does not occur in fractures of the lower portion of the forearm.

The forearm is constantly contused in football. The ulnar side receives the majority of blows in arm blocks and, consequently, the greater amount of bruising.

The forearm splints, like shin splints, are difficult to treat. They occur most often in gymnasts and particularly in those who perform on the side horse.

## The Wrist

The chief traumatic problems of the wrist (Fig. 21–17) are (1) Colles' fracture, (2) navicular fracture, (3) lunate dislocation, (4) wrist sprain, and (5) wrist ganglions.

The Colles' fracture involves the lower end of the radius and/or ulna. The mechanism of the injury is usually a fall upon the outstretched hand, forcing the radius backward and upward. The most frequently fractured bone of the carpus is the navicular. Falls upon the hand compress the navicular bone between the radius and the second row of carpals. The most frequently dislocated bone of the carpus is the lunate. This injury occurs as a result of a fall upon the outstretched hand forcing open the space between the distal and the proximal carpal bones. When the stretching force is released, the lunate is dislocated anteriorly (palmar side).

The most common of the wrist injuries is the sprain. Since the main support of the wrist is derived from posterior and anterior ligaments, these ligaments are most often involved in sprains. The wrist ganglion seen in athletics often results after a wrist sprain. It is believed to be the result of a herniation of the joint capsule and it contains a clear, mucinous fluid.

## The Hand

The major injuries of the hand (Fig. 21–18) are (1) fractures of the metacarpals, (2) fractures of the phalanges, (3) baseball finger (mallet finger), (4) dislocation of the phalanges, (5) sprains of the phalanges, and (6) contusion of the hand and phalanges.

Fractures of the metacarpals are common in contact sports. They arise from striking an object with the fist or from having the hand stepped on. Fractures of the phalanges can occur as the result of a variety of mechanisms: the finger's being stepped upon, being hit by a ball, or being twisted. The mallet finger is common in baseball and basketball and is a condition caused by a blow from a thrown ball that strikes the tip of the finger and results in the avulsion of the extensor tendon from its distal attachment. Having a ball hit the tip of a finger is also the most frequent cause for finger dislocations. The force of injury is usually directed upward from the palmar side, displacing either the first or the second joint dorsally.

The phalanges, particularly the thumb, are prone to sprains caused by a blow delivered to the tip of the finger or by violent twisting. The hand and phalanges, having irregular bony structure combined with little protective fat and muscle padding, are prone to bruising in athletics.

**Fig. 21-17. Major injuries of the wrist.**

Wrist Ganglion

Dislocation of the Lunate

Navicular Fracture

**Fig. 21-18. Major injuries of the hand.**

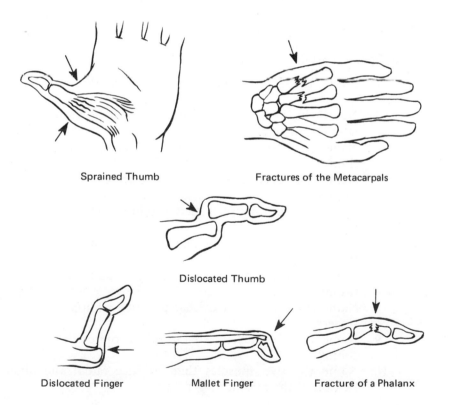

Sprained Thumb     Fractures of the Metacarpals

Dislocated Thumb

Dislocated Finger     Mallet Finger     Fracture of a Phalanx

## 21.21 Movements of the Elbow Joint

## 21.20 Study Guidelines

A. Specific Student Objectives

1. Name the four muscles that produce elbow flexion.
2. Name the two muscles that produce elbow extension.
3. State the role of the forearm muscles in elbow flexion.

### 21.22 Movements of the Radioulnar Joints

A. Specific Student Objectives

1. Name the five muscles that produce pronation of the forearm.
2. Name the four muscles that produce supination of the forearm.

### 21.23 Movements of the Wrist

A. Specific Student Objectives

1. Name the seven muscles that produce flexion of the wrist.
2. Name the seven muscles that produce extension of the wrist.
3. Name the six muscles that produce radial flexion of the wrist.
4. Name the two muscles that produce ulnar flexion of the wrist.

### 21.24 Movements of the Digits

A. Specific Student Objectives

1. Name the four muscles that produce flexion of the thumb.
2. Name the eight muscles that produce flexion of the lateral four fingers.
3. Name the three muscles that produce extension of the thumb.
4. Name the seven muscles that produce extension of the fingers.
5. Name the four muscles that produce abduction of the thumb.
6. Name the three muscles that produce abduction of the fingers.
7. Name the three muscles that produce adduction of the thumb.
8. Name the three muscles that produce adduction of the fingers.
9. Name the six muscles that produce opposition of the thumb.
10. Name the two muscles that produce radial and ulnar flexion of the middle finger.

B. Study Hints

1. In his study of the muscles that produce the movements of the elbow, forearm, wrist, and hand, the student should do a minimal amount of pure memorizing.

   It is much better for the student to study muscle-produced joint actions along with the actual exercises which employ these actions. Exercises of this type are presented in Section 21.15.

21.25  **Conditioning Problems of the Elbow, Forearm, Wrist, and Hand**

    A.  Specific Student Objectives

        1.  Identify the specific structures of the elbow, wrist, and finger joints that are stretched in the flexibility exercises presented in Figure 21–12.

        2.  Identify the specific muscles being tested by the Clark Cable-Tension Strength Tests in Figure 21–13 and in the Martin Breaking Strength Tests in Table 21–1.

        3.  Identify the specific muscles being exercised in Figure 21–14.

    B.  Study Hints

        1.  The strength tests and the exercises presented in this section are excellent for studying muscles in a way in which they can best be palpated. The palpation instructions presented in Tables 20–2 and 20–4, should be used to locate the muscles producing the joint actions demonstrated in the measurements and exercises presented in this section.

21.26  **Postural and Pathological Problems of the Elbow, Forearm, Wrist, and Hand**

    A.  Specific Student Objectives

        1.  Identify the primary postural and pathological problems of the elbow, forearm, wrist, and hand.

21.27  **Traumatic Problems of the Elbow, Forearm, Wrist, and Hand**

    A.  Specific Student Objectives

        1.  Identify and define the major traumatic problems of the elbow.

        2.  Identify and define the major traumatic problems of the forearm.

        3.  Identify and define the major traumatic problems of the wrist.

        4.  Identify and define the major traumatic problems of the hand.

**21.30  Recommended Supplementary Readings**

The student should consult any recent kinesiology text for supplementary readings on the movements and problems of the toes, foot, and ankle. A list of selected kinesiology texts is given in Appendix B. The following readings are especially recommended.

Basmajian, J. V., and Travill, A.: "Electromyography of the Pronator Muscles of the Forearm," *Anat. Rec.,* **139**:45–49, 1961.

DeSousa, O. M., and others: "Electromyographic Study of the Brachioradialis Muscle," *Anat. Rec.,* **139**:125–31, 1961.

Eyler, D. L., and Markee, J. E.: "The Anatomy and Function of the Intrinsic Musculature of the Fingers," *J. Bone Joint Surg.,* **36A**:1-9, 1954.

Little, A. D., and Lehmkuhl, D.: "Elbow Extension Force," *Phys. Ther.,* **46**: 7-17, 1966.

Long, C., and others: "An Electromyographic Study of the Extrinsic-Intrinsic Kinesiology of the Hand: Preliminary Report," *Arch. Phys. Med. Rehab.,* **41**:175-81, 1960.

———: "Electromyographic Kinesiology of the Hand: Part II. Third Dorsal Interosseus and Extensor Digitorum of the Long Finger," *Arch. Phys. Med. Rehab.,* **42**:559-65, 1961.

McFarland, G. B., and others: "Kinesiology of Selected Muscles Acting on the Wrist: Electromyographic Study," *Arch. Phys. Med. Rehab.,* **43**:165-71, 1962.

Pauly, J. E., and others: "An Electromyographic Study of Some Muscles Crossing the Elbow Joint," *Anat. Rec.,* **159**:47-53, 1967.

Sullivan, W. E., and others: "Electromyographic Studies of M. Biceps Brachii During Normal Voluntary Movements at the Elbow," *Anat. Rec.,* **107**: 243-51, 1950.

Taylor, C. L., and Schwartz, R. J.: "The Anatomy and Mechanics of the Human Hand," *Art. Limbs,* **2**:22-35, 1955.

Travill, A., and Basmajian, J. V.: "Electromyography of the Supinators of the Forearm," *Anat. Rec.,* **139**:557-60, 1960.

# APPENDIX A

## Natural Trigonometric Functions

| De-gree | Ra-dian | Sine | Cosine | Tan-gent | De-gree | Ra-dian | Sine | Cosine | Tan-gent |
|---|---|---|---|---|---|---|---|---|---|
| 0° | .000 | 0.000 | 1.000 | 0.000 | | | | | |
| 1° | .017 | .018 | 1.000 | .018 | 46° | 0.803 | 0.719 | 0.695 | 1.036 |
| 2° | .035 | .035 | 0.999 | .035 | 47° | .820 | .731 | .682 | 1.072 |
| 3° | .052 | .052 | .999 | .052 | 48° | .838 | .743 | .669 | 1.111 |
| 4° | .070 | .070 | .998 | .070 | 49° | .855 | .755 | .656 | 1.150 |
| 5° | .087 | .087 | .996 | .088 | 50° | .873 | .766 | .643 | 1.192 |
| 6° | .105 | .105 | .995 | .105 | 51° | .890 | .777 | .629 | 1.235 |
| 7° | .122 | .122 | .993 | .123 | 52° | .908 | .788 | .616 | 1.280 |
| 8° | .140 | .139 | .990 | .141 | 53° | .925 | .799 | .602 | 1.327 |
| 9° | .157 | .156 | .988 | .158 | 54° | .942 | .809 | .588 | 1.376 |
| 10° | .175 | .174 | .985 | .176 | 55° | .960 | .819 | .574 | 1.428 |
| 11° | .192 | .191 | .982 | .194 | 56° | .977 | .829 | .559 | 1.483 |
| 12° | .209 | .208 | .978 | .213 | 57° | .995 | .839 | .545 | 1.540 |
| 13° | .227 | .225 | .974 | .231 | 58° | 1.012 | .848 | .530 | 1.600 |
| 14° | .244 | .242 | .970 | .249 | 59° | 1.030 | .857 | .515 | 1.664 |
| 15° | .262 | .259 | .966 | .268 | 60° | 1.047 | .866 | .500 | 1.732 |
| 16° | .279 | .276 | .961 | .287 | 61° | 1.065 | .875 | .485 | 1.804 |
| 17° | .297 | .292 | .956 | .306 | 62° | 1.082 | .883 | .470 | 1.881 |
| 18° | .314 | .309 | .951 | .325 | 63° | 1.100 | .891 | .454 | 1.963 |
| 19° | .332 | .326 | .946 | .344 | 64° | 1.117 | .899 | .438 | 2.050 |
| 20° | .349 | .342 | .940 | .364 | 65° | 1.134 | .906 | .423 | 2.145 |
| 21° | .367 | .358 | .934 | .384 | 66° | 1.152 | .914 | .407 | 2.246 |
| 22° | .384 | .375 | .927 | .404 | 67° | 1.169 | .921 | .391 | 2.356 |
| 23° | .401 | .391 | .921 | .425 | 68° | 1.187 | .927 | .375 | 2.475 |
| 24° | .419 | .407 | .914 | .445 | 69° | 1.204 | .934 | .358 | 2.605 |
| 25° | .436 | .423 | .906 | .466 | 70° | 1.222 | .940 | .342 | 2.747 |
| 26° | .454 | .438 | .899 | .488 | 71° | 1.239 | .946 | .326 | 2.904 |
| 27° | .471 | .454 | .891 | .510 | 72° | 1.257 | .951 | .309 | 3.078 |
| 28° | .480 | .470 | .883 | .532 | 73° | 1.274 | .956 | .292 | 3.271 |
| 29° | .506 | .485 | .875 | .554 | 74° | 1.292 | .961 | .276 | 3.487 |
| 30° | .524 | .500 | .866 | .577 | 75° | 1.309 | .966 | .259 | 3.732 |
| 31° | .541 | .515 | .857 | .601 | 76° | 1.326 | .970 | .242 | 4.011 |
| 32° | .559 | .530 | .848 | .625 | 77° | 1.344 | .974 | .225 | 4.331 |
| 33° | .576 | .545 | .839 | .640 | 78° | 1.361 | .978 | .208 | 4.705 |
| 34° | .593 | .559 | .829 | .675 | 79° | 1.379 | .982 | .191 | 5.145 |
| 35° | .611 | .574 | .819 | .700 | 80° | 1.396 | .985 | .174 | 5.671 |
| 36° | .628 | .588 | .809 | .727 | 81° | 1.414 | .988 | .156 | 6.314 |
| 37° | .646 | .602 | .799 | .754 | 82° | 1.431 | .990 | .139 | 7.115 |
| 38° | .663 | .616 | .788 | .781 | 83° | 1.449 | .993 | .122 | 8.144 |
| 39° | .681 | .629 | .777 | .810 | 84° | 1.466 | .995 | .105 | 9.514 |
| 40° | .698 | .643 | .766 | .839 | 85° | 1.484 | .996 | .087 | 11.43 |
| 41° | .716 | .658 | .755 | .869 | 86° | 1.501 | .998 | .070 | 14.30 |
| 42° | .733 | .669 | .743 | .900 | 87° | 1.518 | .999 | .052 | 19.08 |
| 43° | .751 | .682 | .731 | .933 | 88° | 1.536 | .999 | .035 | 28.64 |
| 44° | .768 | .695 | .719 | .966 | 89° | 1.553 | 1.000 | .018 | 57.29 |
| 45° | .785 | .707 | .707 | 1.000 | 90° | 1.571 | 1.000 | .000 | ∞ |

# APPENDIX B

## Bibliography

Barham, J. N., and Thomas, W. L.: *Anatomical Kinesiology.* New York, The Macmillan Company, 1969.

Broer, M. R.: *An Introduction to Kinesiology.* Englewood Cliffs, N.J., Prentice-Hall, Inc., 1968.

Broer, M. R.: *Efficiency of Human Movement.* Philadelphia, W. B. Saunders Company, 1966.

Brunnstrom, S.: *Clinical Kinesiology,* 2nd ed. Philadelphia, F. A. Davis Company, 1966.

Bunn, J. W.: *Scientific Principles of Coaching.* Englewood Cliffs, N.J., Prentice-Hall, Inc., 1972.

Cooper, J. M., and Glassow, R. B.: *Kinesiology,* 3rd ed. St. Louis, The C. V. Mosby Company, 1972.

Duvall, E. N.: *Kinesiology: The Anatomy of Motion.* Englewood Cliffs, N.J., Prentice-Hall, Inc., 1959.

Dyson, G.: *The Mechanics of Athletics,* 2nd ed. London, University of London Press, Ltd., 1970.

Jensen, C. R., and Schultz, G. W.: *Applied Kinesiology.* New York, McGraw-Hill Book Company, 1970.

Kelley, David L.: *Kinesiology: Fundamentals of Motion Description.* Englewood Cliffs, N.J., Prentice-Hall, Inc., 1971.

Logan, G. A., and McKinney, W. C.: *Kinesiology.* Dubuque, Iowa, William C. Brown Company, 1970.

MacConaill, M. A., and Basmajian, J. V.: *Muscles and Movement, A Basis for Human Kinesiology.* Baltimore, The Williams & Wilkins Company, 1969.

Morehouse, L. W., and Cooper, J. M.: *Kinesiology.* St. Louis, The C. V. Mosby Company, 1950.

Plagenhoef, S. C.: *Patterns of Human Movement: A Cinematographic Analysis.* Englewood Cliffs, N.J., Prentice-Hall, Inc., 1971.

Rasch, P. J., and Burke, R. K.: *Kinesiology and Applied Anatomy.* Philadelphia, Lea & Febiger, 1967.

Scott, M. G.: *Analysis of Human Motion: A Textbook in Kinesiology,* 2nd ed. New York, Appleton-Century-Crofts, 1963.

Steindler, A.: *Kinesiology of the Human Body.* Springfield, Ill., Charles C Thomas, Publishers, 1955.

Thompson, C. W.: *Manual of Structural Kinesiology,* 6th ed. St. Louis, The C. V. Mosby Company, 1969.

Tricker, R. A. R., and Tricker, B. J. K.: *The Science of Movement.* New York, American Elsevier Publishing Co., Inc., 1967.

Wells, K. F.: *Kinesiology,* 5th ed. Philadelphia, W. B. Saunders Company, 1971.

Williams, M., and Lissner, H. R.: *Biomechanics of Human Motion.* Philadelphia, W. B. Saunders Company, 1962.

Selected Kinesiology Textbooks

Anson, B. J.: *Morris' Human Anatomy,* 12th ed. New York, McGraw-Hill Book Company, 1966.

Basmajian, J. V.: *Muscles Alive: Their Function Revealed by Electromyography,* 2nd ed. Baltimore, The Williams & Wilkins Company, 1967.

Selected Anatomy Textbooks

Best, C. H., and Taylor, N. B.: *The Human Body,* 4th ed. New York, Holt, Rinehart & Winston, Inc., 1963.

Bourne, G. H.: *The Structure and Function of Muscle.* New York, Academic Press, Inc., 1960.

Breathnach, A. S.: *Frazer's Anatomy of the Human Skeleton,* 5th ed. London, J. & A. Churchill, Ltd., 1958.

Edwards, L. F., and Gaughran, G. R. L.: *Concise Anatomy.* New York, McGraw-Hill Book Company, 1971.

Gardner, W. D., and Osburn, W. A.: *Structure of the Human Body.* Philadelphia, W. B. Saunders Company, 1967.

Goss, C. M.: *Gray's Anatomy of the Human Body,* 29th ed. Philadelphia, Lea & Febiger, 1966.

Hall, M. C.: *The Locomotor System: Functional Anatomy.* Springfield, Ill., Charles C Thomas, Publishers, 1965.

Hollinshead, H. W.: *Functional Anatomy of the Limbs and Back,* 2nd ed. Philadelphia, W. B. Saunders Company, 1960.

Lockhart, R. D.; Hamilton, G. G.; and Fyfe, F. W.: *Anatomy of the Human Body.* Philadelphia, J. B. Lippincott Company, 1965.

Miller, M. A., and Leavell, L. C.: *Kimber-Gray-Stackpole's Anatomy and Physiology,* 16th ed. New York, The Macmillan Company, 1972.

Quiring, D. P., and Warfel, J. F.: *The Extremities.* Philadelphia, Lea & Febiger, 1967.

Romanes, G. J.: *Cunningham's Textbook of Anatomy,* 10th ed. New York, Oxford University Press, Inc., 1964.

Woodburne, R. T.: *Essentials of Human Anatomy,* 4th ed. New York, Oxford University Press, Inc., 1968.

## Selected Physics Textbooks

Alley, P. W., and Sells, R. L.: *Introduction to Physics.* Boston, Allyn & Bacon, Inc., 1971.

Beiser, A.: *Foundations of Physics.* Reading, Mass., Addison-Wesley Publishing Co., Inc., 1964.

Blanchard, C., *et al.:* *Introduction to Modern Physics,* 2nd ed. Englewood Cliffs, N.J., Prentice-Hall, Inc., 1969.

Edwards, S.: *Physics: A Discovery Approach.* New York, John Wiley & Sons, Inc., 1971.

Ford, K. W.: *Basic Physics.* Waltham, Mass., Ginn/Blaisdell, 1968.

Fuchs, W. R.: *Physics for the Modern Mind.* New York, The Macmillan Company, 1967.

Lehrman, R. L., and Swartz, C.: *Foundations of Physics.* New York, Holt, Rinehart & Winston, Inc., 1965.

McCormick, W. W.: *Fundamentals of College Physics.* New York, The Macmillan Company, 1965.

Madley, R., and Winter, R.: *Modern Physics: A Student Study Guide.* New York, John Wiley & Sons, Inc., 1971.

Ripley, J. A.: *The Elements and Structure of the Physical Sciences.* New York, John Wiley & Sons, Inc., 1964.

Sears, F. W., and Zemansky, M. W.: *University Physics,* 4th ed. Reading, Mass., Addison-Wesley Publishing Co., Inc., 1960.

Shames, I. H.: *Engineering Mechanics—Statics and Dynamics,* 2nd ed. Englewood Cliffs, N.J., Prentice-Hall, Inc., 1967.

Tyson, H. N.: *Kinematics.* New York, John Wiley & Sons, Inc., 1966.

White, H. E.: *Modern College Physics,* 5th ed. New York, Van Nostrand Reinhold Company, 1966.

# Index